Insights and Recommendations
from the
MAA National Study
of
College Calculus

Edited by

David Bressoud,[1] Vilma Mesa,[2] Chris Rasmussen[3]

[1] Mathematics, Statistics, and Computer Science Department, Macalester College, 1600 Grand Ave., Saint Paul, MN 55105-1899, bressoud@macalester.edu.
[2] School of Education, University of Michigan, 610 East University, Ann Arbor, MI, 48109-1259, vmesa@umich.edu
[3] Department of Mathematics and Statistics, 5500 Campanile Drive, San Diego State University, San Diego, CA 92182-7720, crasmussen@mail.sdsu.edu

Editors' Note: This work was supported by NSF grant DRL 0910240. The opinions expressed in this volume do not necessarily reflect those of the National Science Foundation.

Library of Congress Number: 2015949323

Print ISBN: 978-0-88385-194-4

Electronic ISBN: 978-1-61444-319-3

Printed in the United States of America

Current Printing (last digit):

10 9 8 7 6 5 4 3 2 1

The MAA Notes Series, started in 1982, addresses a broad range of topics and themes of interest to all who are involved with undergraduate mathematics. The volumes in this series are readable, informative, and useful, and help the mathematical community keep up with developments of importance to mathematics.

MAA Notes

14. Mathematical Writing, by *Donald E. Knuth, Tracy Larrabee, and Paul M. Roberts.*

16. Using Writing to Teach Mathematics, *Andrew Sterrett*, Editor.

17. Priming the Calculus Pump: Innovations and Resources, Committee on Calculus Reform and the First Two Years, a subcomittee of the Committee on the Undergraduate Program in Mathematics, *Thomas W. Tucker*, Editor.

18. Models for Undergraduate Research in Mathematics, *Lester Senechal*, Editor.

19. Visualization in Teaching and Learning Mathematics, Committee on Computers in Mathematics Education, *Steve Cunningham and Walter S. Zimmermann*, Editors.

20. The Laboratory Approach to Teaching Calculus, *L. Carl Leinbach et al.*, Editors.

21. Perspectives on Contemporary Statistics, *David C. Hoaglin and David S. Moore*, Editors.

22. Heeding the Call for Change: Suggestions for Curricular Action, *Lynn A. Steen*, Editor.

24. Symbolic Computation in Undergraduate Mathematics Education, *Zaven A. Karian*, Editor.

25. The Concept of Function: Aspects of Epistemology and Pedagogy, *Guershon Harel and Ed Dubinsky*, Editors.

26. Statistics for the Twenty-First Century, *Florence and Sheldon Gordon*, Editors.

27. Resources for Calculus Collection, Volume 1: Learning by Discovery: A Lab Manual for Calculus, *Anita E. Solow*, Editor.

28. Resources for Calculus Collection, Volume 2: Calculus Problems for a New Century, *Robert Fraga*, Editor.

29. Resources for Calculus Collection, Volume 3: Applications of Calculus, *Philip Straffin*, Editor.

30. Resources for Calculus Collection, Volume 4: Problems for Student Investigation, *Michael B. Jackson and John R. Ramsay*, Editors.

31. Resources for Calculus Collection, Volume 5: Readings for Calculus, *Underwood Dudley*, Editor.

32. Essays in Humanistic Mathematics, *Alvin White*, Editor.

33. Research Issues in Undergraduate Mathematics Learning: Preliminary Analyses and Results, *James J. Kaput and Ed Dubinsky*, Editors.

34. In Eves' Circles, *Joby Milo Anthony*, Editor.

35. You're the Professor, What Next? Ideas and Resources for Preparing College Teachers, The Committee on Preparation for College Teaching, *Bettye Anne Case*, Editor.

36. Preparing for a New Calculus: Conference Proceedings, *Anita E. Solow*, Editor.

37. A Practical Guide to Cooperative Learning in Collegiate Mathematics, *Nancy L. Hagelgans, Barbara E. Reynolds, SDS, Keith Schwingendorf, Draga Vidakovic, Ed Dubinsky, Mazen Shahin, G. Joseph Wimbish, Jr.*

38. Models That Work: Case Studies in Effective Undergraduate Mathematics Programs, *Alan C. Tucker*, Editor.

39. Calculus: The Dynamics of Change, CUPM Subcommittee on Calculus Reform and the First Two Years, A. Wayne Roberts, Editor.

40. Vita Mathematica: Historical Research and Integration with Teaching, *Ronald Calinger*, Editor.

41. Geometry Turned On: Dynamic Software in Learning, Teaching, and Research, *James R. King and Doris Schattschneider*, Editors.

42. Resources for Teaching Linear Algebra, *David Carlson, Charles R. Johnson, David C. Lay, A. Duane Porter, Ann E. Watkins, William Watkins*, Editors.

43. Student Assessment in Calculus: A Report of the NSF Working Group on Assessment in Calculus, *Alan Schoenfeld*, Editor.

44. Readings in Cooperative Learning for Undergraduate Mathematics, *Ed Dubinsky, David Mathews, and Barbara E. Reynolds*, Editors.

MAA Service Center
P.O. Box 91112
Washington, DC 20090-1112
1-800-331-1MAA   FAX: 1-240-396-5647

Table of Contents

Preface

David Bressoud, *Macalester College*
Vilma Mesa, *University of Michigan, Ann Arbor*
Chris Rasmussen, *San Diego State University*

Calculus occupies a unique position as gatekeeper to the disciplines in science, technology, engineering, and mathematics (STEM). At least one term of calculus is required for almost all STEM majors. For too many students, this requirement is either an insurmountable obstacle or—more subtly—a great discourager from the pursuit of fields that build upon the insights of mathematics. Over 35 years ago, Robert White, then President of the National Academy of Engineering, declared that the time had come to turn calculus from a filter to a pump. Lynn Steen, former President of the MAA, echoed this sentiment in the National Research Council report *Calculus for a New Century: A Pump not a Filter* (1988). This was the document that heralded the start of the many efforts that collectively became known as Calculus Reform.

Many decades later, we seem to have made little progress. Calculus is still a filter, but until 2010 we knew very little about who takes it, how it is taught, or what makes for effective calculus programs that promote rather than inhibit students' continuation into successful careers in science and engineering. Existing knowledge on the effects of class size, placement procedures, use of technology, or pedagogical approaches was either not specific to calculus or of a very local nature.

This knowledge is more critical now than ever before because the landscape of college calculus has changed. With the explosive growth of Advanced Placement and other calculus courses in high school, roughly three-quarters of all students who eventually study calculus take their first calculus course in high school,[1] and almost half of all students who go directly from high school into a four-year college matriculate with Calculus on their high school transcript. In our large public universities, the primary engines for the production of scientists and engineers, the percentage of students taking Calculus I having already earned a 3 or higher on an AP Calculus exam exceeds 25%. Many of our most mathematically talented students place directly into Calculus II.

At the same time, our colleges and universities find themselves in the vise created by the dramatic growth in the number of incoming students hoping to pursue careers in engineering or science pressed against the drastic budget cuts that have forced departments to reduce the number of full-time faculty and to teach calculus in ever larger classes. In addition, departments have been slow to address the changing demographics of the students who will need to go into STEM fields. Success rates in calculus for women, students from underrepresented minorities, economically disadvantaged students, and first generation college students have always been disappointing. The loss of these students is a luxury our nation cannot afford.

This report, a summary of selected findings from the Mathematical Association of America's (MAA's) study of *Characteristics of Successful Programs in College Calculus* (NSF, DRL 0910240), constitutes two preliminary steps toward addressing these issues. First, it establishes a base of knowledge of who takes Calculus I and why, what their preparation has been, what they experience in the classroom, and how this affects their confidence, enjoyment of mathematics, and intention to persist in the study of mathematics. Second, it identifies institutional practices that contribute to the retention of STEM students. This is the first nationwide investigation of college-level Calculus I in the United States to combine both large-scale survey data and in-depth case study analysis.

---

1 This estimate is based on the following calculations: In 2014, 400,000 US students took an AP Calculus exam. According to the National Center for Education Statistics (NCES, 2012), these represent 53% of all high school calculus students, implying that roughly 750,000 students take calculus in high school each year. From the Conference Board of the Mathematical Sciences (CBMS) data (Blair et al 2013) and our survey data, approximately 500,000 students enroll in Calculus I in college each year, with about half of them repeating the calculus course they took in high school. Therefore, about 250,000 students each year see calculus for the first time as a college Calculus I course.

Why this Report is Relevant to High School Calculus

This report does not address how calculus is or should be taught in high school, yet it is relevant to high school and middle school teachers and administrators because it opens windows into the situation their STEM-intending students will encounter when they enter college. Mathematics is unique among all disciplines in having created a course, calculus, which is both the lodestar of the K-12 curriculum and the bedrock of post-secondary preparation for science and engineering. These distinct perspectives on this course create much of the discontinuity that students experience as they transition from high school to college.

For many high school students, mathematical success is the result of their ability to master a collection of problem types. Learning calculus as a mastery of problem types is a daunting task. The procedures and problems of calculus are sufficiently numerous and complex that acquiring this ability signals a remarkable mental achievement. It may be remarkable, but, by itself, it is not sufficient for success in university-level science or engineering. Students are better prepared for post-secondary mathematics when they have developed an understanding of the undergirding principles which, when accompanied by fluent and flexible application of the concepts and procedures of precalculus mathematics, enable them to understand calculus as a coherent and broadly applicable body of knowledge.

In US universities, successful navigation of Calculus I is merely the start. Subsequent courses build on the knowledge base of calculus and require fluency in the language in which calculus is written, the language of functions, limits, and series. Post-secondary faculty want their students to be able to move easily between the right triangle and the circle understandings of trigonometric functions, instinctively knowing which is the most productive approach in a given context. They expect that students are at ease with exponentials and logarithms and can recognize when the binomial theorem or a finite geometric series is in play.

The problem is that success in AP Calculus does not require this level of proficiency. It is and only claims to be evidence that one can solve the standard problems of calculus. It is not evidence that a student has acquired the preparation needed for future success.

This is why MAA and NCTM issued their joint statement on Calculus in High School.[2] In some sense, the worst preparation a student heading toward a career in science or engineering could receive is one that rushes toward accumulation of problem-solving abilities in calculus while short-changing the broader preparation needed for success beyond calculus.

This disjuncture of expectation is exacerbated by logistical problems. Large universities struggle to accommodate the number of students flooding the precalculus through calculus sequence. Their difficulties range from finding sufficient numbers of qualified instructors to creating mechanisms that identify and address individual student weaknesses. Our colleges and universities want students to succeed. For high school teachers and administrators, this report may open their eyes to the obstacles and struggles our universities face and the very challenging environment students encounter as they make the transition to post-secondary education.

Description of the Study

In 2009, in response to our lack of knowledge of the landscape of college calculus, the MAA launched its study of *Characteristics of Successful Programs in College Calculus*, supported by the National Science Foundation. The goals of this project are

1. To improve our understanding of the demographics of students who enroll in calculus.
2. To measure the impact of the various characteristics of calculus classes that are believed to influence student success.
3. To conduct explanatory case study analysis of exemplary programs in order to identify why and how these programs succeed.
4. To develop a theoretical framework that articulates the factors under which students are likely to succeed in calculus.
5. To use the results of these studies and the influence of the MAA to leverage improvements in calculus instruction across the United States.

The study was structured around two phases of intensive data gathering. The first occurred in 2010. In the spring we selected a stratified random sample[3] of non-profit colleges and universities offering a degree in mathematics (Associate's, Bachelor's, Master's, or Doctoral). Over the summer and fall of 2010, we surveyed those responsible for

---

2 See www.nctm.org/about/content.aspx?id=32351.

3 The sample followed the stratification and percentages established for the CBMS survey (Blair et al 2013), also conducted in 2010. Institutions were stratified by highest degree offered by the department and size of the undergraduate population.

coordinating mainstream[4] Calculus I instruction to get basic information about the course and contact information for instructors. In addition, we surveyed instructors both before the start of the first fall term and immediately after it had concluded, and we surveyed their Calculus I students both in the second and the second-to-last weeks of class. All the data from these five surveys have since been cleaned and compiled into a single file in which student data have been linked to the responses from their instructors and coordinators. A version of this file with all identifiers removed is available to researchers through the MAA (see www.maa.org/cspcc).

The second phase of intensive data gathering occurred in 2012. After analyzing the survey data to identify those institutions that seemed to be doing better than expected controlling for the background of their students, we selected four institutions from each of our four institutional categories for three-day visits by case study teams. Four additional institutions were visited to pilot the protocols developed for interviewing students, faculty, and administrators and for collecting classroom data. While we have decided to allow the sites of the case study visits to self-identify if they so wish, in this report we maintain anonymity for the sake of those institutions and participants that prefer not to be identified.

This report identifies the 20 case study sites as follows. In each case, the numeral 0 indicates one of the pilot sites. Except for the PhD-granting universities, these were chosen for geographical convenience rather than because of special characteristics of their program. Unless otherwise specified, the institutions identified with the numeral 0 are not included in the analyses.

> TY0 to TY4. Two-year colleges and technical colleges, defined as institutions for which the highest degree offered in mathematics is an Associate's degree.
>
> BA0 to BA4. Four-year undergraduate programs for which the highest degree offered in mathematics is a Bachelor's degree (BA or BS).
>
> MA0 to MA4. Four-year undergraduate programs for which the highest degree offered in mathematics is a Master's degree (MA or MS).
>
> LPU1 and LPU2. Large public universities. Offer PhD in mathematics.
>
> LPrU. Large private university. Offers PhD in mathematics.
>
> PTU. Public technical university. Offers PhD in mathematics
>
> PTI. Private technical institute. Offers PhD in mathematics

Overview of Volume Contents

This volume begins with a description of what we have learned about the students who enroll in Calculus I. In Chapter 2, we discuss the results of the hierarchical linear model constructed by Sadler and Sonnert of factors that can potentially influence changes in student attitudes toward mathematics in general and calculus in particular. The hierarchical analyses of the 2010 surveys yield correlations, not causality; nevertheless they played a significant role in our identification of those institutions that seemed to be doing something special.

Chapters 3 through 11 combine the insights from the case study visits conducted in 2012 with the general picture of what is happening across the country obtained from the 2010 surveys. Chapter 3 describes the institutional context: Who teaches calculus, what are the effects of class size, how is technology used, and how are departments supporting innovative approaches to teaching? Chapter 4 describes the variety of curricula including course content, cognitive goals, types of assignments, and assessments. Chapter 5 surveys placement procedures, and Chapter 6 looks at the variety of student support services. Two of the pedagogical factors that were identified as working at the classroom level are collections of highly correlated attributes we are calling "good teaching," described in Chapter 7, and "ambitious teaching," described in Chapter 8.

The last three chapters focus on what we have learned about the PhD-granting universities. They are, for the most part, large, diverse institutions that prepare large numbers of students entering the STEM fields and often have fall enrollments in Calculus I that approach or exceed 1,000 students. They were particularly rich sources of information. While the data we collected are specific to these universities, there are lessons, especially about fostering community and use of data, that are relevant to all calculus programs. Chapter 9 looks at how these universities coordinate calculus instruction and foster a community of practice around the teaching of Calculus I. Chapter 10 looks at preparation of graduate teaching assistants (GTAs) to either teach Calculus I in small classes or to support large lectures through recitation sections. Finally, Chapter 11 describes the kinds of data that are collected at the department or university level and how they are being used to improve the program. We include appendices that provide further details of the methods used in the study and descriptions of all questions asked in the surveys.

---

4 "Mainstream Calculus I" is defined as any first course in calculus that can be used as part of the calculus prerequisite for higher level mathematics courses.

Recommendations

Throughout this volume, you will find insights into what works well and what can be problematic, what changes can create significant improvements and which are less effective. One of the clearest lessons learned from this study is that there are no simple solutions. We did, however, identify seven practices that were common among the colleges and universities chosen for the case study visits. The last seven chapters of this volume each revolve around one of these practices, which we summarize here as recommended best practices;

1. Attention to the effectiveness of placement procedures. (See Chapter 5.)
2. Proactive student support services, including the fostering of student academic and social integration. (See Chapter 6.)
3. Construction of challenging and engaging courses. (See Chapter 7.)
4. Use of student-centered pedagogies and active-learning strategies. (See Chapter 8.)
5. Coordination of instruction, including the building of communities of practice. (See Chapter 9.)
6. Effective training of graduate teaching assistants. (See Chapter 10.)
7. Regular use of local data to guide curricular and structural modifications. (See Chapter 11.)

Research Teams and Advisory and Support Personnel

A very large group of people have worked on this study. David Bressoud, Marilyn Carlson, Vilma Mesa, and Chris Rasmussen coordinated this project with support from Michael Pearson and Linda Braddy at MAA, who also served as co-PIs.

Marilyn Carlson at Arizona State University headed the development and some of the analysis of the 2010 surveys, assisted by Sally Jacobs, Michael Tallman, and Eric Weber. Phillip Sadler and Gerhard Sonnert of Harvard University built the statistical model that emerged from the survey data. Brad Chaney at Westat provided the stratified random sample of colleges and universities for the 2010 surveys.

Chris Rasmussen at San Diego State University coordinated the efforts of the four case study teams and led the team in charge of data collection at the doctoral granting institutions. His team included Jessica Ellis (now at Colorado State University), Dov Zazkis (now at Arizona State University), Natalie Selinski (now at Univesity of Kassel, Germany), Gina Nuñez, and Kady Hanson.

Sean Larsen at Portland State University led the team in charge of the data collection at the baccalaureate granting institutions. His team included Estrella Johnson (now at Virginia Polytechnic Institute and State University), Kate Melhuish, John Caughman, Erin Glover, and Steve Strand.

Eric Hsu at San Francisco State University led the team in charge of the data collection at the master's granting institutions. His team included Addie Evans and Arek Goetz.

Vilma Mesa at the University of Michigan led the team in charge of data collection at the associate's granting institutions. Her team included Helen Burn (Highline College), Nina White, and Cameron Bloom.

We especially appreciate the work of Olga Dixon at the MAA who handled all of the logistics of running this grant. She was assisted by Grace Cunningham, Mehr Sood, and John Wolfe.

The advisory board for this study consisted of Guershon Harel (University of California, San Diego), W. James Lewis (University of Nebraska, Lincoln), David Lutzer (William and Mary College), Stanley Maloy (San Diego State University), William McCallum (University of Arizona), Robert Megginson (University of Michigan), Jeanne Narum (Project Kaleidoscope), Harriet Pollatsek (Mt. Holyoke College), and Ann Watkins (California State University, Northridge). Peter Ewell (National Center for Higher Education Management Systems) was the project evaluator, and Janice Earle (National Science Foundation) was the program officer. The advice they provided was critical to the success of this project.

We also wish to express our appreciation to the faculty, administrators, and staff at the twenty colleges and universities chosen for the case studies. The gave generously of their time and logistical support.

References

Blair, R. M., Kirkman, E. E., & Maxwell, J. M. (2013). *Statistical abstract of undergraduate programs in the mathematical sciences in the United States: Fall 2010 CBMS survey.* Providence RI: American Mathematical Society. www.ams.org/profession/data/cbms-survey/cbms2010

National Center for Education Statistics (NCES). (2012). *An overview of classes taken and credits earned by beginning postsecondary students.* NCES 2013-151rev. Washington, DC: US Department of Education. nces.ed.gov/pubs2013/2013151rev.pdf

Chapter 1

The Calculus Students

David Bressoud, *Macalester College*

Characteristics of Successful Programs in College Calculus has been the most extensive national survey of students enrolled in Calculus I in US colleges and universities. In this chapter, we summarize some of the basic data we collected on student demographics, high school experience including preparation for calculus, and beliefs about and attitudes toward mathematics and how it is learned.

Close to 300,000 students were enrolled in mainstream calculus during the fall term of 2010 when this study was undertaken. The 2010 Conference Board of the Mathematical Sciences (CBMS) departmental survey revealed that just over a third of the Calculus I students, about 110,000, were at PhD-granting universities. An additional 41,000 Calculus I students were at MA-granting universities, 82,000 were at BA-granting four-year colleges, and 65,000 students were enrolled in AS-granting two-year colleges (Figure 1).

Following the sampling procedures of surveys undertaken by the CBMS, we stratified the colleges and universities in our sample according to the highest mathematics degree offered: PhD-granting universities, MA-granting universities, BA-granting four-year colleges, and AS-granting two-year colleges. In this chapter we report our data aggregated by institution type. When total percentages are reported, we first calculated the percentages for each institution type and then combined these with a weighted average determined by the number of Calculus I students at each type of institution.

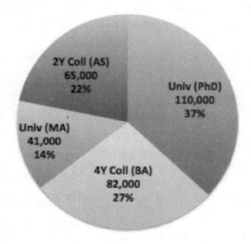

Figure 1: Distribution of Calculus I students by institution type, rounded to nearest thousand. Source: CBMS 2010.

One of the most striking features of the data we collected is the differentiation by institution type. In almost all instances, PhD-granting universities and AS-granting two-year colleges are at opposite ends of the spectrum whether we are looking at age, high school grades, or attitudes toward the learning of mathematics. Calculus students at BA-granting four-year colleges look very much like those at PhD-granting universities, while those at MA-granting universities are similar in many respects to the calculus students of AS-granting two-year colleges. This is not surprising because BA-granting four-year colleges are predominantly selective or highly selective private colleges, while most MA-granting universities are regional public universities with a more open admissions policy.

Basic Demographics

Table 1 shows the basic demographics of the students taking Calculus I in fall 2010. Women made up just under half of the Calculus I students, except at two-year colleges where they are only a third. By comparison, in fall 2010 women constituted 57% of all undergraduates. That fall, White students were 60%, Black students 15%, Asian American students 6%, and Hispanic students 14% of all undergraduates. Non-resident aliens were 2% of all undergraduates. (NCES 2013, Table 306.10)

Table 1: Percentage and weighted percentage of Calculus I students by various characteristics.

	Univ (PhD) N = 7,086	4Y Coll (BA) N = 1,742	Univ (MA) N = 535	2Y Coll (AS) N = 751	Weighted average
Male	55%	53%	53%	66%	57%
White	77%	81%	77%	67%	76%
Black	5%	7%	8%	9%	7%
Asian	15%	10%	9%	12%	12%
Hispanic	9%	10%	7%	16%	11%
Born in US	88%	91%	85%	83%	87%
High school in US	94%	94%	91%	91%	93%

Note: Students could choose multiple races. Responses to "American Indian/Alaska Native" and "Pacific Islander" were under 2%. The "Hispanic" option was a separate question. Source: maalongdatafile.[1]

Absolute numbers of students in Calculus I in the fall term of 2010 are given in Table 2, rounded to the nearest 100. These are based on the absolute number of students taking Calculus I at each institution type from the CBMS (2010) survey and the percentages at each institution type by gender, race, and ethnicity.

Table 2: Number of Calculus I students by gender, race, ethnicity, and institution type.

	All	Male	Female	White	Black	Asian	Hispanic
Univ (PhD)	110,100	60,600	49,500	84,300	5,000	16,200	9,800
4Y Coll	82,300	48,200	34,100	66,100	5,700	7,900	8,200
Univ (MA)	40,900	21,800	19,200	31,500	3,200	3,700	2,700
2Y Coll	65,000	43,000	22,000	42,300	5,500	7,700	10,000
TOTAL	298,400	173,600	124,800	224,200	19,400	35,500	30,800

Note: Students could choose multiple races. They could also choose Pacific Islander, Native American/Alaskan Native, or Other. The "Hispanic" option was a separate question. All numbers rounded to nearest 100; totals may not equal sum of numbers above. Source: CBMS (2010) and maalongdatafile.

---

1 The data source maalongdatafile is the full file of all survey responses. For a description of the anonymous version of this file, maalongdatafile_ ANON, see Appendix B.

The low enrollment of women in Calculus I at two-year colleges relative to the enrollment of men may be related to the fact that two-year college students are largely non-traditional students. As Table 3 shows, calculus students at two-year colleges are older and much less likely to be in the first year of college. In contrast, Calculus I students at PhD-granting institutions are the epitome of the traditional calculus students: 18 years old and in their first year of college.

Table 3: Age, year in college, and full-time status of Calculus I students.

	Univ (PhD) N = 7,081	4Y Coll (BA) N = 1,742	Univ (MA) N = 534	2Y Coll (AS) N = 746	Weighted average
Mean age (SD)	18.3 (2.4)	18.8 (2.9)	20.5 (5.3)	22.0 (7.4)	19.7 (3.5)
Freshman	83%	73%	50%	25%	63%
Sophomore	10%	16%	27%	40%	21%
Junior/Senior	6%	10%	17%	18%	11%
Enrolled full time	99%	98%	91%	76%	92%

Note: Other possible responses to year in college were Graduate Student and Other. Source: maalongdatafile.

The American Freshman survey from fall 2010 (Pryor, Hurtado, DeAngelo, Palucki Blake, & Tran, 2010) asked, "Do you have any concern about your ability to finance your college education?" The responses among all full-time freshmen at four-year institutions were

    34% None (I am confident that I will have sufficient funds)
    55% Some (but I probably will have enough funds)
    11% Major (not sure I will have enough funds to complete college)

The response *Some* appears to line up with those in Table 4 who slightly disagreed, slightly agreed, or agreed with the statement in our survey, "I am anticipating difficulty paying for college," while *Major* appears to correspond to those who strongly agreed with this statement. Comparisons by type of institution are interesting. We see that Calculus I students at BA-granting four-year colleges are significantly less concerned about finances than those at PhD-granting universities (Welch's t-test, $p < 0.001$) whereas those at AS-granting two-year colleges are significantly more concerned about finances (Welch's t-test, $p < 0.001$).

Table 4 records whether the student's parents were born in the United States and whether English was the language spoken at home. It also looks at some of the proxies for socio-economic status: parental education and anticipated difficulty paying for college. Among all full-time freshmen at four-year institutions in fall 2010, 53% had a father who had earned a college degree and 55% had a mother who had accomplished this (Pryor et al. 2010). It is interesting that among calculus students at four-year institutions, 60% had a father who had completed college and 57% had a mother who had completed college, thus a slightly higher level of education for mothers but a much higher level of education for fathers.

Table 4: Parental background and financial situation.

	Univ (PhD) N = 7,055	4Y Coll (BA) N = 1,736	Univ (MA) N = 535	2Y Coll (AS) N = 740	Weighted average
Father born in US	77%	83%	80%	67%	77%
Mother born in US	77%	81%	80%	65%	76%
English spoken at home	86%	90%	85%	76%	85%
Father completed college	65%	58%	49%	44%	56%
Mother completed college	62%	56%	47%	40%	53%
Some concern about paying for college[a]	54%	40%	57%	55%	51%
Major concern about paying for college[b]	13%	10%	13%	23%	14%

Notes: a. To the statement, "I am anticipating difficulty paying for college," responded Slightly Disagree, Slightly Agree, or Agree. b. To the statement, "I am anticipating difficulty paying for college," responded Strongly Agree. Source: maalongdatafile.

As reported in Table 5, home environment is also reflected in the answers to the questions "To what degree was your home environment supportive of your studying math?" and "Who encouraged you to take mathematics classes?"

Table 5: Percentage of reported support at home and from teachers by type of institution.

	Univ (PhD) N = 7,089	4Y Coll (BA) N = 1,743	Univ (MA) N = 535	2Y Coll (AS) N = 746	Weighted average
Home supported my studying math[a]	80%	77%	69%	67%	75%
Parents see me as good at math[b]	69%	65%	65%	63%	66%
Teachers see me as good at math[b]	66%	61%	63%	56%	62%
Father encouraged me to study math[c]	44%	39%	32%	31%	38%
Mother encouraged me to study math[c]	43%	38%	33%	31%	38%
Math teacher encouraged me to study math[c]	40%	36%	33%	28%	35%
No one encouraged me to study math[c]	40%	43%	48%	49%	44%

Notes: a. Percent responding *Strongly* or *Very Strongly* to question, "To what degree was your home environment supportive of your studying math?" b. To the question, "Do the following people see you as good at math?," percent responding 5 or 6 on a Likert scale from 1 = *Not at All* to 6 = *Very Much*. c. To the question, "Who encouraged you to take mathematics classes?," percent that included this person as one of possibly several choices. Source: maalongdatafile. See Appendix B for the full survey.

Looking at whether the home environment was supportive of studying mathematics and the encouragement the student received to study mathematics, we see a sharp distinction between students at PhD-granting universities and four-year colleges on the one hand and MA-granting universities and two-year colleges on the other. Note that a similar proportion of students report that their mothers and fathers encouraged them to study mathematics, both cited slightly more frequently than mathematics teachers.

Academic Background

We begin this section with SAT and ACT scores and then look at previous mathematics courses, when students took them, and how well they did. We also will look at classroom experiences and previous use of graphing calculators.

SAT scores were reported by roughly two-thirds of the students at PhD-granting universities and four-year colleges and about half the students at MA-granting universities and two-year colleges. ACT scores were reported by about two-thirds of the students at PhD- and MA-granting universities as well as students at four-year colleges. Only about a quarter of the students at two-year colleges reported ACT scores. The means and standard deviations are reported in Table 6.

A common high school progression, especially for students who may be headed toward eventually taking calculus, consists of Algebra I in 8th grade, geometry in 9th, Algebra II in 10th, precalculus in 11th, and calculus in 12th. As shown in Figure 2, this is the common experience of students who take Calculus I at a PhD-granting university. In fact, many of them move even faster through this progression: 25% have taken Algebra II by the end of 9th grade, 30% have taken precalculus by the end of 10th, and 11% have taken calculus by the end of 11th.

Table 6: Average SAT/ACT scores and subscores.

	Univ (PhD) SAT (N = 4,983) ACT (N = 5,103) Mean (SD)	4Y Coll (BA) SAT (N = 1,271) ACT (N = 1,198) Mean (SD)	Univ (MA) SAT (N = 278) ACT (N = 375) Mean (SD)	2Y Coll (AS) SAT (N = 451) ACT (N = 228) Mean (SD)
SAT Math	663 (71)	632 (72)	616 (81)	589 (95)
SAT Critical Reading	619 (83)	601 (84)	583 (104)	560 (98)
ACT Math	29.1 (4.0)	27.4 (4.0)	26.2 (4.8)	25.5 (4.5)
ACT Composite	28.2 (3.4)	26.9 (3.7)	25.4 (3.9)	24.6 (4.2)

Notes: SAT N is the number of students who reported scores on SAT. ACT N is the number for the ACT. Source: maalongdatafile.

Table 7 presents a comparison of the percentage of students at our four types of institutions who have followed the progression that would normally lead to calculus in Grade 12. It also shows the average grade and standard deviation in these courses. Only students in the common track are reflected in these percentages. We did not count students who followed an integrated curriculum. It is perhaps surprising that only over half of Calculus I students in two-year colleges had completed Algebra II by the end of 10th grade, while 84% of the Calculus I students in two-year colleges completed Algebra II at some point in high school, and they did it with an average grade between B+ and A−. Over a fifth of them had taken a calculus course in high school. Students who take Calculus I at a two-year college have not done quite as well in high school as those at four-year institutions, but they are not far behind. The other side of the coin is that students who arrive at a two-year college needing developmental courses in mathematics are much less likely to eventually enroll in calculus, an observation borne out by direct studies of this problem (Bailey, Jeong, & Cho, 2010; Tyson, Lee, Borman, & Hanson, 2007).

Table 7: Percentage of students' enrollment in various high school mathematics courses, average grade in course with standard deviation (SD) by type of institution.

	Univ (PhD) N = 7,174		4Y Coll (BA) N = 1,782		Univ (MA) N = 527		2Y Coll (AS) N = 740	
	%	Grade (SD)	%	Grade (SD)	%	Grade (SD)	%	Grade (SD)
Algebra II by end of 10th grade	78%	3.8 (0.5)	71%	3.7 (0.6)	59%	3.6 (0.7)	56%	3.4 (0.8)
Precalculus by end of 11th grade	67%	3.7 (0.6)	58%	3.5 (0.6)	46%	3.6 (0.6)	37%	3.3 (0.9)
Statistics by end of 12th grade	10%	3.8 (0.5)	11%	3.7 (0.6)	9%	3.6 (0.7)	8%	3.5 (0.8)
Calculus by end of 12th grade	67%	3.6 (0.6)	50%	3.5 (0.7)	40%	3.5 (0.7)	22%	3.4 (0.8)

Note: Grades are mean grades on scale A+ = 4.33, A = 4.0, A− = 3.67,..., F = 0. SD is standard deviation. Source: maalongdatafile.

Figure 2 presents the percentage of Calculus I students at PhD-granting universities who had completed a given course at the indicated grade. There are a number of interesting observations from this figure. Essentially every student taking Calculus I at a PhD-granting university who had taken Precalculus by 11th grade also took calculus in 12th grade (out of 4,828 respondents who had completed precalculus by the end of 11th grade, seven did not take calculus in high school). We see that statistics is not a common course option for students who intend to take calculus in college.

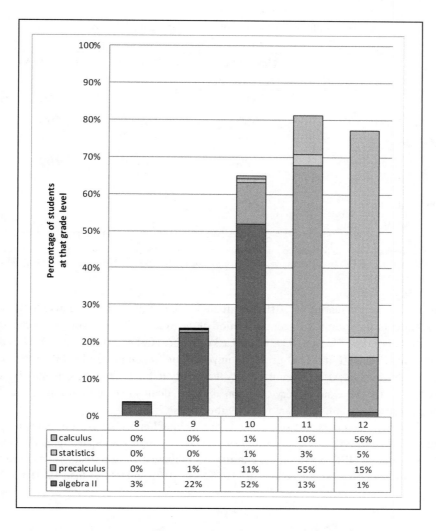

	8	9	10	11	12
▣ calculus	0%	0%	1%	10%	56%
▣ statistics	0%	0%	1%	3%	5%
▣ precalculus	0%	1%	11%	55%	15%
▣ algebra II	3%	22%	52%	13%	1%

Figure 2: Percentage of Calculus I students at PhD-granting universities who had completed a given course at the indicated grade. The graph does not include courses such as integrated mathematics and trigonometry that are not part of a precalculus course. Source: maalongdatafile.

Table 8 displays the percentage of high school calculus students who took an AP Calculus exam, either the AB exam, which covers just slightly more than the first semester of mainstream college calculus, or the BC exam, which covers the full year of college single variable calculus. Every few years, the College Board calibrates these exams by field-testing them with calculus students at major universities. With this calibration, a score of 3 corresponds to a C, 4 to a B, and 5 to an A (Dodd et al, 2002; Ewing et al, 2010; Keng & Dodd, 2008). Students taking the BC exam also get an AB subscore, which is almost always the same as or one point higher than the BC score. In 2010, fewer than 2% of the BC students who earned less than a 3 on the BC exam earned a 3 or higher on the AB subscore (College Board, 2010).

Table 8: AP exam taking among students with calculus in high school.

	Univ (PhD) N = 4,821[a]	4Y Coll (BA) N = 890[a]	Univ (MA) N = 210[a]	2Y Coll (AS) N = 163[a]
Took AB Exam	53%	45%	40%	50%
1 or 2 on AB Exam[b]	36%	46%	50%	63%
3 on AB Exam[b]	32%	29%	40%	17%
4 or 5 on AB Exam[b]	32%	24%	10%	20%
Took BC Exam	11%	7%	6%	11%
1 or 2 on BC Exam[c]	39%	59%	*	*
3 or higher on BC Exam[c]	61%	41%	*	*

Notes: a. Number of survey respondents who reported having taken calculus in high school. Due to rounding, percentages may not add to 100%. b. Percentage of those who took the AB Exam. c. Percentage of those who took the BC Exam. * Numbers are too small for these percentages to be meaningful. Source: maalongdatafile.

Nationally, 40% of those graduating in 2010 that studied calculus in high school also took the AB exam, while 13% took the BC exam.[2] For the spring 2010 administration of the exams, 18% of those taking the AB exam earned a 3 and 38% earned a 4 or 5. For the BC exam, 83% earned a 3 or higher (College Board, 2010). Thus those students who will eventually enroll in Calculus I at a PhD-granting university are much more likely than the average high school student to have taken the Calculus AB exam and slightly less likely to have taken the Calculus BC exam. We also see that a score of 3 or less on the AB exam is very common among Calculus I students at PhD-granting universities, not surprising given that these are students who are retaking this course.

The high school calculus experience of students taking Calculus I at a PhD-granting university is summarized in Figure 3. There are other options for earning credit for calculus taken in high school, including dual enrollment programs and International Baccalaureate (IB). However, the enrollments in these are quite small. Dual enrollment accounted for less than 5% of all high school calculus students in 2010 (CBMS, 2010), and IB less than 1% (IBO, 2010).

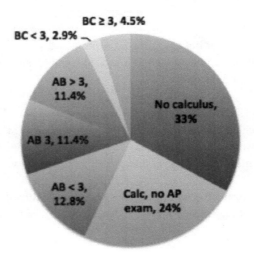

Figure 3: Distribution of students in Calculus I at PhD-granting universities by high school experience in calculus and by AP Calculus score. Source: maalongdatafile.

---

2 The percentages are based on NAEP transcript data on the number of high school students who graduated in 2009 with a calculus course on their transcript (NCES, 2011) and on College Board data on the number of students who took those exams in 2009 (College Board, 2009).

We also recorded the percentages of students who took precalculus at a college or university as well as students who are repeating calculus at the college-level (Table 9).

Table 9: Precalculus and previous calculus at college level.

	Univ (PhD) N = 7,254	4Y Coll (BA) N = 1,800	Univ (MA) N = 546	2Y Coll (AS) N = 771
Took precalculus in college	13%	16%	28%	52%
Previously took calculus in college	14%	15%	18%	19%

Source: maalongdatafile.

We surveyed student experiences with graphing calculators in the last mathematics class they took in high school (Table 10). It should be noted that graphing calculators are required for some parts of the AP Calculus exams (and not allowed on others). It is common for students to use these calculators in both precalculus and calculus classes. We asked about how comfortable the student is in using a graphing calculator, how frequently graphing calculators and calculators with symbolic manipulation capabilities (including symbolic differentiation and integration) were allowed in exams, and how well prepared the student considered herself or himself to be to complete complex calculations without the aid of a calculator.

There are several observations to be made from this table. Students indicate being very comfortable using graphing calculators and noticeably less comfortable doing calculations by hand. In both cases, the degree of comfort was remarkably consistent across all types of institutions. We also see that almost all Calculus I students had been allowed to use graphing calculators on exams at least some of the time, although for most for them it was only some and not all of the time.

Table 10: Percentage of Students Reporting Various Aspects of Graphing Calculator Use.

		Univ (PhD) N = 7,467	4Y Coll (BA) N = 1,840	Univ (MA) N = 575	2Y Coll (AS) N = 792
Comfortable with graphing calculator[a]	Somewhat[b]	14%	14%	18%	18%
	Yes[c]	81%	82%	77%	74%
Graphing calc allowed on exams[d]	Sometimes	60%	55%	53%	48%
	Always	31%	39%	32%	29%
TI-89 or -92 allowed on exams[e]	Sometimes	25%	22%	25%	25%
	Always	31%	37%	30%	28%
Prepared for calculation without calc[f]	Somewhat[b]	28%	29%	30%	27%
	Yes[c]	59%	58%	57%	57%

Notes: a. Response to statement, "I am comfortable using a graphing calculator." b. Combines responses *Slightly Disagree* and *Slightly Agree*. c. Combines responses *Agree* and *Strongly Agree*. Other possible responses were *Strongly Disagree* and *Disagree*. d. Completing the sentence, "In high school I was allowed to use graphing calculators on exams …". Third possible response was *Never*. e. Completing the sentence, "In high school I was allowed to use calculators that performed symbolic operations on exams (e.g., TI-89, TI-92) …". Third possible response was *Never*. f. Response to statement, "My mathematics courses in high school have prepared me to complete complex calculations without a calculator." Source: maalongdatafile.

It is remarkable that the proportion of students who were always allowed to use a graphing calculator on exams was almost identical to the proportion of students who were always allowed to use calculators with symbolic manipulation capabilities on exams, strongly suggesting that those teachers who always allow graphing calculators on exams are almost exclusively using calculators with symbolic manipulation capabilities.

Permission to use graphing calculators on exams is one of the sharp discontinuities between high school and college calculus. Graphing calculators were allowed on exams in college Calculus I for 38% of the students at PhD-granting universities, 41% of those at four-year colleges, 65% of those at MA-granting universities, and 61% of those at two-year colleges (source: maalongdatafile). These percentages are higher than the popular perception of what is allowed in colleges and universities, but they are well below the almost universal use seen in high school.

Field of Study

As important as knowing the background of our students is knowing where they are going or want to go. To the question, "Which of the following BEST describes your current career goal?" we provided 12 choices (see Table 11). In the table we present these options ordered roughly from most mathematically intensive to least mathematically intensive.

As Table 11 shows, there is a tremendous amount of variation in career goals by gender, race/ethnicity, and institution type. If we define a science, technology, engineering, or mathematics (STEM) career as any of the choices above the Total STEM row, we see that generally about three quarters of the students taking Calculus I intend a STEM career, with the lowest being students at four-year colleges, where only 65% intend a STEM career. Sixty-five percent of Asian American students intend a STEM career whereas 80% of African-American students in Calculus I intend a STEM career. Among Asian-American students, 9% are undecided about career goals, while only 5% of African-American students indicate being undecided.

Asian-American students are also unusual in that a relatively small percentage intend to be engineers (19%). This is a recent trend. In 2004, more Asian-Americans graduated with a bachelors degree in engineering (8,046 total degrees) than in the biological sciences (7,838), but then their interest in the biological sciences took off. In 2012, the most recent year for which we have data, Asian-Americans earned 66% more bachelor's degrees in the biological sciences (16,169) than in engineering (9,733; see NCES 2013, Table 322.30). It is also notable that almost one in six of the Asian-Americans in mainstream Calculus I are going into business. This result is all the more surprising because Asian-Americans are heavily represented at PhD-granting universities where there often is a choice between mainstream calculus and business calculus.

Table 11: Distribution of career goals by gender, race, ethnicity, and institution type.

	Gender			Ethnicity				Type of Institution			
	All N=9,445	Male N=5,231	Female N=4,202	White N=7,166	Black N=500	Asian N=1,255	Hispanic N=876	Univ (PhD) N=6,984	4Y Coll (BA) N=11,965	Univ (MA) N=528	2Y Coll (AS) N=737
Math	2%	2%	1%	2%	2%	2%	1%	1%	1%	3%	2%
Physical Science	4%	5%	4%	5%	5%	3%	3%	3%	4%	6%	5%
Engineer	31%	38%	14%	29%	26%	19%	26%	35%	20%	22%	29%
Comp Sci/ IT	5%	10%	2%	6%	9%	6%	7%	4%	7%	7%	10%
Geo/Environ Science	2%	2%	3%	3%	2%	1%	2%	2%	3%	5%	2%
Bio Science Med.	30%	19%	43%	27%	36%	34%	33%	31%	30%	27%	28%
Total STEM	74%	76%	67%	72%	80%	65%	72%	76%	65%	70%	76%
Teacher	5%	4%	10%	8%	3%	3%	6%	3%	9%	13%	7%
Soc Science	1%	1%	2%	1%	2%	2%	2%	1%	2%	1%	1%
Business	7%	9%	7%	6%	7%	16%	8%	7%	8%	7%	7%
Other	4%	3%	5%	5%	4%	4%	4%	4%	5%	5%	3%
Undecided	8%	7%	9%	8%	5%	9%	7%	8%	10%	4%	6%

Note: Percentages computed first by institution type, then combined using weights determined by the percentage of students under this category at each institution type. Source: maalongdatafile.

The most striking differences are between men and women (Figure 4). Whereas 38% of men in Calculus I intend to become engineers, only 14% of the women in the sample have this goal. While 43% of the women in Calculus I intend a career in the medical or biological sciences, this is true of only 19% of the men. Computer science accounts for 10% of the men and only 2% of the women. Teaching attracts 10% of the women but only 4% of the men. Combining these fields, engineering and computer science account for 48% of the men and 16% of the women whereas life sciences and teaching account for 53% of the women and 23% of the men.

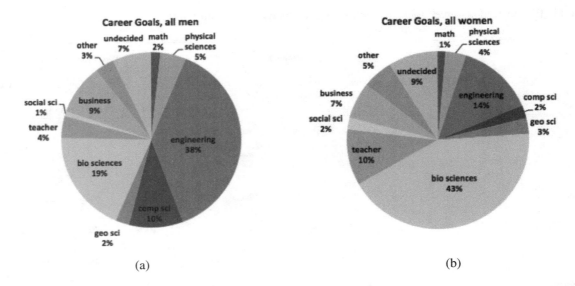

(a)   (b)

Figure 4: Distribution of career goals of men (a) and women (b) in Calculus I. Source: maalongdatafile.

Computer science and IT loom large at two-year colleges, accounting for 10% of the Calculus I students, whereas at PhD-granting universities they make up only 4% of the students. Teaching is a dominant career goal at MA-granting universities (13%) and four-year colleges (9%), but accounts for a very small percentage of Black and Asian students (3% each).

Finally, it is notable that very few prospective mathematics majors and relatively few students heading into chemistry or physics take Calculus I. These data reinforce the anecdotal evidence that most of the students heading into these fields have a sufficiently strong high school background in calculus that they skip Calculus I when they get to college or university.

Time Management

At the start of the term, we asked how much time per week students anticipated they would spend working at a job, participating in extracurricular activities, and studying for all of their classes, including calculus. The survey listed sports, college paper, or clubs as examples of extracurricular activities. At the end of the term, we asked students to estimate how much time per week they had actually spent on each of these activities and also asked how many hours per week they had spent preparing for calculus, including studying, reading, and doing homework or lab work. The results are reported in Table 12.

Fewer than half of the students at PhD-granting universities and four-year colleges did any paid work during the term. At PhD-granting universities, only 23% of the students worked at a job for more than 5 hours per week. At four-year colleges, 26% were working more than 10 hours per week. At MA-granting universities, 30% were working more than 15 hours per week. And at two-year colleges, 62% were working more than 15 hours per week, with 27% working more than 20 hours per week.

Students at the end of the term reported spending less time than they had anticipated in all the three categories: work, extracurricular activities, and studying. At four-year colleges, two-year colleges, and MA-granting universities, the drop in the amount of time they spent preparing for all of their classes was both large (1.5 to 2.5 hours) and statistically significant. The drop at PhD-granting universities (half an hour) was small but still significant. Across all institutions except two-year colleges, more than half of the students reported having spent at most five hours per week preparing for calculus. The fraction of students reporting this upper bound was 56% at PhD-granting universities, 67% at four-year colleges, and 53% at MA-granting universities. At two-year colleges, 58% of the students reported spending six or more hours per week preparing for calculus.

Table 12: Average and standard deviation (SD) of anticipated and reported time allocation to various activities by type of institution.

		Univ (PhD) N = 7,047 Mean (SD)	4Y Coll (BA) N = 1,720 Mean (SD)	Univ (MA) N = 530 Mean (SD)	2Y Coll (AS) N = 747 Mean (SD)
Working at job	Start	4½ (7½)	7½ (10½)	10½ (11½)	14 (12½)
	End	3½ (7) ***	7½ (11½)	9½ (11½)	12½ (12½) *
Extra-curricular activities	Start	8 (7)	11½ (10½)	7 (8)	5½ (7½)
	End	6 (7) ***	10½ (10½) *	6 (8)	5 (7)
Prep for all classes (including calculus)	Start	19 (9)	19 (9½)	18 (9½)	16½ (10)
	End	18½ (9½) ***	16½ (9½) ***	15½ (9½) **	15 (10) **
Prep for calculus	End	6½ (5)	5½ (5)	7 (6)	8½ (7)

Note: Students were offered the options *0, 1–5, 6–10, 11–15, 16–20, 21–30,* or *Over 30 hours per week.* The average in each category was used to estimate means, standard deviations, medians, and quartiles. We used *35* for the option *Over 30.* Cell entries are times rounded to nearest half hour per week. Start: students' anticipated time at start of term. End: students' reported time at end of term. Welch's *t*-test was used to assess the statistical significance of change from start to end of term. * $p < 0.05$, ** $p < 0.01$, *** $p < 0.001$. Source: maalongdatafile.

There are dangers in comparing students' responses at the start and end of the term: At the start of the term, we had a good cross-section of all of the students in Calculus I. Students who answered the survey at the end of the term were, for the most part, those who had successfully negotiated this course. For this reason, we also compared responses from all students at the start of the term with the responses at the start of the term from those who answered the questions at both the start and end of the term. The only statistically significant difference was in answer to the question about hours working at a job, and this only held among students at PhD-granting universities. Those who would go on to also answer the survey at the end of the term anticipated at the start of the term that they would spend an average of 3½ hours per week working at a job. This suggests that the difference in Table 12 between the start and end of the term for this cell is an artifact of selection bias at the end of the term. The question for which we saw the most dramatic change, the amount of time spent preparing for all classes, had higher anticipated times among those who would also complete the end of term survey. This suggests that those students who were successful had started out with slightly higher expectations for how much time they would spend studying, though the differences were small (under 30 minutes) and not statistically significant.

Student Attitudes and Beliefs

We asked many questions that sought to identify student attitudes and beliefs, including the three outcome variables—confidence in mathematical ability, enjoyment of mathematics, and intention to continue the study of mathematics (see Chapter 2).

We asked for a self-assessment at the start of the term of three skills they would need for calculus: factoring expressions, solving inequalities, and solving word problems, as well as how well they felt they had understood the mathematics they already had studied and whether they now possessed the knowledge and abilities needed to succeed in calculus. The results are reported in Table 13. We see that the results are remarkably consistent across all types of post-secondary institutions, with much higher self-confidence in the ability to factor expressions and solve inequalities than in the ability to solve word problems.

Table 13: Percentage of students' self-assessment of high school preparation, start of term.

		Univ (PhD) N = 7440	4Y Coll (BA) N = 1833	Univ (MA) N = 574	2Y Coll (AS) N = 781
Can factor expressions	Somewhat[c]	13%	14%	19%	17%
	Yes[d]	85%	83%	79%	77%
Can solve inequalities	Somewhat[c]	17%	18%	20%	21%
	Yes[d]	80%	80%	78%	74%
Can solve word problems	Somewhat[c]	27%	28%	28%	25%
	Yes[d]	69%	68%	66%	66%
Understand what I have studied[a]	Somewhat[c]	23%	28%	25%	24%
	Yes[d]	75%	69%	72%	73%
Ready for calculus[b]	Somewhat[c]	16%	19%	18%	17%
	Yes[d]	81%	79%	77%	81%

Notes: For the first three questions, the prompts began "My mathematics courses in high school have prepared me to …," followed by "factor expressions," "solve inequalities," and "solve word problems." a. "I understand the mathematics that I have studied." b. "I believe I have the knowledge and abilities to succeed in this course." c. Combines *Slightly Disagree* and *Slightly Agree*. d. Combines *Agree* and *Strongly Agree*. Source: maalongdatafile.

It is interesting to compare students' sense of readiness for Calculus I at the start of the term (Table 13) with the more realistic self-assessment they expressed at the end of the term of how ready they really were for the course (Table 14). The difference is all the more striking when one remembers that the end of term survey was completed only by students who had been successful in the course, roughly 40% getting an A, 40% a B, and 20% a C.

Table 14: Percentage of Students' Self-assessment of High School Preparation, End of Term.

		Univ (PhD) N = 3,664	4Y Coll (BA) N = 1,524	Univ (MA) N = 333	2Y Coll (AS) N = 441
Was ready for calculus[a]	Somewhat[b]	31%	33%	35%	31%
	Yes[c]	56%	54%	51%	57%

Notes: Students were asked for level of agreement with the statement, "My previous math courses prepared me to succeed in this course." b. Combines *Slightly Disagree* and *Slightly Agree*. d. Combines *Agree* and *Strongly Agree*. Source: maalongdatafile.

The last table, Table 15 presents student self-assessment of ability to compute derivatives and integrals, ability to use calculus to solve word problems, and whether this course increased interest in continuing the study of mathematics. Even among these students who successfully completed this course, only two-thirds expressed confidence in their ability to compute derivatives and integrals. Only around 40% were confident in their ability to use the ideas of calculus. What is perhaps surprising is that this calculus course was most successful in increasing students' interest in mathematics at the MA-granting universities and two-year colleges.

Table 15: Percentage of Students' Self-assessment of Abilities and Interest, End of Term.

		Univ (PhD) N = 3,677	4Y Coll (BA) N = 1,526	Univ (MA) N = 333	2Y Coll (AS) N = 441
Can compute derivatives and integrals[a]	Somewhat[d]	30%	35%	34%	30%
	Yes[e]	66%	60%	61%	66%
Can solve word problems[b]	Somewhat[d]	46%	49%	47%	42%
	Yes[e]	41%	40%	40%	45%
Course has increased interest in math[c]	Somewhat[d]	46%	46%	43%	34%
	Yes[e]	29%	29%	38%	48%

Notes: Prompts were a. "I am good at computing derivatives and integrals." b. "I am able to use ideas of calculus (e.g., differentiation, integration) to solve word problems that I have not seen before." c. "This course has increased my interest in taking more mathematics." d. Combines *Slightly Disagree* and *Slightly Agree*. d. Combines *Agree* and *Strongly Agree*. Source: maalongdatafile.

The strong growth of interest in the life sciences among Asian American students is increasingly reflected among all students pursuing a bachelor's degree in a STEM field (Figure 5). Since the year 2000, the number of students heading into engineering or the physical or mathematical sciences has roughly doubled, but the number heading into the life sciences has more than tripled, and recent trends suggest that this dramatic growth in the life sciences is not slowing down. The traditional Calculus I course was designed for engineers and physical scientists. It is not clear that such a course will meet the needs for the future.

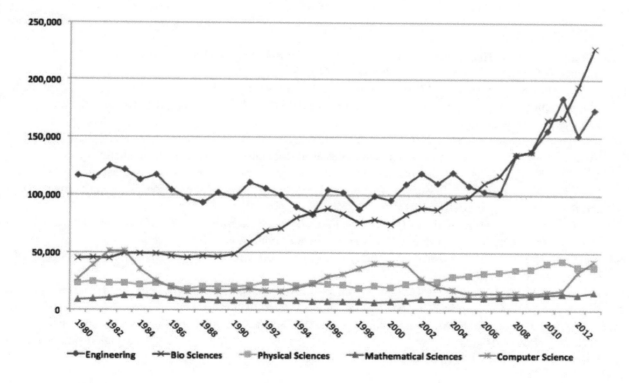

Figure 5: Number of intended majors among full-time freshmen at four-year institutions. Source: Eagan et al. 2013.

Conclusion

We see that the students who enroll in mainstream Calculus I are predominantly White or Asian-American, have highly educated parents, and have done well in high school mathematics in a track that led or could have led to calculus by 12th grade. As we shall see and further explore in Chapter 2, they enter with high confidence in their mathematical abilities although, as reflected in their responses to questions about word problems, they express some uncertainty about their ability to apply the mathematics they have learned to unfamiliar problems. We see that men and women are taking calculus for very different reasons, with men predominantly heading into engineering, computing, or the physical sciences and women going largely into the life sciences or teaching.

References

Baily, T., Jeong, D. W., & Cho, S. W. (2010). Referral, enrollment, and completion in developmental education sequences in community colleges. *Economics of Education Review, 29*, 255–270.

Barnett, M. D., Sonnert, G., & Sadler, P. M. (2014). Productive and ineffective efforts: How student effort in high school mathematics relates to college calculus success. *International Journal of Mathematical Education in Science and Technology, 45*, 996–1020. DOI: 10.1080/0020739X.2014.902131

Cass, C. A. P., Hazari, Z., Cribbs, J., Sadler, P. M., & Sonnert, G. (2011). *Examining the impact of mathematics identity on the choice of engineering careers for male and female students.* Paper presented at 41st ASEE/IEEE Frontiers in Education Conference. October 12–15, 2011, Rapid City, SD. DOI: 10.1109/FIE.2011.6142881

College Board (2009). *AP program summary report for 2009.* Accessed July 30, 2014. media.collegeboard.com/digitalServices/pdf/research/program-summary-report-09.pdf

College Board (2010). *AP student score distributions for 2010.* Accessed July 30, 2014. Available at media.collegeboard.com/digitalServices/pdf/research/Student-Score-Distributions-2010.pdf

Dodd, B. G., Fitzpatrick, S. J., De Ayala, R. J., & Jennings, J. A. (2002). *An Investigation of the validity of AP grades of 3 and a comparison of AP and non-AP student groups.* College Board Research Report No. 2002-9. Accessed July 30, 2014. research.collegeboard.org/publications/content/2012/05/investigation-validity-ap-grades-3-and-comparison-ap-and-non-ap-stude-0

Eagen, K., Lozano, J. B., Hurtado, S., & Case, M. H. (2013). *The American freshman: National norms, Fall 2013.* Los Angeles, CA: Higher Education Research Institute, UCLA.

Ewing, M., Huff, K., & Kaliski, P. (2010). Validating AP exam scores. In P. Sadler, G. Sonnert, R. H. Tai, & K. Klopfenstein (eds.), *AP: A critical examination of the Advanced Placement program* (pp 63–84). Cambridge, MA: Harvard Education Press.

International Baccalaureate Organization (IBO). (2010). *The IB diploma programme statistical bulletin.* Accessed August 12, 2014. www.ibo.org/facts/statbulletin/dpstats/documents/May2010Statisticalbulletin.pdf

Keng, L. & Dodd, B. G. (2008). *A comparison of college performance of AP and non-AP student groups.* Accessed July 30, 2014. research.collegeboard.org/publications/content/2012/05/comparison-college-performances-ap-and-non-ap-student-groups-10-subject

National Center for Education Statistics (2011). *America's high school graduates: Results of the 2009 NAEP high school transcript study.* Washington, DC: US Department of Education

National Center for Education Statistics (NCES). (2013). *Digest of education statistics, 2013 tables.* Washington, DC: US Department of Education

Pryor, J. H., Hurtado, S., DeAngelo, L., Palucki Blake, L., & Tran, S. (2010). *The American freshman: National norms, Fall 2010.* Los Angeles, CA: Higher Education Research Institute, UCLA.

Tyson, W., Lee, R., Borman, K. M., & Hanson, M. A. (2007). Science, Technology, Engineering, and Mathematics (STEM) pathways: High school science and math coursework and postsecondary degree attainment. *Journal of Education for Students Placed at Risk, 12*, 243–270, DOI: 10.1

Chapter 2

The Impact of Instructor and Institutional Factors on Students' Attitudes[1]

Gerhard Sonnert, *Harvard University*
Philip Sadler, *Harvard University and Smithsonian Institution*

In this chapter we examine how pedagogical strategies and characteristics of the calculus instructor as well as institutional features and policies of the mathematics department influence college calculus students' attitudes towards mathematics, using the survey data collected as part of the project. We employed factor analyses to develop a composite measure of students' attitudes toward mathematics, three composites of pedagogical features, and four composites of institutional characteristics. We used multivariate regression analyses to model the impact of these pedagogical and institutional characteristics on students' mathematics attitude, while accounting for a host of control variables.

The CSPCC project used a stratified random sampling to obtain a national sample of colleges and universities. It was difficult to get students and instructors to take both pre- and post-surveys, and to secure the responses of the institution's department chair or of the calculus coordinator. This contributed to many incomplete observations: Overall, 13,965 students, from 213 institutions, completed at least one of the surveys, but the final sample with all five surveys completed, which was used in this chapter, included 3,103 students in 308 classrooms at 123 institutions. Before presenting the results, we describe our methods, specifically the variables used and the analyses performed.

Dependent Variables

The dataset contains several candidates for dependent variables: Three of them concern students' attitudes towards mathematics in the areas of confidence, enjoyment, and persistence. On a 6-point scale, ranging from 0: (*Strongly Disagree*) to 5: (*Strongly Agree*), students rated the statements *I am confident in my mathematics abilities* and *I enjoy doing mathematics*. They also indicated their desire to study more mathematics on a 4-point scale, where 0 stood for *If I had a choice, I would never take another mathematics course*, and 3 stood for *If I had a choice, I would continue to take mathematics*. Each of these questions was asked in the pre-survey and the post-survey, so that it was possible to examine the change in their values from the start to the end of the students' calculus course.

The three variables indicating students' mathematics confidence, enjoyment, and persistence correlated considerably with each other (from $r = 0.52$ to $r = 0.70$). This made it useful to form a composite, called (final) mathematics attitude, to be used as a dependent variable. This choice required standardizing each of the three variables from the post-survey, averaging them, and then adjusting the standard deviation of the resulting composite to the standard deviation of the initial mathematics attitude composite and centering it on the average decline in the mathematics attitude score between the beginning and end of the semester. To create that composite of initial mathematics attitude, we had standardized, averaged, and re-standardized the corresponding variables from the beginning-of-the-semester survey.

1 The work presented in this chapter was, in part, published previously in Sonnert, Sadler, Sadler, & Bressoud (2015).

The composite mathematics attitude variable had the additional advantage that the normality of its distribution was boosted. Table 1 presents statistical information about the components of the attitude composite.

Table 1: Mean, standard deviation (SD), standard error (SE), effect size (ES), and standard error of ES of variables included in the attitude composite.

Variable	Timing	Mean	SD	SE	Δ	ES[a]	ES SE
Confidence in Math	Pre-survey	3.89	1.01	0.02			
	Post-survey	3.42	1.18	0.02	−0.47	−0.46	.02
Enjoyment of Math	Pre-survey	3.63	1.27	0.02			
	Post-survey	3.28	1.37	0.02	−0.35	−0.27	.02
Choice to take more Math	Pre-survey	1.93	1.02	0.02			
	Post-survey	1.84	1.08	0.02	−0.09	−0.09	.02
Δ Attitude Composite						−0.30	.02

Note: On average, student attitudes toward mathematics declined from beginning to end of a college calculus course. a. Effect Size is the change from pre- to post-survey in units of the pre-survey standard deviation for each variable.

The students' pre- and post-surveys also contained the participants' response to the question *Do you intend to take Calculus II?* We do not report on this variable because of problems that became obvious in the course of our analyses. We noticed that an institution at which every student was required to take Calculus II showed the strongest gains on that variable during the semester. Clearly, these gains had little to do with the pedagogy in Calculus I, but were presumably caused by initially oblivious students becoming aware of this universal requirement. In general, because course-taking intentions may be strongly influenced by study requirements and the students' awareness thereof, they appeared less suited as indicators of the quality of students' educational experience in Calculus I. Indeed, this variable exhibited a rather low correlation with the other three.

Control Variables

In correlational studies such as this, it is important to control for variables that can be reasonably expected to affect the outcome variable. Indeed, the believability of results from statistical models depends upon whether alternative hypotheses have been accounted for. This can be done by using variables that control for differences in students, classroom, and institutions, especially those differences that do not represent decisions that can be made or conditions that can be modified. Table 2 shows the control variables in the study.

Student Level
These variables included students' background characteristics, such as their gender and race or ethnicity (Hispanic, Black, Asian, and Other, with White serving as the baseline).[2] Students' socioeconomic status (SES) was modeled by the average of their parents' educational levels (on a 5-point scale: 1 = *Did not finish high school*; 2 = *High school*; 3 = *Some college*; 4 = *Four years of college*; 5 = *Graduate school*). If educational information was missing for one parent, the information for the other parent was used as the SES indicator. Several variables described the students' prior mathematics experience and preparation in high school. These included the students' grades in their most advanced mathematics class during high school (i.e., 4.33 = A+, 4 = A, 3.67 = A−, etc.) and whether the student had taken a non-AP calculus, AP Calculus AB, or AP Calculus BC class, respectively. The students' SAT mathematics score (200-800) was also used. If students reported no SAT mathematics score, but an ACT mathematics score, the latter was mapped onto the SAT mathematics scale, following the College Board (1999) concordance. Furthermore, we included potentially relevant college-related characteristics of students, such as the students' year of college, represented by the dummy variables sophomore, junior, senior, graduate student, and special student, with freshman as the baseline, and

---

2 The Hispanic category contains only those students selecting this category in ethnicity. They are not counted in other categories. The other categories are, more precisely, Non-Hispanic Black, Non-Hispanic Asian, etc., though we drop the "Non-Hispanic" part to facilitate the writing.

whether the students had previously taken a college precalculus class or a college calculus class. Students' career plans may also influence their attitudes toward mathematics, so the dummy variables engineering (including computing), science and mathematics, and medicine (including health) were used, with other career intentions serving as the baseline. Of course, the beginning-of-semester counterpart to the end-of-semester mathematics attitude composite also appeared as a control in our models.

Instructor Level

We used three control variables at the classroom/instructor level: the class average of the students' SAT mathematics scores (this variable is different from the individual students' SAT mathematics scores), the size of the calculus class, and the status of the instructor. The latter was modeled by a dummy variable distinguishing between graduate teaching assistants (coded as 1) and instructors of all other statuses (coded as 0).

Institution Level

At the institutional level, we added a control variable of institutional type. Using the Carnegie classification of institutions of higher education, we divided the 123 participating institutions into four broad categories by the highest degree in mathematics granted by the institution: AS-granting two-year colleges (N = 24); BA-granting four-year colleges (N = 13); MA-granting universities (N = 24); and finally PhD-granting universities (N = 62). In our regression analyses, three dummy variables represented institutional type, with the AS-granting institutions serving as the baseline.

Variables of Interest

A veritable multitude of items—121 items in total—that characterized instructor pedagogy and institutional characteristics was available from the surveys. To reduce this large number of variables to a smaller number of meaningful and robust composites, and to create parsimonious models, exploratory factor analysis was used. Because the items tended to correlate with others, groups of items might be viewed as indicators of a single underlying feature. Factor analysis is a procedure that helps to group items into a smaller number of underlying features, or factors, in a methodical way. Factor loadings, representing the correlations between items and factors, indicate how strongly items are associated with particular factors.

Instructor Pedagogy

The students' post-survey included 61 items about their calculus instructor's pedagogical practices, behaviors, and characteristics. The means of the student ratings of their individual instructor on each of these variables were used as indicators of the instructor's characteristics. A series of models with a different number of factors was run. Guiding considerations were parsimony and interpretability of the factors. We decided upon a three-factor solution (which explained 49.3% of the variance). The three factors were VARIMAX rotated[3], and variables with loadings below 0.4 were excluded from the composites to be formed. Thus, for the first composite, 22 variables were retained; for the second, 17; and for the third, 14, whereas eight variables were dropped from inclusion in any of these three factors.

As indicated by the factor analysis, the appropriate variables were then combined into three composites of pedagogical characteristics. To make the different formats of the individual variables commensurate, all variables were standardized (with a mean of zero and a standard deviation of 1), before adding them together. (Variables that loaded negatively on a factor were inverted (multiplied by –1) before addition.) The resulting composites were again standardized to ease comparison and interpretation. The three composites and their components are presented in Table 3.

Inspection of the variables loading on the first factor suggests that they represent what can be considered traditionally accepted good teaching practices (e.g., providing explanations that the students understood, and listening carefully to students' questions and comments). We call the composite derived from this factor *Good Teaching*. The second factor appears to aggregate variables related to the use of instructional technology (e.g., using graphing calculators, or computers). We call it *Technology*. Finally, the constituents of the third factor appear to be associated with pedagogical reform and novel approaches that aim at increasing the interactivity of the classroom experience and its relevance (e.g., emphasis on group work, students explaining their thinking, and having class discussions). We call this composite *Ambitious Teaching*.

---

3 A VARIMAX rotation rotates the coordinate system formed by the factors in a way that MAXimizes the sum of the VARIances of the squared loadings. The purpose is to have factors with a few high-loading items and a remainder of low-loading items, because this makes the interpretation of the factors easier. The factors remain orthogonal in the rotation.

Table 2: Mean and standard deviation (SD) of control variables used in predictive models.

Name	Description	N[a]	Mean	SD
Student level				
Gender	Gender (male = 1)	3,080	0.554	0.497
SES	Parental education (ranging 1-5)	3,094	3.657	1.000
Hispanic	Hispanic (yes = 1)	3,078	0.092	0.289
Black	Black(yes = 1)	3,071	0.033	0.178
Asian	Asian (yes = 1)	3,071	0.122	0.328
Other	Other (yes = 1)	3,071	0.039	0.195
Non-AP Calc.	Took non-AP calculus (yes = 1)	2,961	0.189	0.392
AP AB Calc.	Took AP Calculus AB (yes = 1)	2,961	0.378	0.485
AP BC Calc.	Took AP Calculus BC (yes = 1)	2,961	0.086	0.281
Highest grade	Grade in highest math class in high school (on 4-point scale)	2,961	3.557	0.720
SAT/ACT math	Mathematics SAT (ranging 200-800)	2,690	653	75
College precalc	Took a pre-calculus course in college prior to this course (yes = 1)	3,069	0.139	0.346
College calc	Took a calculus course in college prior to this one (yes = 1)	3,096	0.107	0.309
Sophomore	Sophomore (yes = 1)	3,090	0.118	0.323
Junior	Junior (yes = 1)	3,090	0.050	0.219
Senior	Senior (yes = 1)	3,090	0.020	0.139
Grad. stud.	Graduate student (yes = 1)	3,090	0.005	0.070
Special stud.	Special student (yes = 1)	3,090	0.024	0.153
Medicine	Career goal in medicine and health (yes = 1)	2,743	0.255	0.436
Science and math	Career goal in science or mathematics (yes = 1)	2,743	0.559	0.497
Engineering	Career goal in engineering or computing (yes = 1)	2,743	0.392	0.488
Class level				
Grad. instructor	Graduate teaching assistant (yes = 1)	308	0.114	0.318
Class size	Class size (N)	308	44.138	45.666
Avg. SAT math	Class average of mathematics SAT	297	639	56
Department level				
BA	BA-granting institution (yes = 1)	123	0.106	0.309
MA	MA-granting institution (yes = 1)	123	0.195	0.398
PhD	PhD-granting institution (yes = 1)	123	0.504	0.502

Note: a. N for variables represents the number of students, instructors, or coordinators answering the questions. For students, a number different from 3,103 shows that we needed to use multiple imputation. Similarly for instructors, a number different from 308 suggests that multiple imputation was used.

Table 3: Results of factor analysis of pedagogical variables.

Pedagogical Characteristics: Rotated Factor Pattern	Factor Loading
Factor 1: Good Teaching	
My calculus instructor provided explanations that were understandable	0.914
My calculus instructor listened carefully to my questions and comments	0.889
My calculus instructor helped me become a better problem solver	0.888
My calculus instructor allowed time for me to understand difficult ideas	0.862
My calculus instructor made me feel comfortable in asking questions during class	0.857
My calculus instructor presented more than one method for solving problems	0.836
My calculus instructor made class interesting	0.817
My calculus instructor asked questions to determine if I understood what was being discussed	0.803
My calculus exams were a good assessment of what I learned	0.776
My calculus instructor discussed applications of calculus	0.748
My calculus instructor acted as if I was capable of understanding the key ideas of calculus	0.745
How frequently did your instructor ask questions?	0.736
My calculus instructor encouraged students to seek help during office hours	0.716
My calculus instructor was available to make appointments outside of office hours, if needed	0.713
How frequently did your instructor prepare extra material to help students understand calculus concepts or procedures?	0.709
My exams were graded fairly	0.694
My calculus instructor encouraged students to enroll in Calculus II	0.643
My homework was graded fairly	0.627
How frequently did your instructor show how to work specific problems	0.553
Assignments completed outside of class time were challenging but doable	0.443
My calculus instructor made students feel nervous during class	-0.608
My calculus instructor discouraged me from wanting to continue taking calculus	-0.719
Factor 2: Technology	
Computing technologies during your calculus class: graphing calculator[a]	0.802
How did your instructor use technology during your class? To find answers to problems[a]	0.779
How did you use technology during your class? To find answers to problems[a]	0.757
Indicate how often the following occurred: My instructor used technology[b]	0.751
I used a graphing calculator during class[b]	0.742
How did your instructor use technology during your class? To illustrate ideas[a]	0.741

Table 3: Results of factor analysis of pedagogical variables. *continued*

Pedagogical Characteristics: Rotated Factor Pattern	Factor Loading
How did your instructor use technology during your class? To check answers after we worked them out by hand[a]	0.735
The assignments completed outside of class time required that I use technology to understand ideas	0.725
My instructor demonstrated mathematics with a graphing calculator[b]	0.724
Were you allowed to use a graphing calculator during your exams?[a]	0.700
How did you use technology during your class? To understand underlying mathematical ideas[a]	0.665
How did you use technology during your class? To check written answers after I worked them out by hand[a]	0.638
Computing technologies during your calculus class: computers[a]	0.619
My instructor demonstrated mathematics with computer algebra system[b]	0.580
How did your instructor use technology during your class? To illustrate motion/dynamic animations[a]	0.527
I used a computer algebra system[b]	0.465
Computing technologies during your calculus class: none[a]	-0.871

Factor 3: Ambitious Teaching	
How frequently did your instructor have students work with one another	0.718
Assignments completed outside of class time were submitted as a group project	0.714
The exam questions required that I solve word problems	0.695
The assignments completed outside of class time required that I solve word problems	0.640
How frequently did your instructor require you to explain your thinking on your homework?	0.613
The assignments completed outside of class time required that I solve problems unlike those done in class or in the book	0.609
How frequently did your instructor ask students to explain their thinking?	0.600
How frequently did your instructor hold whole-class discussion	0.577
The exam questions required that I solve problems unlike those done in class or in the book	0.575
How frequently did your instructor assign sections in your textbook for you to read before coming to class?	0.563
How frequently did your instructor have students give presentations?	0.555
How frequently did your instructor require you to explain your thinking on exams?	0.460
Assignments completed outside of class time were returned with helpful feedback/comments	0.451
How frequently did your instructor lecture?	–0.425

Notes: A three-factor solution was generated from 53 out of 61 student-reported variables of their instructor's pedagogical practices and decisions. Only variables with factor loadings greater than 0.400 (or for reversed scales, -0.400) are included. Unless otherwise noted, the item had a 6-point scale response. a. Item had a 5-point scale response. b. Item had a 4-point scale response.

Institutional Characteristics

The course coordinator questionnaire asked many questions about the institutional environment and characteristics of the mathematics departments. Analogously to our procedure for the instructor variables, we used exploratory factor analysis to reduce the available 60 variables in this area. In a four-factor solution (explaining 43% of the variance), 31 variables loading on the same factors were combined into composites of departmental characteristics (12 variables being retained for the first composite, 8 for the second, 6 for the third, and 5 for the fourth). To make the different formats of the individual variables commensurate, all variables were standardized (with a mean of zero and a standard deviation of 1) before adding them. The resulting four composites were again standardized to ease comparison and interpretation. The four composites and their components are presented in Table 4.

The first factor was labeled *Student Centered*, because it includes a variety of departmental measures designed to recruit undergraduate students and retain them, such as having a recruitment program, a mentoring program for students, special lectures and activities for undergraduate students, and faculty rewards for teaching excellence. The second factor we called the *TA Quality* factor. It bundles aspects of providing a high quality TA service by carefully selecting TAs, observing their teaching, mentoring them, and giving them opportunities for professional development. This factor also included the existence of special mathematics programs for minorities and women. The third factor was the *Tutoring Center* factor. It groups the resources and activities provided by a tutoring center, such as internet resources, computer-aided instruction, organized small-group tutoring or study sessions, and computer software. Finally, the fourth factor was labeled *Technology*. It includes the availability of training in mathematical software, of online course websites training, of online homework training, and of clickers training.

As one might expect, the departmental characteristics co-vary with the type of institution in which they are located. An Analysis of Variance (ANOVA) showed that the first factor, Student Centered, was significantly related to institutional category ($R^2 = 0.13$; $p = .0010$), with Associate-granting institutions scoring much lower than all others. On the second factor, TA Quality, we found that the PhD-granting institutions scored much higher than the others ($R^2 = 0.35$; $p < .0001$). On the third factor, Tutoring Centers, the Associate-granting institutions showed particularly elevated levels ($R^2 = 0.09$; $p = .0083$). No significant differences were found for the fourth factor, Technology ($p = .34$). Teaching assistants play the biggest role in teaching at PhD-granting institutions, obviously because these institutions have sizeable graduate student populations and teaching assistantships are typical jobs for graduate students. At the opposite end of the institutional scale, Associate-granting institutions focus on the model of the tutoring center for helping their students. See Chapters 6 and 10 for more details on student support and TA training, respectively.

Table 4: Results of factor analysis of institutional variables.

Institutional Characteristics: Rotated Factor Pattern	Factor Loading
Factor 1: Student Centered	
Department has a program to recruit promising high school students[a]	0.667
Department has a program that matches promising students with faculty mentors[a]	0.642
Department has a guest lecture series accessible to first year students[a]	0.633
Department has a program to recruit students from undeclared or undecided majors[a]	0.628
Weight given to excellence in teaching for untenured faculty for promotion and compensation[b]	0.620
Opportunities for Calc I students: Special mathematics lectures/colloquia not part of a mathematics club	0.573
Opportunities for Calc I students: Participation in undergraduate research in mathematics	0.480
Department has a program that matches promising students with upper classmen or graduate students[a]	0.449
Opportunities for Calc I students: Mathematics outreach to local K-12 schools	0.446
Opportunities for Calc I students: Assigned faculty advisors	0.439
Instructors who excel in the classroom are publicly acknowledged and/or rewarded for their teaching excellence[b]	0.437
Department has a career fair specifically targeted at careers in mathematics[a]	0.423
Factor 2: Teaching Assistant Quality	
Effective seminar or class for the purpose of TAs' professional development	0.777
Effective faculty observation of TAs for the purpose of evaluating their teaching	0.768
Effective screening of TAs before assigning them a recitation section	0.699
Effective pairing of new TAs with faculty mentors	0.628
Tutoring center: tutoring by graduate students	0.571
Effective interview process to select prospective TAs	0.492
Special mathematics programs to encourage minorities	0.444
Special mathematics programs to encourage women	0.442
Factor 3: Tutoring Center	
Tutoring center: internet resources	0.842
Tutoring center: computer-aided instruction	0.800
Tutoring center: organized small-group tutoring or study sessions	0.715
Tutoring center: media such as CDs or DVDs	0.646

Tutoring center: computer software such Maple, Mathematica, Matlab, etc.	0.586
Tutoring center: tutoring by part-time mathematics faculty	0.426
Factor 4: Technology	
Mathematica, Maple, Matlab, etc. training available	0.759
Online course websites training available	0.746
Online homework training available	0.718
Clickers training available	0.598
Mathematica, Maple, Matlab, etc. available, recommended, or required[b]	0.429

Notes: A four-factor solution was generated from 60 institution-level variables. Only the 31 variables with factor loadings greater than 0.400 (or for reversed scales, –0.400) are included. Unless otherwise noted, the response was dichotomous. a. Item had a 5-point scale response. b. Item had a 4-point scale response.

Methods of Analysis

Because we are primarily interested in explaining the variance in students' attitude at the end of their calculus course through differences at the course or instructor level and institutional level, we employ a statistical method that helps to account for differences at the higher levels, while controlling for subjects' backgrounds. Hierarchical linear modeling (HLM) is the most appropriate method here, because it allows us to analyze data that are structured at several levels (in our case, students within classrooms within institutions). This also helps to deal with the different numbers of students in classrooms and institutions; otherwise the larger groups would overly impact our results. In the course of our analyses, we found that, although the theoretical data structure is three-tiered (students-class-department), the introduction of the class- and department-level predictors absorbed the variance at these two levels so that simplified (i.e., flat) models containing only the student level became feasible.

Missing values are always an issue in studies such as these in which students may not fill out every question for a variety of reasons. Even though the individual variables included in our multivariate models typically have quite low percentages of missing values (2% on average; max 13%), the percentages accumulate and lead to rather high losses in the standard method of listwise deletion of observations (29%). Hence, the method of multiple imputation of missing values was used (Rubin 1976, 1987, 1996). All statistical analyses were carried out in the SAS 9.2 statistical software package.

Results

Before building multivariate models to investigate what effects different instructor pedagogy and departmental characteristics had on students' mathematics attitudes, we note the changes in students' mathematics attitudes (i.e., mathematics confidence, enjoyment, and persistence) that occurred between the beginning and end of their calculus courses. All changes were in the negative direction. The students' mathematics confidence dropped, on average, 0.47 points on the 6-point rating scale, corresponding to an effect size of 0.46 (in units of the standard deviation of the pre-course rating). The students' self-reported enjoyment of mathematics dropped 0.35 points (or 0.27 in the effect size metric). The students' desire to persist in studying mathematics fell 0.09 points of the 4-point rating scale (effect size: 0.09). Finally, the mathematics attitude composite fell by 0.30 (in units of the standard deviation of the pre-course composite).

At the beginning of the multivariate analysis, unrestricted means hierarchical linear models (HLM) were run to determine how the outcome variance was partitioned into the three levels (students, classrooms, departments). As one might expect, the lion's share of the variance was associated with the student level: prior experience with, preparation in, and, most of all, prior attitudes towards mathematics powerfully shape students' attitudes at the end of their calculus class. Nonetheless, there was significant variance at the class (or instructor) level, and at the departmental level. As mentioned, the independent variables absorbed the variance at those two upper levels, so that the models could be simplified to ordinary regressions. Table 5 summarizes the results of our regression models for the mathematics attitude composite. Both a main effects and an interaction model are listed. Each of these models of final mathematics attitude explains more than 50% of the variance.

We briefly survey the main effects of the various control variables. The students' initial attitudes powerfully predicted their attitudes at the end of the semester. It showed a large effect size—a one standard deviation difference corresponded to almost a two-thirds of a standard deviation difference in the outcome (0.65). This suggests that this attitude is fairly viscous, which one might expect if one realizes that mathematics education is a protracted and incremental process that, at that point, has been going on for more than a decade.

As expected, the effects of strong prior mathematics experiences and preparation, such as taking more rigorous calculus courses in high school and achieving a good grade in the most advanced high school mathematics class, were strong and pervasive.

On the other hand, it is noteworthy that having previously taken either a precalculus or calculus course in college had no significant effect. Sophomores reported a more positive mathematics attitude than did freshmen. The students' career plans had the expected effects, with students bound for a science or mathematics career scoring higher on mathematics attitude than did students with a career interest outside the STEM fields.

Moreover, male students scored significantly higher than females on the mathematics attitude composite. The racial or ethnic background did not make much of a difference, with the exception that the Other group reported lower scores than did Whites. None of the three classroom or instructor level variables was significant, and neither were the dummy variables representing type of institution.

We now turn to the variables of interest. In the main effects models, Good Teaching had a positive effect. The use of Technology was not significant. Ambitious Teaching had a negative effect. In terms of relative effect sizes, the positive effect of Good Teaching far outweighed the negative effect of Ambitious Teaching, the former being nearly three times as large. As to the institutional composites, TA Quality was negatively associated with students' mathematics attitudes, whereas Tutoring Center had a positive association. The latter effect appears quite straightforward, but the former is, at first view, counterintuitive. In this case, it behooves us to remember that our statistical models are correlational, not causal. Rather than departmental attention to quality TAs depressing students' mathematics attitudes per se, it may be more plausible that departments focused on improving TA quality in a reaction to problems in this area that to some extent might still linger on.

We further estimated the following series of models with various sets of interactions: among the instructor characteristics and institution characteristics themselves, between the instructor and institution characteristics and the students' prior attitudes, between the instructor and institution characteristics and the students' SAT/ACT mathematics score, between the instructor and institution characteristics and the classroom or instructor level controls (class size, class SAT mathematics average, and instructor status), and between instructor and institution characteristics and institutional type. All interactions thus identified as significant were then entered into a single model, and the ones that dropped below significance level were deleted. Model 2 includes the remaining four significant interactions.

Two of them were between the students' prior attitudes and instructor characteristics. Good Teaching improved the mathematics attitudes of students with initially negative attitudes more than it did the attitudes of students who already came to the calculus class with a more positive attitude. By contrast, Ambitious Teaching was more beneficial (in terms of influencing students' mathematics attitudes) for students with initially more positive attitudes than for students with initially more negative attitudes. In addition, a graduate teaching assistant who used a lot of Technology was a particularly disadvantageous combination. Finally, Ambitious Teaching worked better in larger than in smaller classrooms.

Discussion

We focused on two major categories of factors in our analysis of the survey, at the instructor level and at the institution level. We discuss the effects we observed.

Table 5: Regression models predicting students' final mathematics attitude.

	Model 1		Model 2	
Parameter	Estimate	Sig.	Estimate	Sig.
Intercept	−0.787	**	−0.821	**
Student Level				
Prior attitude	0.646	***	0.628	***
Gender	0.095	**	0.089	**
SES	−0.005		−0.008	
Hispanic	−0.072		−0.080	
Black	−0.002		0.007	
Asian	0.064		0.076	
Other	−0.203	**	−0.194	***
Non-AP Calculus	0.140	**	0.144	**
AP AB Calculus	0.196	***	0.202	***
AP BC Calculus	0.235	***	0.234	***
Highest grade	0.071	***	0.070	**
SAT/ACT math	0.001	**	0.001	**
College precalculus	−0.04		−0.030	
College calculus	0.034		0.032	
Sophomore	0.125	*	0.095	
Junior	0.078		0.055	
Senior	−0.061		−0.119	
Grad. student	0.377		0.361	
Special student	0.135		0.125	
Medicine	0.022		0.015	
Science & math	0.223	***	0.224	***
Engineering	0.062		0.058	
Class Level				
Grad. instructor	−0.066		−0.118	
Class size	0.000		0.001	**
Avg. SAT/ACT math	−0.001		−0.001	
Good Teaching	0.247	***	0.241	***
Technology	0.002		0.019	
Ambitious Teaching	−0.085	***	−0.148	***
Department Level				
BA	0.025		0.044	
MA	0.041		0.030	
PhD	0.034		−0.014	
Student-Centered	0.021		0.002	
TA Quality	−0.080	***	−0.051	*
Tutoring Center	0.044	*	0.039	
Technology	0.006		−0.003	

	Model 1	Model 2	
Interactions			
Prior attitude x Good Teaching		–0.050	**
Prior attitude x Ambitious Teaching		0.038	**
Graduate instructor x Technology (class)		–0.168	*
Class size x Ambitious Teaching		0.002	***
R^2	0.509	0.510	
N	3,103	3,103	

Notes: A main effects model (Model 1) and an interaction model (Model 2) are presented. $* p < .05; ** p < .01; *** p < .001$.

Instructor Factors

The students' mathematics attitudes became substantially more negative (close to a third of a standard deviation), on average, during their college calculus course. To some degree, this trend might be owed to a general reality check that occurs when students enter college. The weaker high school students are no longer present, and the levels of challenge and expected performance are raised. Some calculus professors may accept the decline in students' mathematics attitudes as a fact of life, others may bemoan it—but, as we found, professors do exert at least some degree of influence on the trend. It would be interesting to compare the calculus results with those in other disciplines, such as physics and other STEM fields, to determine to what extent the drop in students' mathematics attitudes parallels trends in other fields, and to what extent it might be unique to mathematics.

Going beneath the surface level of declining averages, our multivariate analyses explored what difference students' experiences in the college calculus classroom made in shaping their mathematics attitudes, after controlling for many of their background characteristics and prior experiences. In college calculus, the amount of Technology use does not influence students' attitudes about mathematics one way or the other. In this respect, the math wars controversies concerning the use of technology (Ball et al., 2005; Schoen, Fey, Hirsch, & Coxford, 1999) turn out to be not really relevant. As to Good Teaching, it may not come as a surprise that these practices improve students' attitudes about mathematics. The underlying characteristics are what most people would consider traits and behaviors of good teachers—and what students typically appreciate in their teachers. Some of these features are further explored in Chapter 7 of this volume. What may require more probing is why Ambitious Teaching is negatively related to students' attitudes. Is it that students tend to dislike professors' attempts at engaging them in more active modes of participation? Do they resent having to talk or listening to other students talk in class? Do students not share their instructors' ideas about what is good for them (the students)? Is Ambitious Teaching often implemented poorly or in ways that put students off?

Institutional Factors

Although we found significant effects of department-level variables on calculus students' mathematics attitudes and interest, we should also note that the pedagogy students experienced in their calculus class had stronger effects—and even stronger effects were located at the student level, especially students' prior attitudes, but also various indicators of their mathematics preparation.

On the whole, the leverage of departmental characteristics on students' mathematics attitudes appears limited in this dataset. We should note, however, that a better study of the effects of departmental characteristics would be a longitudinal one that observes students' mathematics attitudes and attitudinal changes over a period of time before and after a change in the departmental environment.

One might also contemplate indirect effects, that is, that the effects of departmental characteristics on students' mathematics attitudes are mediated through the instructors' pedagogical practices. For instance, one might surmise that a Student-Centered department (which, among other things, rewards good teaching) would be associated with instructors' Good Teaching, which in turn is, as we have found, positively associated with students' mathematics attitude. Interestingly, however, the correlation between a Student-Centered department and the instructors' Good Teaching was negative ($r = -.14, p = .0115$). This might reinforce the earlier interpretation of departments' student-centeredness being an indicator of (or even a countermeasure against) troubles at the teaching front. By contrast, departmental student-centeredness positively correlated with instructors' Ambitious Teaching ($r = .20, p = .0005$). Instructors at Student-Centered departments were more likely to engage in the ambitious practices—but those practices were found to have negative effects on students' mathematics attitudes. Again, causality is uncertain, and it is unclear what these correlations really mean.

Finally, we readily acknowledge that the outcomes discussed in this chapter are only half of the story. The other half is, of course, the amount of mathematics knowledge and skills learned in the class, which was not a focus of this study. Nonetheless, the students' attitudes toward mathematics are also crucial because they may influence future career-related choices. In addition, if more students emerge from their college mathematics education with a sense of confidence and enjoyment, and fewer with a sense of dread, this will help make the general societal outlook on mathematics more favorable—itself a necessary condition of success for a society grounded in high tech and science.

Conclusion

Students taking college calculus exhibited a reduction in positive attitude toward mathematics, which can affect their career aspirations and desire to take more mathematics. This may be the result of increased rigor when compared with pre-college coursework.

Instructor pedagogy, identified through the factor analysis of 61 student-reported variables, was investigated for its impact on students' mathematics attitudes:

1. Instructors who employed generally accepted good teaching practices (e.g., clarity in presentation and answering questions, useful homework, fair exams, help outside of class), were found to have the most positive impact, particularly with students who began with weaker initial mathematics attitudes.
2. Use of educational technology (e.g., graphing calculators, for demonstrations, in homework), on average, was found to have no impact on attitudes, except when used by graduate student instructors, which negatively affected students' mathematics attitudes.
3. Ambitious teaching (e.g., group work, word problems, flipped reading, student explanations of thinking) had a small negative impact on student attitudes.

Furthermore, some departmental/institutional differences played out in their impact on student attitudes. Neither a student-centered approach nor the use of technology was found to influence student attitudes. The existence and support of a tutoring center where students could get help outside of class were found to have a positive impact. By contrast, students' mathematics attitudes were negatively associated efforts to improve teaching assistant quality.

This study provides support for efforts to improve calculus teaching by training faculty and graduate students to use traditional good teaching practices through professional development workshops and courses. As currently implemented, technology and ambitious pedagogical practices, while no doubt effective in certain classrooms, do not appear to have a reliable, positive impact on student attitudes toward mathematics. Hence, mathematics departments may find that efforts to improve student support through fostering good teaching (especially in courses for students who are mathematically weaker) and tutoring centers will have a bigger payoff than increasing the use of technology or student-centered activities, which tend to most benefit the already mathematics-prone students.

References

Ball, D. L., Ferrini-Mundy, J., Kilpatrick, J., Milgram, R. J., Schmid, W., & Schaar, R. (2005). Reaching for common ground in K-12 mathematics education. *Notices of the AMS, 52*(9), 1055–1058.

College Board Office of Research and Development (1999). *Concordance between SAT I and Act scores for individual students.* Report RN-07 (June 1999). New York: The College Board.

Rubin, D. B. (1976). Inference and missing data. *Biometrica, 63*, 581–592.

Rubin, D. B. (1987). *Multiple imputation for nonresponse in surveys.* New York: John Wiley & Sons.

Rubin, D. B. (1996). Multiple imputation after 18+ years. *Journal of the American Statistical Association, 91*, 473–489.

Schoen, H. L., Fey, J. T., Hirsch, C. R., & Coxford, A. F. (1999). Issues and options in the math wars. *Phi Delta Kappan, 80*, 444–453.

Sonnert, G., Sadler, P. M., Sadler, S. M., & Bressoud, D. M. (2015). The impact of instructor pedagogy on college calculus students' attitude toward mathematics. *International Journal of Mathematical Education in Science and Technology, 46*(3), 370–387.

Chapter 3

The Institutional Context

Natalie E. Selinski, *Leibniz-Universität Hannover*
Hayley Milbourne, *San Diego State University*

In this chapter we provide insight into the context of Calculus I at the 17 institutions selected for the case study visits and, when possible, compare selected institutions to the other colleges and universities using the national survey data. In doing so, we introduce the reader to the atmosphere at each of the selected institutions and provide the context for studies of other factors associated with success in Calculus I.

Our discussion on institutional context begins with features specific to the Calculus I course: variations in mainstream Calculus I at different institutions, the format of the mainstream Calculus I courses, class size, and the professional rank of Calculus I instructors. We then broaden the discussion to the mathematics department and the institution. The reader is introduced to key aspects of the departmental and institutional environment, with an emphasis on support for instructional innovation. Lastly, we examine the types of technologies that were used in the teaching and learning of Calculus I.

Variations in Calculus I and the Format of Calculus I Courses

As expected, some variations in Calculus I are based on students' intended majors, such as specific calculus courses for business, management, economics, the social sciences or other non-science, technology, engineering, and mathematics (STEM) fields. Other variations exist within the mainstream calculus sequence for STEM-intending students. As detailed in the introduction to this volume, our study was restricted to mainstream Calculus I courses.

Institutions tailored the mainstream Calculus I variations they offered and the format of their classes, including recitation and lab sessions, based on the goals of the institution, the needs of the students, and the resources available to the department. At PTI[1], for example, the university has seven-week terms, instead of the more common 14- to16-week terms, and hence the standard offering of Calculus I meets for an intense seven-week period. The chair from PTI described their situation as follows:

> *So we have four, seven-week terms. Students… particularly in Calculus, they meet four times a week for an hour with the instructor. They meet for an instructional conference with a graduate student or a PLA [peer learning assistant] for one hour a week. And then they have lab for another hour a week, so Calculus is six hours a week for seven weeks. Now the calculus material is divided into four [terms].*

---

1 See the Preface for the list of institution identifiers used in the study.

PTI also offers a "stretched out" Calculus I that lasts for two seven-week terms. While this variation was found at only one selected institution, PTI, stretched out Calculus I is a notable example of how the selected institutions adapted to their specific situations. At PTI, a short, intensive Calculus I course was the norm, given the institution's seven-week terms. The stretched out calculus was offered for students needing more algebraic review, and this was done in the context of the calculus course.

There were other variations in the format and frequency of classes in Calculus I courses at the selected institutions. For example, Calculus I courses at AS-granting two-year colleges typically met two or three times per week, while Calculus I courses at other institution types typically met three or more times per week, including recitation and lab sessions. Recitation sessions were offered at some selected BA-granting four-year colleges, MA-granting universities, and PhD-granting universities, specifically at BA2, MA 1, LPrU, PTU, LPU2, and PTI. Less common were lab sessions offered at one AS-granting two-year college (TY2) and two PhD-granting institutions (PTU and PTI).

Several selected institutions offered mainstream Calculus I courses that varied in the pacing or depth of the course. One common variation of these mainstream courses was Honors Calculus I. Honors courses were found at five of the selected institutions (TY2, MA3, MA4, LPrU, and LPU2). While the majority of these courses were at MA-granting universities and PhD-granting universities, there was one AS-granting two-year college offering mainstream Calculus I in this more in-depth and higher-paced variation.

Scheduling was also a concern for students, and some institutions (TY2, TY4, BA4, and LPrU) accommodated students' needs by offering daytime and evening Calculus I sections. This was particularly true at AS-granting two-year colleges, which worked to accommodate students who balance work and family commitments with their studies.

Furthermore, some universities offered a way for students who started the term in Calculus I but then found that their prerequisite knowledge was lacking to drop back and take precalculus. At LPU1, for example, when students did poorly on the first exam, they were given the opportunity to exit calculus and enroll in a precalculus course that started after that exam. The benefit for the students was that they received a just-in-time preparatory course without any indication on their transcripts that they initially enrolled in calculus. This also benefits the delivery of Calculus I, because students who remained in the course were better prepared.

The variations we identified at the selected case-study institutions are similarly documented in the literature. Existing research shows the variety of discipline-specific calculus courses available at many schools, ranging from Business Calculus to Calculus for the Life Sciences. For example, Klingbeil, Mercer, Rattan, Raymer, & Reynolds (2004) described a calculus course that was designed for engineering students by including applications related to engineering, and showed it retained more students in the major.

Even within mainstream Calculus I courses variations exist in the pace and format of the course. For example, at Syracuse University, there are two versions of Calculus I: one for students who had calculus in high school and one for those who had not (Doerr, Staniec, & O'Niel, 2012). At Macalester College, it was found that students tended to come in having already taken calculus in high school but showed little interest in taking more mathematics in college (Bressoud, 2009). In response, the college designed a new calculus course that would be attractive to students. This course is different from students' high school calculus in that it emphasizes mathematical modeling, active pedagogy, and technology using the software R.

Class Size

Class size has been a topic of increasing importance as enrollment numbers grow and budgets shrink (Blair, Kirkman, & Maxwell, 2013; Hornsby & Osman, 2014). However, studies on the effect of class size on student success have not been conclusive. For example, several studies, not specific to mathematics, show a negative association between class sizes and student achievement (Keil & Parell, 1997; Kokkelenberg, Dillon, & Christy, 2008). In contrast, Williams, Cook, Quinn, & Jensen (1985) found that class size was, in fact, not a good predictor of student achievement. Additionally, others (e.g., Stockton, 1960; Warren, 1988) found that there was no significant difference in student achievement between large and small class sizes. Both Millett (2002) and Spencer (1995) suggest that the class size makes far less of a difference than what happens in the classroom. While the class sizes at SUNY Potsdam are small, Spencer (1995) argues that they cannot be identified as the source of success. Similarly, Millet (2002) noted that large classes could be effective by creating a "small class" environment.

Consistent with the literature, we found that class size is not a definitive indicator of student success in Calculus I. Consider Table 1, which shows the mean class size for Calculus I sections at selected and non-selected institutions by institution type. We conducted an independent-samples t-test to compare mean class sizes at each institution type for selected and non-selected institutions as reported by instructors on the national survey. These tests showed no significant difference in the means between selected and non-selected institutions.[2]

Also of interest in Table 1 are the large standard deviations at PhD-granting institutions, both selected and non-selected. We attribute this occurrence at PhD-granting institutions and no other institution type to the larger number of Calculus I sections and greater variation in class size among Calculus I sections at PhD-granting institutions.

Table 1: Comparison of mean class sizes for Calculus I sections at selected and non-selected institutions.

Institution Type[a]	Selected		Non-selected	
	M (SD)	N	M (SD)	N
4Y-Coll (BA)	25.46 (4.457)	14	25.29 (6.585)	47
Univ (MA)	26.50 (5.334)	12	29.72 (12.989)	30
Univ (PhD)	54.70 (57.045)	47	52.95 (53.661)	164

Note: a. Two-year colleges were omitted from this analysis due to small sample size.

Data from site visits at selected institutions depicted a similar pattern in class size. Most AS-granting two-year colleges, BA-granting four-year colleges, and MA-granting universities had Calculus I sections averaging 25-40 students. In addition to the smaller total student enrollment typical of these institution types, the institutions also adhered to maximum class sizes. For example, at three out of the five selected AS-granting two-year colleges, class sizes were strictly capped at 30-35 students. The purpose of restricting class size varied as well. While some institutions attributed smaller caps on class size to limited physical space in classrooms, individuals at several institutions expressed an appreciation for the more active learning possible with a smaller class size. One instructor at MA 3 described this sentiment:

> *I think that it's so important for students to be active and not passive in the classroom, and with these small classes you can be active. And I think that most of the people here do want to have student involvement, have active classrooms, and more students participate.*

Thus, small class size was seen as benefiting students' active engagement, and thus important to maintain. Administrators voiced the importance of small classes as well. For example, the provost at LPU1 noted,

> *Most students, in my observation, draw energy from each other and so they're actually much more engaged when they have an opportunity to talk to each other than when they're just sitting in a class listening.*

The exception to the small-class-size trend is at PhD-granting universities. At two of five selected PhD-granting universities (LPU2 and LPrU), the majority of class sessions occurred in large lectures of 150-250 students. In these situations, students were simultaneously enrolled in recitation sections of 30-40 students. These two universities demonstrate that it is possible to have successful Calculus I programs that utilize large-lecture formats. A student at LPrU describes aspects of how these large lectures can be used by students:

> *I'm in one of the sections where we have the big lecture with over 100 people as well as the smaller class [recitation section] with 30-40 people. So the big lecture, I don't raise my hand at all.... I pay attention, I take notes, and it's helpful. Then when I get to the smaller lecture, that's the time when I can ask questions if I want to, make comments, go up to the board, maybe do a problem, and it's a lot more interactive.*

---

2 The data source for our statistical analysis of class size and all other statistical tests comes from the national survey data (see Hsu, Mesa, & The Calculus Case Collective, 2014).

Thus, the students use the large lecture, as one may expect, primarily to be focused on the instructor exposing the class to the material and the students attentively following and taking notes. Then these lectures are coupled with small sections with a more student-centered, interactive environment. As suggested by the quoted student, a student should be engaged in both formats, be it paying attention to the lecture or doing problems on the board in recitation, for this combination to be successful.

Who Teaches Calculus I?

At selected institutions we found the majority of Calculus I courses to be taught by ladder-rank faculty with some notable exceptions. Table 2 shows the percentage of faculty teaching Calculus I of different professional ranks at selected and non-selected institutions by each institution type. Faculty were asked in the national survey to identify themselves as tenured or tenure-track (Tenure-track), full-time non-tenure-track (Full-time-Other), part-time faculty (Part-time), or, in the case of MA- and PhD-granting universities, graduate teaching assistants (GTAs).

No statistical significance was found in the relationship between faculty professional rank and type of institution, except for the PhD-granting universities. Nevertheless, the percentages in Table 2 highlight a couple of interesting trends.

First, at BA-granting four-year colleges and MA-granting universities, full-time faculty—most of whom are tenure-track—taught Calculus I. Interviews conducted during the case-study visits confirmed these findings for the selected institutions, with a few notable additions and exceptions. Full-time non-ladder-rank faculty were often assigned to teach Calculus I only when they were highly experienced, having previously taught the course for the department. The importance of experience also applied to adjunct faculty teaching Calculus I, such as at BA4, where known and trusted adjunct instructors taught the evening sections. Faculty of all ranks were aware of the importance of experience, as explained by one instructor at MA 1: "As I told you, first of all the faculty are veterans. You know every one of us has taught this several times and that's a help."

Second, Table 2 calls attention to the role of GTAs in teaching Calculus I at universities granting graduate degrees in mathematics. While the quantitative analysis of the national survey data in Table 2 only accounts for GTAs who were the teacher of record, our review of the case study data showed GTAs play a much broader role. In the case of the MA- and some PhD-granting universities, GTAs were employed to assist the teacher of record with in-class activities or to conduct recitation or problem-solving sessions. At some of the selected PhD-granting universities, GTAs were employed to help create a "small class" feeling within the larger sections during recitation sections. For example, at LPU2 one instructor stated, "The main purpose for the TAs ideally is that they have a more intimate relationship with the students." More on the specific role of GTAs can be found in Chapter 10.

Table 2: Percentage of faculty teaching Calculus I of different professional ranks at selected and non-selected institutions.

Institution[a] and Rank	Selected Institutions N = 83	Non-Selected Institutions N = 264
4Y-Coll (BA)	N = 12	N = 42
Tenure-track	86%	79%
Full-time-Other	7%	15%
Part-time	7%	6%
Univ (MA)	N = 12	N = 32
Tenure-track	83%	78%
Full-time-Other	8%	6%
Part-time	8%	13%
GTA	0%	3%
Univ (PhD)**	N = 59	N = 190
Tenure-track	10%	33%
Full-time-Other	41%	37%
Part-time	5%	5%
GTA	44%	25%

Note: N refers to number of institutions. a. Two-year colleges were omitted from this analysis due to small sample size. ** $p < .05$. Source: maalongdatafile.

Table 2 seems to indicate a unique situation regarding Calculus I instructors at PhD-granting universities, namely the predominance of GTAs as the teacher of record at selected institutions. This is not an accurate representation, because there were differences in the number of GTAs assigned to teach Calculus I by individual institutions. Table 3 elucidates this point by indicating the percentage of Calculus I instructors of the different professional ranks at each of the selected PhD-granting universities. Thus, LPU1 had significantly more instructors teaching Calculus I than all the other institutions combined, the majority of whom were GTAs. Thus, when calculating the percentage of GTA Calculus I instructors for all selected PhD-granting universities, the results were skewed by the large percentage of GTAs at LPU1.

Table 3: Number and percentage of faculty teaching Calculus I of different professional ranks at selected PhD-granting universities.

University	Tenure-track		Full-time – Other		Part-time		GTA	
	N	%	N	%	N	%	N	%
LPU2	0	0	4	100	0	0	0	0
LPrU	3	100	0	0	0	0	0	0
PTI	1	13	5	62	2	25	0	0
LPU1	1	3	10	29	0	0	23	68
PTU	1	10	5	50	1	10	3	30

Another unique feature of the PhD-granting universities is the prevalence of full-time non-ladder-rank faculty teaching Calculus I. A closer examination of these positions in the case-study data showed that two of the universities (LPU2 and LPU1) have non-research, teaching-specific secured-employment positions, in particular for but not limited to Calculus I instructors and course coordinators. These positions were created to allow dedicated members of the faculty to focus solely on teaching and course coordination. Such positions are part of a larger trend of full-time faculty in mathematics departments (Vélez, Maxwell, & Rose, 2014) and university mathematics teaching positions with security of employment (Blair et al., 2013).

Much as we have seen in our analyses, higher education research has documented increased diversity in faculty members' professional rank. As a result, studies are emerging regarding the effect of faculty status on student outcomes. The findings are mixed and inconclusive. For example, Ehrenberg & Zhang (2005) considered the data from the College Board on the percentages of tenure or tenure-track faculty and the graduation rates in all departments at institutions across the United States. From these data they concluded that a 10-percentage point increase in the number of part-time faculty at an institution results in about a 2.65-percentage point reduction in graduation rates. In contrast, Cross & Goldenberg (2003) concluded through a study of course evaluation data that the use of non-tenure-track faculty is highly effective for lower division courses. Their measurement of teacher effectiveness was based on how high students ranked their professor in the evaluations, and thus accounting for how students responded to the instructor. Cross & Goldenberg (2003) went on to hypothesize that these higher evaluation scores resulted from hiring teaching specialists, those qualified to teach in particular areas, for the evaluated positions. Thus, the instructors were "extremely dedicated [to] and highly competent [for]" their specific teaching positions (Cross & Goldenberg, 2003, p. 56). Their results suggest the possible advantages of teaching positions with secure employment like those at LPU2 and LPU1.

Institutional and Departmental Environment

As mentioned earlier, the size of the class and format of the course are not necessarily the most important factors in having a successful Calculus I program. Stigler & Hiebert (2004) explain the importance of broader cultural and environmental factors:

> *A focus on teaching must avoid the temptation to consider only the superficial aspects of teaching: the organization, tools, curriculum, content, and textbooks. The cultural activity of teaching—the ways in which the teacher and students interact about the subject—can be more powerful than the curriculum materials that teachers use. ... We must find a way to change not just individual teachers, but the culture of teaching itself. (p. 16)*

In a similar call to not focus solely on superficial features, the MAA's *Curriculum Guide* (CUPM, 2004) identifies six recommendations for undergraduate mathematics: regular evaluations of courses and programs, an emphasis on developing mathematical thinking and communication skills, a stress on interconnections within the mathematical sciences, promotion of interdisciplinary connections, use of technology to support problem solving and promote understanding, and faculty support for curricular and instructional improvement. These research findings suggest there are aspects of the institutional and departmental environment that are critical to success in the classroom. This section focuses on identifying these aspects of institutional and departmental environment that fostered successful Calculus I programs.

A review of the case study data, including but not limited to interviews from the visits and summaries about the Calculus I program at each selected institution following the case study visits, gave rise to three general environmental aspects to which almost all selected institutions, at least in part, attribute their success: communication and collegiality, quality teachers, and support for pedagogical innovations.

Communication and Collegiality

Almost every selected institution identified an atmosphere of collaboration, collegiality, and open communication as part of their success. Administration, faculty, and students reported frequent, open communication between each group and among themselves. The chair at BA1 described this atmosphere:

We're a group of people who care deeply about teaching, and so we have hallway conversations about teaching, we have department meetings about teaching, and so we're small enough and collaborative enough that we have open conversations about our instruction. Everybody here is willing to share all their materials. People create stuff and immediately make it available to everybody else. People will come to your classroom if you ask them to give you some feedback on what you're doing. So I think in those ways, we're all supporting each other's innovations and efforts to improve.

Many tangible and less-discernible features facilitated this emphasis on communication and collegiality. One feature that often reflected the importance of collegiality was the physical space where faculty and students work. For example, adjunct faculty at BA4 shared a common office space in which they could work on and discuss the courses they were teaching together. A common physical space played an even greater role in facilitating communication and collaboration at MA 2, as explained by one instructor:

We've got the fishbowl here in the middle and that's where the students congregate and then they're constantly coming out and asking us questions or things. So it's very much an open door sort of policy and the faculty and students interact almost non-stop I'd say. And I'm probably one of the more reclusive ones, if anything, in terms of I don't venture into the fishbowl real often to interact with students there, but many of the faculty I think are extremely involved in working with the students on a daily basis.

As explained by the instructor at MA 2, communication and collegiality were forged by the creation of a common workspace, which he refers to as the "fishbowl," where students and faculty frequently interacted.

Students at many institutions also described close, collaborative communities among themselves. Of particular note are two PhD-granting universities, LPrU and PTI. LPrU was founded by a religious organization, and 99% of the student population is affiliated with this religion. This provided a common set of values for most students. Among the values of the religion is commitment to education, which many students openly embraced and cited in their interviews.

Even for institutions that were not founded on such common cultural foundations, it is possible to build a common value system and collaborative environment. For example, students at PTI acknowledged a close relationship with and support regarding their academic pursuits from their peers. This student culture was built through structures such as student cohorts for the calculus sequence (which almost all students take) and an approach to teaching and learning that is intended to prepare students for working on difficult problems in industry by creating an environment where students are comfortable working in teams, taking intellectual risks, tackling big projects, and solving open-ended problems. More generally, the system of coordination at PhD-granting institutions seems to greatly contribute to communication and collegiality (see Chapter 9).

Quality Teachers

When asked what was the reason for the Calculus I program's success, administration, faculty, and students at nearly every institution cited quality teachers. Hiring and retaining high quality teachers was supported in explicit and meaningful ways that elevate the importance of teaching at the selected institutions. For example, at TY3 administration shielded faculty from non-teaching concerns, so instructors could focus on their responsibilities as teachers. At institutions where scholarship was expected, teaching was just as important in hiring and promotions. Above all, having quality teachers in Calculus I was an expectation and point of pride for these department, as expressed by one instructor at PTU: "One thing I've really been impressed with in the math department here … is people really care whether or not someone's a good teacher." Further investigation into what makes for quality teachers, in particular what defines good teaching and beyond, are discussed in Chapters 7 and 8.

Support for Pedagogical Innovations

Departments and institutions showed their support for pedagogical innovations in a variety of ways. Such innovations include but are not limited to implementing new instructional techniques in the classroom (e.g., flipped classrooms, inquiry-oriented learning, etc.) and exploring the use of technology in the classroom (e.g., clickers or smart boards). At some selected institutions such as TY1 and BA0, there was an expectation that instructors continually enhance their teaching and pursue innovations, despite having no incentives for such innovations. Even when external incentives, support, or funds were available, the impetus to improve one's teaching and try out more student-centered pedagogical techniques came from the instructor. As one instructor at MA1 explained, "interest [in pedagogical innovations] … it has to be organically motivated from the instructors themselves. If they're not interested in doing this it's not something that they're going to be successful with."

Nevertheless, it is difficult for faculty to pursue innovations in pedagogy, or even be aware of ways to enhance their teaching, without support. Departments at the selected institutions identified a variety of ways in which they supported innovations. These ways included but were not limited to travel funds for conferences, professional development centers and workshops, opportunities to collaborate with mathematics education researchers or other instructors, and participation in Project NExT.

Interest and implementation were also key to having Calculus I programs that supported innovation. For example, at BA1 and BA3, some instructors were already trying flipped classes for their Calculus I. LPU1 requires all instructors to use a mixture of small-group work and instructor-led discussion. Interest in active and inquiry-oriented learning is growing among Calculus I faculty, and thus it is slowly making its way into the classroom. BA4 adopted a new general education model, which is a move toward incorporating cooperative and active learning into classes with emphasis on critical thinking and problem solving. These examples exhibit the importance of institutions in supporting faculty not only to learn about innovative pedagogies, but the necessity of faculty and administration alike to muster the courage and resources to implement them.

Use of Technology

The use of technology in the classroom has become more prevalent as its availability has increased. Instructors can use graphing calculators, computer algebra systems (CAS), computer simulations, clickers, and online homework grading systems. However, it is not certain if the use of technology makes for a more successful learning and teaching experience. Our analysis of Calculus I programs showed mixed results regarding the use of technology at selected versus non-selected institutions. We conducted multiple independent-sample t-tests on the national survey data to compare the use of graphing calculators between selected and non-selected institutions.

To begin, consider Table 4, which compares the mean usage of graphing calculators (including those with and without symbolic algebra capabilities) as reported by students during class at selected and non-selected institutions by each institution type. At all institution types, the difference between selected and non-selected institutions was statistically significant. At BA-granting four-year colleges and MA- and PhD-granting universities, more frequent student use of graphing calculators during class was seen at the selected institutions. However, at AS-granting two-year colleges, the opposite was true. Students at the selected institutions reported less frequent graphing calculator use compared to non-selected institutions.

Table 4: Comparison of mean student reported graphing calculator use during class at selected and non-selected institutions.

Institution Type	Selected N = 1,255		Non-selected N = 3,490	
	M (SD)	N	M (SD)	N
2Y-Coll (AS)	2.43 (1.485)	97	3.00 (1.448)	309
4Y-Coll (BA)	3.50 (1.190)	226	2.69 (1.405)	601
Univ (MA)	3.58 (1.132)	84	2.58 (1.371)	215
Univ (PhD)	2.88 (1.518)	848	2.11 (1.284)	2,365

Note: Responses were reported on a five-point scale, where 1 = *Never*, 2 = *Some class sessions*, 3 = *About half of class sessions*, 4 = *Most of class sessions*, 5 = *Every class session*. All differences between selected and non-selected institutions are significant with $p < .001$.

Comparing across institution types at selected institutions, we see that graphing calculators are used in class less frequently at AS-granting two-year colleges and PhD-granting institutions compared to BA- and MA-granting institutions. At selected PhD-granting institutions larger class sizes may be a reason why students reported less frequent in-class use of graphing calculators, but this cannot be the reason at AS-granting two-year colleges, which had smaller class sizes. Hence the lower reported use of graphing calculators may be due to selected institutions valuing procedural fluency without technology.

In Table 5, we present the mean instructor use of graphing calculators (both those with the ability to perform symbolic algebra and those without) during class at selected and non-selected institutions. At all institution types, the difference between selected and non-selected institutions was statistically significant. At BA-granting four-year colleges and MA- and PhD-granting universities, increased use of graphing calculators by the instructor during class was seen at the selected institutions.

Table 5: Comparison of mean instructor reported graphing calculator use during class at selected and non-selected institutions.

Institution Type[a]	Selected N = 72		Non-selected N = 231	
	M (SD)	N	M (SD)	N
4Y-Coll (BA)**	2.21 (.893)	14	1.64 (.750)	44
Univ (MA)**	2.17 (.835)	12	1.62 (.677)	29
Univ (PhD)**	1.59 (.652)	46	1.34 (.626)	158

Note: a. Two-year colleges were omitted from this analysis due to small sample size. Responses were reported on a five-point scale, where 1 = *Never*, 2 = *Some class sessions*, 3 = *About half of class sessions*, 4 = *Most of class sessions*, 5 = *Every class session*. All differences between selected and non-selected institutions are significant with $p < .05$.

Similar to the student reported use of graphing calculators in class, instructor reported use of graphing calculators in class was lower among PhD-granting institutions compared to other institution types. Again, the more typical large lecture classes at PhD-granting universities or what is valued may contribute to less frequent instructor use of graphing calculators in class.

Based on student and instructor reported use of graphing calculators in class at selected institutions, we conjectured that we would see a similar pattern of graphing calculator use permitted on exams. In Table 6, we see this conjecture held. Very few instructors reported not allowing graphing calculators on exams at the BA-granting four-year colleges and MA-granting universities, whereas 31% of instructors at PhD-granting universities did not permit any type of graphing calculators on exams.

In the case of BA-granting four-year colleges, the difference between selected and non-selected institutions regarding technology use on exams, namely graphing calculators both with and without the ability to perform symbolic algebra, was statistically significant. The relationship between technology permitted on exams and the selection of institutions at MA-granting universities was not statistically significant. In the case of PhD-granting universities, the relationship was statistically significant. There, selected institutions showed a greater percentage of instructors permitting graphing calculator use on exams (just under 70%), particularly graphing calculators that perform symbolic algebra (GC w/ SA).

Table 6: Percentage of instructors permitting technology on Calculus I exams at selected and non-selected institutions.

Institution and Type of Technology	Selected N = 84	Non-selected N = 298
4Y-Coll (BA)***	N =13	N = 50
None	0%	26%
Graphing Calculator (GC)	43%	42%
GC w/ SA	50%	28%
Univ (MA)	N = 17	N = 87
None	9%	30%
Graphing Calculator (GC)	33%	41%
GC w/ SA	42%	16%
Univ (PhD)***	N = 54	N = 161
None	31%	51%
Graphing Calculator(GC)	25%	25%
GC w/ SA	37%	16%

Note. a. Two-year colleges were omitted from this analysis due to small sample size. ***: $p < .001$.

Existing studies on the use of technology in the classroom show similarly mixed results. Some researchers have shown that graphing calculators can be effective in prompting discussions (Doerr & Zangor, 2000; Drijvers & Doorman, 1996). Others (Cunningham, 1991; Palmiter, 1991; Park & Travers, 1996; Tiwari, 1999) have shown that the use of CAS leads to increases on exam scores for both computational and conceptual problems. However, Melin-Conejeros (1992) found just the opposite: the use of CAS in a college calculus class was related to decreased exam scores. Research done on the use of computer simulations and CAS demonstrations generally shows positive results, but they all emphasize the importance of considering how the technology was used in the classroom. For example, computer animations have been shown to be more effective than static images in developing computations skills in many STEM courses (Aldahmash & Abraham, 2009; Keller, Finkelstein, Perkins, & Pollock, 2007; Nicholls, Merkel, & Cordts, 1996; Steinberg, 2000; Szabo & Pookhay, 1996). Tabaghi (2010) was able to show that computer simulations, such as GeoGebra, could support a pictorial concept image of advanced mathematical concepts like linear transformations.

Finally, while some institutions have been implementing online homework grading systems (Kehoe, 2010), there is little data as yet to determine whether this medium supports student understanding and retention in mathematics courses.

Despite the at times contradictory findings on technology use in our data, many selected institutions noted the varied but important use of technology during the site visits. Often at the discretion of the instructor, many institutions reported some use of technology in the teaching and learning of Calculus I. The two most frequently cited forms of technology used at selected institutions were online homework systems and graphing calculators. In terms of online homework systems, a wide variety of such systems are available such as MyMathLab (available at TY1) and WeBWork (used at BA3). Furthermore, selected institutions using online homework systems occasionally coupled this with group homework assignments (as at LPU1) or other written homework assignments (as at LPrU). As for graphing calculators, their use was often noted for homework and exams, with only one institution (LPrU) opting to prohibit the use of calculators on exams and assign homework explicitly not needing a calculator.

The next most discussed form of technology during the site visits was CAS (e.g., Mathematica, Maple, MATLAB). Multiple institutions including TY3, PTU, and PTI required students to complete projects or labs using CAS such as Maple and Mathematica. At other institutions, CAS was used based on the interests of the instructor. As one MA3 instructor explained, CAS can give students the chance to "play" with the mathematical material, thus motivating the concepts and ideas of Calculus I:

I wanted the students to be in a position where they could interact with aspects of the mathematics in as close to a tactile way as possible. I did not want a syntactical layer to be between them and the ideas.

At other institutions (e.g., two-year institutions), the use of CAS in Calculus I was restricted because of lack of funding for such programs.

Some institutions and faculty members opted for a greater use of technology, often depending on the resources and support available at their institution. For example, at MA2, one instructor noted the freedom to incorporate podcasts into his Calculus I course:

By giving me the freedom to teach the material and in whatever order... So when I did the podcasting I talked to my department chair ... and my colleagues and they thought it was a good idea and worth trying. So while they didn't make anyone else use it, they didn't stop me. They made sure it was possible for me to be in a classroom that was equipped for the podcasting. They were genuinely interested in the results and outcomes.

Thus, this instructor felt supported by his department in his innovative use of podcasts in his Calculus I sections despite no other faculty member using that technology. Such open and generous support was critical to many instances of innovative uses of technology. An instructor at BA1 described the great degree to which some institutions pursue new technological endeavors:

We got a $174,000 [internal] grant from our provost ... to buy iPads and to put Apple TVs into four classrooms and change [them] from standard lecture classrooms to tables for group work.

Thus, though iPads and Apple TVs could not be installed in all classrooms, the administration made funds available to test these technologies in at least some classrooms to encourage faculty to pursue innovations in their instructional approach. In one of the two-year colleges, all the rooms in the math and science building had finished installing smart boards. These examples underscore an important characteristic of the selected institutions: while the use of technology was not uniform, most selected institutions reported support for instructors and departments to pursue the use of technology as they saw fit for their situation.

Conclusions and Recommendations

The selected institutions were diverse in their size, focus, and student body and showed similar variation in the mainstream Calculus I courses available, the format of the class, class size, professional rank of faculty, and technology use during class. However, there were also common aspects of the institutional and departmental culture found at all selected institutions. Below we highlight our findings from each of these categories and make recommendations based on our analyses.

Many of the selected institutions offered a variety of different Calculus I courses in diverse formats to fit the needs of their student bodies. Variations seen in mainstream Calculus I included intensive Honors Calculus I courses, a drop-back precalculus course, and a slower-paced stretched-out Calculus I course. Selected institutions also worked to provide students with convenient times to take these courses and added components such as recitations and labs to improve the experience. For example, some selected institutions offered evening courses for those students who were working. At two of the PhD-granting universities, where it was more common to have large lecture sections of Calculus I, there were additional recitation sessions to provide students with an interactive forum. Some institutions had a lab component to give students experience with the software they might be using later in their studies or careers.

While we can make no broad recommendation on what variations of Calculus I or formats for class are best for every college and university, our analysis shows that institutions benefit when the variations and format of Calculus I courses are tailored specifically to the needs of an institution's students. For institutions with a large number of students with some exposure to calculus but not enough to satisfy the college or university's requirements, an accelerated course or one adapted to the students' specific majors may be beneficial. When many students have daytime commitments, flexibility in scheduling including evening courses and formats that meet fewer times each week may be beneficial. Whatever variations in the Calculus I course or format of the class that are offered, students should not be at a disadvantage for opting into these alternatives; that is, the alternatives should be of equivalent credit, permitting students to progress normally in their studies without jeopardizing their on-time graduation.

We also found that class size varied across the selected institutions. While in all the selected institutions, administrators, faculty, and students alike valued small classes as encouraging student engagement and giving students a voice in their learning of Calculus I, small class size was not a necessary condition to be a selected institution. Two of the selected PhD-granting universities offered large sections of Calculus I. In these instances, students expressed an awareness of what they could learn in lecture versus what was best done in accompanying recitation sections. Thus, we recommend that institutions guide students in specific ways to make the most of their Calculus I offerings, be it large lectures, small standard sections, or recitations. We also posit that some smaller forum, be it the regular class meeting, a recitation, or a lab, is important to ensure the teacher of record or supporting teaching staff like GTAs have a chance for direct communication with students.

Our results also showed that no broad generalizations can be made about what professional rank of Calculus I instructors result in the successful, selected Calculus I programs. Many selected institutions employed part-time or full-time non-ladder-rank instructors who were experienced in teaching Calculus I and well respected within the department. Consistent with national trends, some selected PhD-granting universities offered non-research, teaching positions with secured employment, which permitted faculty to concentrate on the teaching and coordination of Calculus I. As such, we conjecture that it is not the faculty's professional rank that impacts the success in Calculus I, but rather the experience of the instructors and trust and respect for these instructors' ability to teach Calculus I that is important.

Beyond these features were common aspects of departmental and institutional environment seen at all selected institutions. These include support for collaboration and innovation and an expectation for quality teachers. For example, many of the selected institutions had specific areas where faculty and students were able to collaborate and have open communication. At two of the PhD-granting universities we observed different student cultures centered around religious affiliation and academic interest that helped connect the students to their institution, department, and peers. While we know not all institutions will have the naturally unifying situations seen at LPrU and PTI, we strongly recommend other institutions to take note of ways they can encourage collegiality. Cohorts, common physical space for faculty and students, and a general openness of communication all support collegiality and can be universally applied.

Another aspect of the departmental environment frequently discussed at the selected institutions was that of supporting quality teachers. At each selected institution, the administration, faculty, and students reported that they felt that good teachers were expected in the classroom and in the hiring and promotion process. Many interviewees cited quality teachers as the main reason for their institution's success in Calculus I. As such, we recommend departments and institutions take steps to explicitly state and reward quality teachers. Giving faculty time and resources to focus on teaching as a main part of their job and integrating teaching clearly into the hiring and promotion processes are two ways in which this can be achieved.

All selected institutions supported innovative pedagogy, though how this support was shown varied. At some of the institutions there was an expectation that instructors continually enhance their teaching and pursue innovations, despite the lack of external funding or incentives for such innovations. Others provided support in the form of funding to send instructors to teaching conferences, hosting professional development centers and workshops, and providing opportunities for instructors to work and communicate with other instructors and with mathematics education researchers. In all of these instances, interest was important in the implementation of pedagogical innovations. Thus, we suggest institutions provide whatever resources they can to make faculty feel supported in pursuing pedagogical innovations. This can be as simple as supporting an instructor to take a risk in the techniques used to teach a Calculus I section, but can be expanded to include funding for conferences, hosting seminars focusing on innovations in pedagogical innovations, or providing access to new technologies.

The use of more standard technologies, such as graphing calculators and CASs, varied widely across selected institutions of all institution types. While some institutions required the use of specific technologies such as CAS in labs, the majority of technology use was left to the discretion of the instructor. However, our results indicate that it is not so much that selected institutions were successful because they used technology, but rather successful use of technology depended on departmental and institutional support in trying out and innovating with technologies. Thus we recommend departments keep an open mind towards the ways in which technology can be adapted to the specific needs of their Calculus I courses.

References

Aldahmash, A. H. & Abraham, M. R. (2009). Kinetic vs. static visuals for facilitating college students' understanding of organic reaction mechanisms in chemistry. *Journal of Chemical Education, 86*(12), 1442–1446.

Blair, R., Kirkman, E. E., & Maxwell, J. W. (2013). *Statistical abstract of undergraduate programs in the mathematical sciences in the United States. Fall 2010 CBMS Survey.* Washington, DC: American Mathematical Society.

Bressoud, D. (2009). Is the sky still falling? *Notices of the AMS, 56*(1), 20–25.

Cunningham, R. (1991). *The effects on achievement of using computer software to reduce hand-generated symbolic manipulation in freshman calculus* (unpublished doctoral dissertation). Temple University. *Dissertation Abstracts International, 52*(07) 2448.

CUPM (2004). *CUPM Curriculum Guide 2004.* Washington, DC: Mathematical Association of America.

Doerr, H. M., Staniec, A. C., & O'Neil, A. H. (2012). *Designing for improved success in first year mathematics.* ASEE Annual Conference, San Antonio, TX.

Ehrenberg, R. & Zhang, L. (2005). Do tenured and tenure-track faculty matter? *The Journal of Human Resources, 40*, 647–659.

Hornsby, D. J. & Osman, R. (2014). Massification in higher education: large classes and student learning. *Higher Education, 67*, 711–719.

Hsu, E., Mesa, V., & The Calculus Case Collective (2014). *Synthesizing measures of institutional success* (CSPCC-Technical Report #1*)*. Washington DC: Mathematical Association of America.

Kehoe, E. (2010). AMS homework software survey. *Notices of the American Mathematical Society, 57*, 753–757.

Keil, J. & Partell, P. J. (1997). *The effect of class size on student performance and retention at Binghamton University.* Office of Budget and Institutional Research, Binghamton University, Binghamton, NY.

Keller, C. J., Finkelstein, N. D., Perkins, K. K., & Pollock, S. J. (2007). Assessing the effectiveness of a computer simulation in conjunction with Tutorials In Introductory Physics in undergraduate physics recitations. *AIP Conference Proceedings*, Salt Lake City, UT.

Klingbeil, N. W., Mercer, R. E., Rattan, K. S., Raymer, M. L., & Reynolds, D. B. (2004). Rethinking engineering mathematics education: A model for increased retention, motivation and success in engineering. *ASEE Annual Conference Proceedings*, Salt Lake City, Utah.

Kokkelenberg, E. C., Dillon, M., & Christy, S. M. (2008). The effects of class size on student grades at a public university. *Economics of Education Review, 27*, 221–233.

MacArthur, J. R. & Jones, L. L. (2008). A review of literature reports of clickers applicable to college chemistry classrooms. *Chemistry Education Research and Practice, 9*, 187–195.

Melin-Conejeros, J. (1992). *The effect of using a computer algebra system in mathematics laboratory on the achievement and attitude of calculus students* (Unpublished doctoral dissertation). University of Iowa. Dissertation Abstracts International, 53(7) 2283A.

Millett, K. (2002). Making large lectures effective: an effort to increase student success. In D. Holton, D. (ed.), *The teaching and learning of mathematics at university level: an ICMI study* (pp. 137–152). Netherlands: Springer.

Nicholls, C., Merkel, S., & Cordts, M. (1996). The effects of computer animation on students' understanding in microbiology. *Journal of Research on Computing in Education, 20*(2), 359–371.

Palmiter, J. R. (1991). Effects of computer algebra systems on concept and skill acquisitions in calculus. *Journal for Research in Mathematics Education, 22*(2), 151–186.

Park, K. & Travers, K. (1996). A comparative study of a computer-based and a standard college first-year calculus course. *CBMS Issues in Mathematics Education, 6*, 155–176.

Reay, N. W., Li P., & Bao, L. (2008). Testing a new voting machine question methodology. *American Journal of Physics, 76*(2), 171–178.

Reay, N. W., Bao, L., Li P., Warnakulasooriya, R., & Baugh, G. (2005). Toward the effective use of voting machines in physics lectures. *American Journal of Physics, 73*(6), 554–558.

Spencer, A. (1995). On attracting and retaining mathematics majors—Don't cancel the human factor. *Notices of American Mathematical Society, 42*(8), 859–862.

Steinberg, R. N. (2000). Computers in teaching science: To simulate or not to simulate? *Physics Education Research: American Journal of Physics Supplemental, 68*(7), 37–41.

Stockton, D. (1960). An experiment with a large calculus class. *The American Mathematical Monthly, 67*(10), 1024–1025.

Szabo, M. & Poohkay, B. (1996). An experimental study of animation, mathematics achievement and attitude toward computer-assisted instruction. *Journal for Research on Computing in Education, 28*(3), 390–402.

Tiwari, T. K. (1999). *Integrating computer algebra systems as an instructional aid in an introductory differential calculus course* (PhD thesis). Mississippi State University.

Vélez, W. Y., Maxwell, J. W., & Rose, C. (2014). Report on 2012–2013 Academic recruitment and hiring. *Notices of the American Mathematical Society, 61*(7), 1–6.

Warren, E. (1988). *The association between class size, achievement, and opinions of university students in first-semester calculus.* (Unpublished doctoral dissertation.) University of North Texas, TX. Dissertations & Theses A&I database, AAT 8817053.

Williams, D. D., Cook, P. F., Quinn, B., & Jensen, R. (1985). University class size: Is smaller better? *Research in Higher Education, 23*(3), 307–318.

Chapter 4

The Calculus I Curriculum

Helen Burn, *Highline College*
Vilma Mesa, *University of Michigan, Ann Arbor*

Curriculum is a broad term with multiple meanings (Lattuca & Stark, 2009; Stein, Remillard, & Smith, 2007). This chapter focuses on four interdependent elements of the Calculus I curriculum: (1) course content, (2) cognitive goals, (3) types of assignments, and (4) how student learning is assessed. Additional elements of the Calculus I curriculum related to instruction can be found in Chapters 7 and 8. These four curricular elements were selected because they are known to be paramount as mathematics faculty plan, reason, and make decisions about courses (Burn, 2012; Kaput, 1997; Lattuca & Stark, 2009). These elements have also proven useful in framing research on the school mathematics curriculum (Mesa, Gómez, & Cheah, 2013; Rico, 1997). We begin by describing methods of analysis and limitations of the available data. Following this, the four curricular elements are addressed in separate sections that include selected literature and findings. The chapter concludes with recommendations for practice and suggestions for relevant literature for the interested reader. The information in this chapter will be of interest to mathematics faculty, administrators, and mathematics education researchers.

Methods

In order to describe the four curricular elements (content, cognitive goals, assignments, and assessment), we worked with different sources. The content of Calculus I presented in this chapter derives from a synthesis of four sources. First is the course description for Advanced Placement (AP) calculus (The College Board, 2012). The AP courses (AB and BC courses[1]) are modeled on comparable college courses and developed in consultation with university faculty. The second source is Sofronas et al.'s (2011) "brain trust" study with 24 calculus experts who identified content and goals critical for student understanding of first-year calculus. Third, topics included in the Khan Academy website (Khan Academy, 2014) were examined because of their widespread use and because the topics reflect student need. Lastly, the content analysis drew on the expertise of the CSPCC research team, including Johnson, Ellis, and Rasmussen's (2014) analysis of course content listed in master syllabi collected from the PhD-granting universities selected for case study. In the content section, we discuss Calculus I content that appeared in at least two of the aforementioned sources.

Data for the analysis of cognitive goals, assignments, and assessment in Calculus I derive from the national survey[2] of Calculus I faculty (Hsu, Mesa, & The Calculus Collective, 2014). The sample included all faculty who responded to pre- or post-course instructor surveys (N = 503). We calculated frequencies and used cross tabulations of selected survey questions and, depending on the question type, conducted either *t*-tests or Chi-square tests of independence to explore differences between faculty in institutions selected for case study (N = 104) and those not selected for case

---

1 Calculus BC is an extension of Calculus AB. Throughout this document, the AP course description refers to the AB course description unless otherwise noted.
2 Data derived from the CSPCC_Data instructor file.

study (N = 399). We refer to these two groups as *selected* and *non-selected institutions*, respectively. Only statistically significant differences between selected and non-selected institutions at a significance level of 5% are reported. In several cases, we collapsed item response categories due to sparse cell counts. Faculty response rates to survey questions analyzed ranged from a minimum of 65% (329/503) to a maximum of 84% (421/503), with an average response rate across the survey questions of 72% (362/503). For ease of reading, response rates are reported only in tables, figures, and footnotes.

As with any survey research, limitations due to construct validity need to be considered. For example, Calculus I faculty were not asked directly about cognitive goals for Calculus I; instead, selected survey questions served as proxies. A second limitation in any study using self-reported data relates to potential differences between what faculty say they do and what they actually enact in classrooms—that is, between the intended and the enacted curriculum (Travers & Westbury, 1989). However, there is no reason to believe that faculty would respond to questions without accuracy, given that there were no repercussions for the responses provided.

Content of Calculus I

Mathematics faculty tend to consider content first in planning courses because their primary goal is for students to learn fundamental concepts and principles of the discipline (Lattuca & Stark, 2009). Calculus I in colleges and universities in the United States covers basic differential and some integral calculus. The content of Calculus I has remained relatively stable over the decades regardless of calls for a "lean and lively calculus" (Douglas, 1986), the calculus reform movement of the 1990s (Hughes-Hallett, n.d.), or the general trend toward reducing content in mathematics courses (Hillel, 2001). To be sure, course content in Calculus I has changed over time. Delta-epsilon proofs are no longer considered a standard part of the Calculus I curriculum. The "rule of four" calling for a mix of graphical, numerical, symbolic, and verbal approaches has had a lasting impact on current textbooks. The availability of technology has enabled increased emphasis on visualizing graphs of functions and their derivatives and other graphical connections. Further, Calculus I courses more often include employability or transfer skills, such as communication, teamwork, and technology skills (Houston, 2001).

We identified four major content areas of Calculus I, which will be familiar to our readers: (1) limits and continuity, (2) derivatives, (3) integrals, and (4) sequences and series. In addition, many courses begin with a review of functions. After describing each content area, this section concludes by examining survey questions about time constraints and pressure faculty feel to cover course content.

Limits and Continuity
The limit concept is necessary for the limit definition of the derivative and the integral. Students are expected to develop an intuitive understanding of the limiting process, calculate limits using algebra, estimate limits from graphs or tables, and find limits at infinity. Continuity (intuitive understanding and in terms of limits) is included in the AP course description, the Khan Academy website, and the master syllabi of four of the five selected PhD-granting institutions. It is noteworthy that continuity was not identified as critical content by calculus experts.

Derivatives
The analysis revealed four major content areas related to derivatives: the concept of the derivative, derivative computations, visualizing derivatives and graphical connections, and applications of derivatives. First, Calculus I content on the derivative concept includes the derivative as the instantaneous rate of change of a function, as the limit of the difference quotient, and as a measure of sensitivity of one variable to another when linked by an equation. The next content area is derivatives of basic functions (power, exponential, logarithmic, trigonometric, and inverse trigonometric), derivative rules (sum, power, product, quotient, chain), and implicit differentiation. Some Calculus I courses may include hyperbolic trigonometric functions. The third content area related to derivatives is visualizing graphs of functions and their derivatives and other graphical connections (e.g., using secant lines to approximate tangent slope, approximating rates of change from graphs or tables, analysis of f, f', and f'' and graphical connections). A final content area concerns the applications of derivatives, including analysis of curves, modeling, interpreting rates of change, optimization, and related rates. The mean value theorem (assumptions and geometric interpretations), L'Hospital's rule, and numerical solutions via Euler's method are also course content in Calculus I.

Integrals

This content includes the indefinite integral as antiderivative and the definite integral as a limit of Riemann sums (Riemann sums are used to approximate the definite integral) and interpretation and application of the definite integral (e.g., integral as area, as net change/accumulated total change). Additional content includes the Fundamental Theorem of Integral Calculus and techniques of integration (computing antiderivatives following from basic functions and substitution of variables). Calculus I courses increasingly include some treatment of simple differential equations (e.g., $y' = ky$), slope fields, and the relationship of slope fields to solution curves for differential equations.

Sequences and Series

The AP course description (BC version) and the Khan Academy website include sequences and series. The AP course (BC version) includes sequences and series, series of constants (e.g., geometric series with applications) and Taylor series. The Khan Academy website includes sequences, sequence convergence and divergence, series, geometric series, power series function representation using algebra, and Taylor and Maclaurin series.

Faculty Responses to Survey Questions about Time and Pressure to Cover Course Content

Faculty were asked whether they had enough time during class to help students understand difficult concepts using a scale that ranged from 1 (*Not at all*) to 6 (*Very often*). The median instructor response was 4, with 72% responding 4 or higher. Using the same scale, faculty were asked whether they felt pressured to go through the material quickly to cover all the required topics. The median instructor response was 3, with 64% of faculty responding 3 or less. Taken together, the national survey suggests Calculus I faculty believe they have enough time to cover required material and do not feel undue pressure to move too quickly through material. For more information on the relationship between how quickly or deeply calculus material is covered and how this is related to students' instructional experience and their persistence in a STEM major, see Ellis, Johnson, & Rasmussen (2015).

Cognitive Goals for Students in Calculus I

Knowing what instructors want students to do with Calculus I content adds depth to knowing the topics to be covered. *Cognitive goals* refer to cognitive processes students are expected to deploy in order to learn Calculus I content. The processes—remembering, understanding, applying, analyzing, evaluating, and creating—can be more or less cognitively demanding depending on the cognitive resources required to activate them (Anderson & Krathwohl, 2001; Bloom & Krathwohl, 1956). For example, asking students to remember a fact (definition) or to apply a procedure requires fewer mental resources than asking students to make interpretations or provide explanations of the same fact or procedure. Classroom instruction that maintains higher levels of cognitive demand has been associated with higher levels of student achievement in mathematics (Boaler & Staples, 2008; Silver & Stein, 1996; Stigler, Givvin, & Thompson, 2004). Cognitive processes are activated with four types of knowledge: factual, procedural, conceptual, and metacognitive, all of which are considered necessary for having expertise in any given subject (Anderson & Krathwohl, 2001).

To discern the cognitive goals Calculus I faculty intend, we examined problem types faculty include on assignments and exams and explored whether faculty ask or require students to explain their thinking on assignments, exams, or during class. We also analyzed survey questions revealing faculty beliefs about their primary role as instructors, what it takes for students to succeed in Calculus I, and students' approach to studying.

Problem Types Faculty Include on Assignments and Exams

Figure 1 shows median responses to the percentage of different problem types faculty include on assignments and exams. Faculty reported nearly identical percentages for assignments and exams.

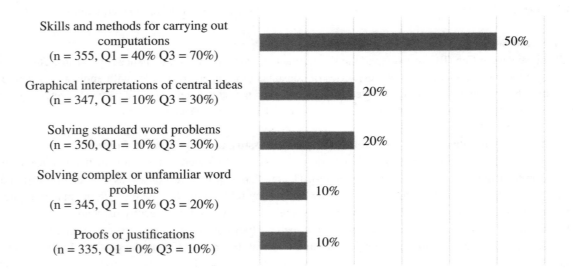

Figure 1: Median responses to the percentage (0% to 100%) of different problem types faculty include on assignments and exams. Q1 = 25th percentile; Q3 = 75th percentile.

Faculty reported assigning a higher percentage of problems focused on skills and methods for carrying out computations, with a median instructor response of 50% and an interquartile range of 30 percentage points (Q1 = 40%, Q3 = 70%). This finding is partially explained by the fact that 66% of faculty agreed somewhat or strongly with the statement: *Understanding ideas in calculus typically comes after achieving procedural fluency.* Figure 1 suggests faculty are less likely to assign problems involving graphical interpretations of central ideas, standard word problems, complex or unfamiliar word problems, or proofs and justifications.

Faculty in selected institutions were less likely than faculty in non-selected institutions to report assigning problems focused on skills and methods for carrying out computations ($M_{selected}$ = 40%; $M_{non-selected}$ = 50%, $t(353)$ = -2.84, $p < .005$). Instead, faculty in selected institutions were more likely than faculty in non-selected institutions to assign problems involving graphical interpretation of central ideas ($M_{selected}$ = 30%; $M_{non-selected}$ = 20%; $t(87)$ = 3.36, $p < .001$) and complex or unfamiliar word problems ($M_{selected}$ = 20%; $M_{non-selected}$ =10%, $t(343)$ = 4.35, $p < .001$). These differences represent small-to-medium effect sizes (Cohen's d: 0.36 for skills and computations, 0.49 for graphical interpretations, and 0.47 for complex or unfamiliar word problems.)

Asking or Requiring Students to Explain Their Thinking in Calculus I

Faculty reported how frequently they asked students to explain their thinking during class or required them to explain their thinking on assignments or exams using a scale that ranged from 1 (*Not at all*) to 6 (*Very often*). A response of 5 is interpreted to mean *Often*. Faculty frequently asked students to explain their thinking on exams, with 44% responding *Often* or *Very often* (Median = 4). Similarly, 41% of faculty reported that they *Often* or *Very often* asked students to explain their thinking during class (Median = 4). In contrast, 34% of faculty reported that they *Often* or *Very often* required students to explain their thinking on assignments (Median = 3).

Faculty Beliefs about Student Success, Their Primary Role as Instructors, and Students' Approach to Studying Calculus I

Table 1 shows faculty responses to three survey questions that relate to cognitive goals by revealing faculty beliefs about their primary role as instructors, what it takes for students to succeed in Calculus I, and students' approach to studying.

Table 1: Mean and standard deviation for survey questions about faculty beliefs about their primary role as instructors, what it takes for students to succeed in Calculus I, and students' approach to studying.

Survey questions and scales[a]	N	Mean (SD)
My primary role as a Calculus instructor is to: 1 (*work problems so students know how to do them*) to 6 (*help students reason through problems on their own*)	421	4.90 (1.03)
From your perspective, student success in calculus relies on their ability to: 1 (*solve specific kinds of problems*) to 6 (*make connections and form logical arguments*)	420	3.99 (1.28)
When studying Calculus I in a textbook or in course materials, students tend to: 1 (*memorize it the way it was presented*) to 6 (*make sense of the material so that they understand it*)	421	3.14 (1.21)

Note: a: Survey questions and scale are presented verbatim and required faculty to interpolate.

When faculty were asked whether their primary role is to *work problems so student know how to do them* (response = 1) or to *help students reason through problems on their own* (response = 6), the mean response was 5, and 90% of faculty responded 4 or higher. When asked whether student success in calculus relies more on their *ability to solve specific kinds of problems* (response = 1) or *to make connections and form logical arguments* (response = 6), the mean response was 4, and 66% of faculty responded 4 or higher. In contrast, when asked whether, when studying Calculus I in a textbook or in course material, students tend to *memorize it the way it was presented* (response = 1) or *make sense of the material so that they understand it* (response = 6), the mean response was 3, with 37% responding 4 or higher. Taken together, these survey questions suggest a potential mismatch between faculty expectations and students' approach to studying. Whereas faculty desire that students develop and apply higher order thinking skills in Calculus I (e.g., making connections, reasoning on their own), faculty believe that students tend to resort to memorizing—a less cognitively demanding activity.

Assignments in Calculus I

Course content is typically encountered by students through academic tasks or assignments that mediate learning by determining how students direct their attention, process information, and what students learn (Doyle, 1983; Stein, Smith, Henningsen, & Silver, 2000). Tasks are also the way in which instructors can create a space for cognitive goals to be actualized. While assignments are sometimes completed in class, it is more common in college classrooms for students to complete assignments outside of class (Mesa & Griffiths, 2012). Assignments influence learning in part by promoting time on task—a recognized good practice in undergraduate instruction (Chickering & Gamson, 1991). Further, assignments are a primary means to provide students with timely, supportive, and corrective feedback, which is known to make a difference in students' learning (Angelo & Cross, 1993; McKeachie & Svinicki, 2006).

In this section we examine how frequently students turned in assignments, whether students did presentations, projects, or pre-reading assignments, and how homework was submitted and graded in Calculus I.

Frequency of Assignments in Calculus I

The majority of faculty reported that students regularly turn in assignments in Calculus I. Specifically, the national survey asked faculty how often students turn in assignments (either hard copy or online) using the scale 1 (*Never*), 2 (*Some class sessions*), 3 (*About half the class sessions*), 4 (*Most class sessions*), or 5 (*Every class session*). The modal response was to have students turn in assignments in *Some class sessions* (32%), followed by *About half the class sessions* (21%), *Most class sessions* (20%), and *Every class session* (15%). Only 12% of faculty never had students turn in assignments.

There were statistically significant differences between selected and non-selected institutions in how often students were required to turn in assignments (χ^2 (4, N = 359) = 18.81, p < .001). Nearly half the faculty in the selected institutions (47%) said that they collected assignments in *Most* or *Every class session* compared to roughly a third (32%) of faculty in non-selected institutions. In fact, 32% of faculty in selected institutions reported collecting assignments in *Every class* session compared to 11% of faculty in non-selected institutions.

Use of Projects, Presentations, and Pre-Reading Assignments

Faculty reported how many projects (group or individual) they assigned during the term (*0, 1, 2,* or *more than 2*), how frequently they had students give a presentation, and whether they assigned sections of the textbook for students to read before coming to class. The latter two questions used a scale that ranged from 1 (*Not at all*) to 6 (*Very often*). One-quarter of the faculty reported assigning projects, and these projects tended to count for 40% of the students' course grade. Thirty-four percent of faculty reported that they had students give presentations during class time. Overall, 70% of faculty reported assigning sections in the textbook for students to read before coming to class, although only 35% reported doing this *Often* or *Very often*.

There were statistically significant differences between selected and non-selected institutions in the use of projects (χ^2(1, N = 364) = 7.54, p < .006) and student presentations (χ^2(3, N = 358) = 23.82, p < .001). While in both cases, about 25% of faculty assigned students projects, more faculty in selected institutions (20%) than non-selected institutions (9%) assigned two or more projects. Further, 43% of faculty in selected institutions had students give presentations (15% responded *Often* or *Very often*) compared to 32% of faculty in non-selected institutions (2% responded *Often* or *Very often*).

Calculus I Homework

Figure 2 shows the frequency of methods of submitting and grading Calculus I homework.

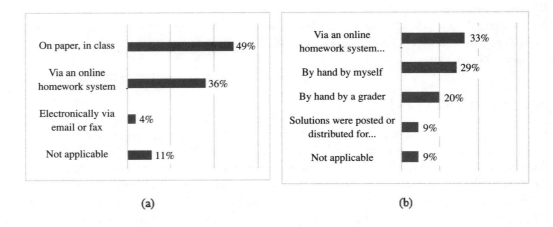

(a)   (b)

Figure 2: Frequency of instructor responses to how Calculus I homework was submitted (a) and graded (b). Faculty were asked to "Check all that apply."

About half the faculty (49%) reported that students submitted homework on paper, and 36% had students submit homework via an online homework system. Nearly half (49%) said that they grade homework manually either by themselves (29%) or with a grader (20%). One-third reported that homework was graded via an online homework system. In a separate survey question, 81% of faculty reported that homework problems were of the format *free response questions* rather than *multiple-choice items*.

While the nature of the questions in Figure 2 precludes the use of tests of independence (faculty could *Check all that apply*) it is noteworthy that faculty in selected institutions were more likely than faculty in non-selected institutions to grade homework with an online homework system (41% versus 30%) or by hand (33% versus 22%) and were less likely to have a homework grader (11% versus 22%). For more information on structure, content, and feedback of Calculus I homework and the role of homework in students' mathematical success in selected research universities, see Ellis, Hanson, Nuñez, & Rasmussen (in press).

How Student Learning is Assessed

Assessment (measuring learning outcomes) is conducted mainly to determine whether students are achieving course objectives (Lattuca & Stark, 2009). At the course level, assessment in mathematics is most often *summative*—that is, timed quizzes and examinations are used to evaluate student performance (Hillel, 2001). In contrast, *formative* assessment intended to monitor student learning and to provide feedback that shapes instruction is less frequently used in mathematics classes (Angelo & Cross, 1993; Wiliam, 2013). In addition to assigning grades, mathematics faculty use assessment results to evaluate and make adjustments to their courses. Because Calculus I is a gateway course for science majors, some institutions use the results of student achievement in Calculus I as an indicator of program effectiveness (Hillel, 2001).

Mathematics faculty tend to have a high degree of confidence in exams and quizzes as indicators of student learning in part because assessing whether students have mastered concepts and principles is presumed to be more easily quantifiable in mathematics (Lattuca & Stark, 2009). Yet students can be held to different standards depending on the types of problems assigned by their faculty. White and Mesa's (2014) analysis of exam items from five Calculus I instructors in the same department revealed statistically significant differences in the types of problems instructors assigned. Some faculty required students to demonstrate mastery on a larger share of problems characterized as *rich tasks* and *complex procedures* while others more often assessed student proficiency with problems characterized as *simple procedures*.

To explore how student learning is assessed in Calculus I, we examined survey questions on the frequency of exams and quizzes, faculty use of pre-assessment, the use of a common final exam, and how the final exam is graded. The section also includes questions about the use of technology on exams.

Frequency of Exams and Quizzes

Figure 3 shows faculty responses to how many exams faculty gave, not including the final, and how frequently they gave a short quiz using the scale 1 (*Never*), 2 (*Some class sessions*), 3 (*About half the class sessions*), 4 (*Most class sessions*), or 5 (*Every class session*). The modal response was for faculty to give three exams (36%) and to give a short quiz in *Some class sessions* (47%).

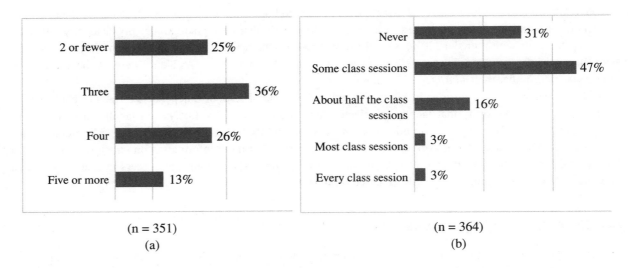

(n = 351)   (n = 364)

(a)   (b)

Figure 3: Frequency of faculty reporting number of exams assigned not including final (a); and frequency of faculty reporting frequency of giving short quizzes (b).

It is noteworthy that faculty in selected institutions tended to give fewer exams (X^2(2, N = 351) = 24.23, $p < .001$) and instead tended to give more short quizzes (X^2(2, N = 364) = 9.15, $p < .010$). Nearly half (47%) of faculty in selected institutions reported giving two or fewer exams compared to 20% of faculty in non-selected institutions. Furthermore, 21% of faculty in selected institutions gave four or more exams compared to a much higher 43% of faculty in non-selected institutions. In contrast, 60% of faculty in selected institutions gave short quizzes in *Some class sessions* compared to 44% of faculty in non-selected institutions. In fact, 35% of faculty in non-selected institutions reported never giving short quizzes compared to a smaller 17% of faculty in selected institutions.

Use of Pre-Assessments
Faculty were asked how frequently they used pre-assessments in their current class when they prepare to teach a challenging idea, using the scale 1 (*Never*), 2 (*Occasionally*), 3 (*Frequently*), and 4 (*Always*). Pre-assessments are an example of a formative assessment technique (Angelo & Cross, 1993). One-third of faculty reported *Occasionally* using pre-assessments while most (55%) reported never using this pedagogical technique.

Use of Common Final and Grading Practices
The majority (64%) of Calculus I faculty surveyed reported that a common final was used for all sections of Calculus I at their institution. Further, nearly three out of four (73%) reported using a rubric in grading their final, either their own (37%) or a common rubric (36%). Nearly one-third (31%) of faculty reported grading the final exam with a group of instructors using a common rubric.

Faculty in selected institutions more often reported using a common final than faculty in non-selected (80% versus 60%, respectively; X^2(2, N = 362) = 13.17, $p < .001$). Faculty in selected institutions also more often reported grading their final exam with a group of instructors using a common rubric (56% versus 27%; X^2(2, N = 345) = 23.00, $p < .001$). These results could be an artifact of the oversampling of PhD-granting institutions in the study, which tend to have multiple sections with graduate teaching assistants (GTAs). For more information on the role of GTAs in Calculus I, see Chapter 10.

Use of Technology on Exams
Faculty in selected institutions were more permissive about the use of technology on exams than faculty in non-selected institutions. Specifically, 78% of faculty in selected institutions permitted the use of technology on their exams and 55% required it, compared to 61% (permitted) and 26% (required) of faculty in non-selected institutions (X^2(2, N = 367) = 15.15, $p < .001$). In addition, 44% of faculty in selected institutions required graphing calculators that do not perform symbolic algebra and 11% required computer algebra systems compared to 20% and 6%, respectively, of faculty in non-selected institutions (X^2(2, N = 398) = 24.54, $p < .001$).

Discussion

This chapter focused on four interdependent elements of the Calculus I curriculum: content, cognitive goals, assignments, and how student learning is assessed. Our discussion centers on recommendations for practice and suggests relevant literature for the interested reader. The discussion begins with the challenge of curriculum change in Calculus I followed by suggestions for promoting higher-order thinking in Calculus I. Lastly, we propose ways to leverage assessment to improve learning and equality of outcomes in Calculus I.

The Challenge of Curriculum Change in Calculus I

Research tells us that the stable nature of the Calculus I curriculum is a consequence of the common disciplinary training of college and university mathematics faculty and their socialization into the teaching norms of the discipline (Becher, 1989; Biglan, 1973; Braxton & Hargens, 1996). Moreover, colleges and universities in the United States have been characterized as *loosely coupled*—that is, there are softer linkages between the units of the organization and weaker coordination and regulation compared with the private sector, resulting in much localized freedom and independence (Birnbaum, 1991; Weick, 1976). Curriculum change, when it does occur, tends to start with faculty working locally within their institutions or in regional partnerships (Lattuca & Stark, 2009). These factors help explain the stability of the Calculus I curriculum. The reader interested in understanding curriculum change in postsecondary education in the United States is directed to Kezar (2001) as a starting point and to Henderson, Beach, & Finkelstein (2011) for a literature review on facilitating change in undergraduate STEM instructional practices.

Promoting Higher-Order Thinking in Calculus I

The findings in this chapter suggest a possible mismatch between faculty members' desire to develop and apply higher-order thinking skills and their belief that students tend to resort to memorizing rather than making sense of the material so that they understand it. We make three recommendations related to promoting higher-order thinking. First, faculty should consider whether students resort to memorizing because of weaknesses in understanding fundamental concepts. There is extensive research documenting common misconceptions in Calculus I. This includes students' understanding of limits (e.g., Oehrtman, 2009; Swinyard & Larsen, 2012), covariational reasoning (e.g., Carlson, Jason, Coe, Larsen, & Hsu, 2002), the derivatives (e.g., Zandieh, 2000), functions (e.g., Carlson, 1998; Trigueros & Martínez-Planell, 2011), and variables (e.g., Trigueros & Ursini, 2003).

A second recommendation related to promoting higher-order thinking in Calculus I is to consider the role of student motivation, self-efficacy, and other non-cognitive factors on student learning. The interested reader is referred to Kuh, Kinzie, Buckley, Bridges, & Hayek's (2006) literature review on this topic. As well, Yeager's (2011) research on self-efficacy, Dweck's (1986, 2006) *growth mindset* research, and Wigfield & Eccles's (2002) *expectancy-value theory of achievement motivation* are all good points of departure for mathematics faculty interested in developing instructional practices aimed at improving student motivation and other non-cognitive factors. Today's students are more utilitarian in their approach to learning than in the past (Astin, 1998; Brint, 2002). This is felt most strongly by faculty teaching in community colleges and non-selective institutions. The interested reader is referred to Cox's (2009) seminal study of community college students.

Faculty have the means at their disposal for promoting higher-order thinking yet may be missing opportunities afforded by the assignments used in Calculus I. For example, projects and presentations are prime opportunities for students to engage in higher-order thinking, yet their overall reported use was relatively low. That said, on the national survey faculty reported that students frequently submitted assignments in Calculus I, and faculty in selected institutions collected assignments more often. Yet faculty reported that assignments included a higher percentage of problems focused on skills and methods for carrying out computations, with fewer problems on graphical interpretations of central ideas and standard word problems, and the least percentage of problems on complex or unfamiliar word problems or proofs and justifications. Furthermore, faculty reported that they require students to explain their thinking on assignments less frequently than on exams or during class. Thus, our third recommendation is that faculty modify assignments to more frequently include questions that require students to apply knowledge, make interpretations, or provide explanations related to Calculus I concepts.

A potential barrier to modifying assignments to include more higher-order thinking could be faculty concerns about the time required for grading problems that require more extended problem solving, explanations, or justifications. For example, it may be difficult to ask questions that promote higher-order thinking in a way that can be automatically graded by an online homework system. One suggestion is to post solutions for students and to hold students individually accountable for the material by including one or two questions from enhanced assignments on quizzes or exams. Another suggestion is for faculty to investigate the role of group or teamwork in helping students develop higher-order thinking skills. Grading can be cut down considerably when groups turn in a single assignment. Faculty may require professional development to be able to implement group work effectively in ways that promote individual student accountability and mitigate freeloading behaviors. The interested reader is directed to research on effective group work in undergraduate mathematics such as Dubinsky, Matthews, & Reynolds (1997) or Rogers, Reynolds, & Davidson (2001).

Leveraging Assessment to Improve Student Learning and Equality of Outcomes

Turning finally to how learning is assessed in Calculus I, White and Mesa's (2014) research with the two-year data suggests that, working in isolation, faculty will design tests with different cognitive complexity. Given that student performance on timed examinations is a major arbiter of student grades, we recommend that faculty collaborate around assessment and, if necessary, seek professional development related to test-item construction and rubric development. This could lead not only to improved student learning but, perhaps more importantly, equality of outcomes. It is noteworthy that faculty in selected institutions were more likely than faculty in non-selected institutions to use a common final and to grade final exams with a group of instructors using a common rubric. Again, this could be an artifact of oversampling of PhD-granting institutions in the national survey. Regardless, the merits of a common final must be weighed against faculty professional autonomy, and faculty should consider whether the same aim can be achieved through a limited number of common final questions. For more details on the ways in which selected PhD-granting institutions coordinated calculus, including common final examinations, see Chapter 9.

Although there were limited questions on the national survey related to faculty use of formative assessment, this is potentially a fruitful area of focus for faculty interested in improving student outcomes in Calculus I. Formative assessment can be achieved through interacting with students during class, as this helps faculty gauge levels of understanding and guides instruction (Lattuca & Stark, 2009; Wiliam, 2013). The interested reader is referred to Wiliam (2013) or Angelo & Cross's (1993) seminal work on using classroom assessment techniques to gain useful formative feedback that can shape instruction in a timely fashion. Mesa's (2011) research on classroom questioning patterns will be of interest to faculty desiring to improve their classroom discussions and increase their tendency to ask students questions that engage higher-order thinking skills. Faculty who teach large-lectures sections can benefit from exploring clicker technology (Trees & Jackson, 2007) and other techniques for engaging students in this context (Mazur, 2009).

Lastly, examinations and quizzes can serve both summative and formative purposes. It was most typical for faculty to give three exams, not including the final, and to use short quizzes in some classes. However, faculty in selected institutions gave fewer exams (typically two or fewer) and instead gave short quizzes in class more often. Short quizzes provide frequent feedback to students and make key learning objectives explicit prior to a major exam, and can help faculty diagnose major problems in understanding before it is too late to help students.

In sum, there are opportunities for faculty to improve student outcomes in Calculus I while maintaining traditional content. We recommend that faculty promote higher-order thinking by considering the potential barriers posed by student misunderstandings of fundamental concepts or non-cognitive factors such as motivation and self-efficacy. Next, we recommend modifying assignments in Calculus I in ways that promote higher-order thinking. Lastly, we recommend that mathematics faculty collaborate intentionally around outcomes assessment. Together, these actions should improve student learning and equality of outcomes in Calculus I.

References

Anderson, L. W., & Krathwohl, D. R. (eds.) (2001). A taxonomy for learning, teaching, and assessing: A revision of Bloom's taxonomy of educational objectives. New York: Longman.

Angelo, T. A. & Cross, K P. (1993). *Classroom assessment techniques: A handbook for college teachers*. San Francisco: Jossey-Bass.

Astin, W. (1998). The changing American college student: Thirty-year trends, 1966-1996. *The Review of Higher Education, 21*(2), 115–135.

Becher, T. (1989). Academic tribes and territories: Intellectual enquiry and the cultures of the disciplines. Stony Stratford: The Society for Research into Higher Education & Open University Press.

Biglan, A. (1973). The characteristics of subject matter in different academic areas. *Journal of Applied Psychology, 57*, 195–203.

Birnbaum, R. (1991). How colleges work: The cybernetics of academic organization and leadership. San Francisco: Jossey-Bass.

Bloom, B. S. & Krathwohl, D. R. (1956). Taxonomy of educational objectives: the classification of educational goals. Handbook I: cognitive domain. New York, NY: Longmans, Green.

Boaler, J. & Staples, M. (2008). Creating mathematical futures through an equitable teaching approach: the case of Railside School. *Teachers' College Record.* 110(3), 608–645.

Braxton, J. M. & Hargens, L. L. (1996). Variation among academic disciplines: Analytical frameworks and research. In J.C. Smart (ed.), Higher education: Handbook of theory and research, XI, (pp. 1–46). Bronx, NY: Agathon Press.

Brint, S. (2002). The rise of the "practical arts." In S. Brint (ed.), The future of the city of intellect: The changing American university, pp. 231-258. Stanford: Stanford University Press.

Burn, H. E. (2012). Factors that shape curricular reasoning about college algebra reform. *MathAMATYC Educator, 4*(1), 23–28.

Carlson, M., Jacobs, S., Coe, E., Larsen, S., & Hsu, E. (2002). Applying covariational reasoning while modeling dynamic events: A framework and a study. *Journal for Research in Mathematics Education, 33*(5), 352–378.

Carlson, M. P. (1998). A cross-sectional investigation of the development of the function concept. *Research in Collegiate Mathematics Education,* III, 114-162.

Chickering, A. W. & Gamson, Z. F. (1991). Seven principles for good practice in undergraduate education. *New Directions for Teaching and Learning, 47*, 63–71.

Cox, R. D. (2009). The college fear factor. Cambridge, MA: Harvard University Press.

Douglas, R. G. (ed.). (1986). Toward a lean and lively calculus (MAA Notes No. 6). Washington, DC: Mathematical Association of America.

Doyle, W. (1983). Academic work. *Review of Educational Research, 53*(2), 159–199.

Dweck, C. S. (1986). Motivational processes affecting learning. *American Psychologist, 41*(10), 1040–1048.

Dweck, C. S. (2006). *Mindset.* New York: Random House.

Dubinsky, E., Mathews, D., & Reynolds, B. E. (1997). *Readings in cooperative learning for undergraduate mathematics* (MAA Notes No. 44). Washington, DC: Mathematical Association of America.

Ellis, J., Johnson, E., & Rasmussen, C. (2015). *It's about time: How instructors and students experience time constraints in Calculus I.* Paper presented at the annual conference on Research in Undergraduate Mathematics Education, Pittsburgh, Pennsylvania.

Ellis, J., Hanson, K., Nuñez, G., & Rasmussen, R. (in press) *Beyond plug and chug: An analysis of calculus homework. International Journal of Research in Undergraduate Mathematics Education.* DOI: 10.1007/s40753-015-0012-z

Henderson, C., Beach, A., & Finkelstein, N. (2011). Facilitating change in undergraduate STEM instructional practices: An analytic review of the literature. *Journal of Research in Science Teaching, 48*(8), 952–984.

Hillel, J. (2001). Trends in curriculum: A working group report. In D. Holton (ed.), *The teaching and learning of mathematics at university level,* (pp. 59–69). Dordrecht: Kluwer.

Houston, K. (2001). Assessing undergraduate mathematics students. A working group report. In D. Holton (ed.), *The teaching and learning of mathematics at university level,* (pp. 407–422). Dordrecht: Kluwer.

Hsu, E., Mesa, V., & The Calculus Case Collective (2014). *Synthesizing measures of institutional success.* Technical report #1, Mathematical Association of America, Washington DC

Hughes Hallett, D. (n.d.) *What have we learned from calculus reform? The road to conceptual understanding.* Retrieved from math.arizona.edu/~dhh/NOVA/calculus-conceptual-understanding.pdf

Johnson, E., Ellis, J., & Rasmussen, C. (2014). *How to make time: The relationship between concerns about coverage, material covered, instructional practices, and student success in college calculus.* Paper presented at the annual conference on Research in Undergraduate Mathematics Education, Denver, Colorado.

Kaput, J. J. (1997). Rethinking calculus: Learning and thinking. *The American Mathematical Monthly, 104*(8), 731–736.

Kezar, A. (2001). *Understanding and facilitating organizational change in the 21ˢᵗ century: Recent research and conceptualizations.* Washington. DC: ASHE-ERIC Higher Education Reports.

Khan Academy. 2014. Calculus. *Khan Academy.* Retrieved from www.khanacademy.org/math/calculus

Kuh, G. D., Kinzie, J., Buckley, J. A., Bridges, B. K., & Hayek, J. C. (2006). *What matters to student success: A review of the literature. Commissioned paper for the National Symposium on Postsecondary Student Success: Spearheading a dialogue on student success.* Washington, DC: National Postsecondary Education Cooperative. Retrieved from nces.ed.gov/npec/pdf/kuh_team_report.pdf

Lattuca, L. R. & Stark, J. S. (2009). *Shaping the college curriculum: Academic plans in context* (2nd ed.). San Francisco: Jossey-Bass.

Martínez-Planell, R. & Trigueros, M. (2012). Students' understanding of the general notion of a function of two variables. *Educational Studies in Mathematics, 81*(3), 365–384.

Mazur, E. (2009). Farewell lecture. *Science. 323*(5910), 50–51.

McKeachie, W. J., & Svinicki, M. D. (2006). *Teaching tips: Strategies, research, and theory for college and university teaching* (12th ed.). Boston: Houghton Mifflin.

Mesa, V. (2011). Similarities and differences in classroom interaction between remedial and college mathematics classrooms in a community college. *Journal of Excellence in College Teaching, 22*(4), 21–56.

Mesa, V., Gómez, P., & Cheah, U. (2013). Influence of international studies of student achievement on mathematics teaching and learning. In Clements, M.D. (ed.), *Third international handbook of mathematics education,* (pp. 861–900). New York: Springer.

Mesa, V. & Griffiths, B. (2012). Textbook mediation of teaching: An example from tertiary mathematics instructors. *Educational Studies in Mathematics, 79*(1), 85–107.

Oehrtman, M. (2009). *Layers of abstraction: Theory and design for the instruction of limit concepts.* Retrieved from hub.mspnet.org/media/data/Oehrtman_Layers_of_Abstraction_Final.pdf?media_000000003121.pdf

Rico, L. (ed.). (1997). *Bases teóricas del currículo de matemáticas en educación secundaria* [Theoretical basis for mathematics curriculum in secondary education]. Madrid, Spain: Síntesis.

Rogers, E. C., Reynolds, B. C., & Davidson, N. A. (2001). *Cooperative learning in undergraduate mathematics: Issues and strategies that work* (MAA Notes No. 55). Washington, DC: Mathematical Association of America.

Silver, E. A. & Stein, M. K. (1996). The QUASAR project: The "revolution of the possible" in mathematics instructional reform in urban middle schools. *Urban Education, 30*, 476–521.

Sofronas, K. S., DeFranco, T. C., Vinsonhaler, C., Gorgievski, N., Schroeder, L., & Hamelin, C. (2011). What does it mean for a student to understand the first-year calculus? Perspectives of 24 experts. *Journal of Mathematical Behavior, 30*(2), 131–148.

Stein, M. K., Remillard, J., & Smith, M. S. (2007). How curriculum influences student learning. In F. K. Lester (ed.), *Second handbook of research on mathematics teaching and learning,* (pp. 319–370). Charlotte, NC.: National Council of Teachers of Mathematics.

Stein, M. K., Smith, M. S., Henningsen, M. A., & Silver, E. A. (2000). *Implementing standards-based mathematics instruction: A casebook for professional development.* New York: Teachers College Press.

Stigler, J. W., Givvin, K. B., & Thompson, B. J. (2010). What community college developmental mathematics students understand about mathematics. *The MathAMATYC Educator, 1*(3), 4–16.

Swinyard, C. & Larsen, S. (2012). Coming to understand the formal definition of limit: Insights gained from engaging students in reinvention. *Journal for Research in Mathematics Education, 43*(4), 465–493.

The College Board. (2012). *Calculus AB, Calculus BC Course Descriptions.* AP Central. Retrieved from apcentral.collegeboard.com/apc/public/courses/teachers_corner/2178.html

Trees, A. R. & Jackson, M. H. (2007). The learning environment in clicker classrooms: Student processes of learning and involvement in large university-level courses using student response systems. *Learning, Media and Technology, 32*(1), 21–40.

Trigueros, M. & Martínez-Planell, R. (2011). *How are graphs of two variable functions taught?* Paper presented at the annual meeting of the North American chapter of the International Group for Psychology in Mathematics Education, Reno, Nevada.

Trigueros, M. & Ursini, S. (2003). First-year undergraduates' difficulties in working with different uses of variable. *Research in Collegiate Mathematics Education. V,* 1–29.

White, N. J. & Mesa, V. (2014). Describing cognitive orientation of calculus I tasks across different types of coursework. *ZDM The International Journal on Mathematics Education.* doi: 10.1007/s1185801405889.

Wigfield, A. & Eccles, J. S. (2000). Expectancy-value theory of motivation. *Contemporary Educational Psychology, 25,* 68–81.

Wiliam, D. (2013). Assessment: The bridge between teaching and learning. *Voices from the Middle, 21*(2), 5–20.

Weick, K. E. (1976). Educational organizations as loosely coupled systems. *Administrative Science Quarterly, 21,* 1–9.

Yeager, D. S. & Walton, G. M. (2011). Social-psychological interventions in education: They're not magic. *Review of Educational Research, 81*(2), 267–301.

Zandieh, M. J. (2000). A theoretical framework for analyzing student understanding of the concept of derivative. *Research in Collegiate Mathematics Education, IV,* 103–127.

Chapter 5

Placement and Student Performance in Calculus I

Eric Hsu, *San Francisco State University*
David Bressoud, *Macalester College*

In this chapter we consider the range of placement policies departments use to decide who is allowed to take Calculus I and to support those students. Often this issue is narrowly framed as a question of finding an effective test to determine which math class a student should take. In this chapter, we will indeed discuss various placement tests in use, their frequency of use, and studies of their effectiveness as predictors of success and failure. However, student placement is always only a part of a larger institutional strategy for ensuring student success. At the colleges and universities we surveyed, we found a surprising variety of approaches to the issue of placement. This variety reflects differences in local priorities and different broader strategies for helping students accomplish their academic goals. We also found differences between the institution types that roughly parallel the increasing departmental autonomy and selectivity as one moves from AS-granting two-year colleges to MA-granting universities to BA-granting four-year colleges to PhD-granting universities.

Why Have a Placement Policy?

The effectiveness of a placement policy clearly depends on the results desired. The policy could be as simple as restricting access to the course because of a limited number of seats available. More common is to restrict access in order to raise the passing rate. Only allowing the strongest students into the course should raise the passing rate, but, as the following discussion illustrates, this may not be in the best interests of many of the students.

At most post-secondary institutions, the stated intention of the placement policy relevant to Calculus I is to prevent or discourage students from entering this course when they are inadequately prepared or unlikely to succeed. The policy should be such that it would direct those students toward the sequence that will enable them to succeed when they get to Calculus I. Implicit in this process is the assumption that those who are directed toward precalculus or other remediation find in the course effective preparation for Calculus I.

Too often, this is not the case. There is ample documentation of two problems with precalculus as preparation for Calculus I. The first is that many of those students who intend to study calculus and are successful in precalculus do not continue into Calculus I. A Texas Tech study (Jarrett, 2000) found that a third of their students who earned a B or higher in their precalculus course did not enroll in Calculus I. There are similar data from Arizona State University (Thompson et al., 2007): Among declared engineering majors who earned a C or higher in precalculus, 38% did not enroll in Calculus I. It was worse for other majors: 55% of physical science majors, 56% of mathematical science majors, and 65% of life science majors who earned a C or higher in precalculus did not enroll in Calculus I. Herriott & Dunbar (2009) report comparable data from the University of Nebraska-Lincoln and several colleges in Illinois.

We now have evidence of a second and more serious problem. Precalculus as currently taught in most post-secondary institutions in the United States does very little to improve student chances of success in Calculus I and can actually be detrimental. In a recent study of over 10,000 Calculus I students across the United States, Sonnert & Sadler (2014) compared grades in Calculus I of students with the same high school preparation in mathematics (courses taken, grades earned, SAT/ACT scores) who either had or had not taken a post-secondary precalculus class. They found that students below the mean composite secondary school preparation score did appear to benefit from precalculus, but by a meager and not statistically significant single point on a 100-point grading scale. They also found that for students above the mean, placement in precalculus *lowered* their Calculus I grade by a statistically significant average of six points. The meager gains from precalculus do not appear to offset the considerable risk that students directed to precalculus will not persist to Calculus I.

Bailey, Jeong, & Cho (2010) described two large studies of community college students as follows: "Calcagno & Long (2008) and [Martorell & McFarlin Jr. (2011)] analyzed the effects of remediation on subsequent outcomes in Florida and Texas, respectively... These studies find no positive effect of remediation on college credit accumulation, completion, or degree attainment." They examined students who ignored their remedial placement and enrolled above their placement in the "gatekeeper" course ("the first college-level courses the student must take after remediation"), and found that their pass rate (72%) was slightly below that of students who had accepted their remedial placement, passed the course, and then enrolled in the gatekeeper (79%). Similar to the Sonnert & Sadler (2014) study, this suggests that the placement plus remediation process may slightly lift the performance of students who complete it. However, the dropout rate for students in remediation was large, giving a net passing rate of 27% for all students who complied with their remediation referral. Eleven percent of the students in the remediation track dropped out even after passing all remediation classes taken. The placement policy as a whole was potentially hurting more students than it helped.

Hsu, Murphy, & Treisman (2008) also document the ineffectiveness of many college precalculus courses in preparing students for calculus. In some studies, students who took precalculus had a significantly lower success rate compared to non-takers, even when matching comparison groups by SAT score. Without an effective precalculus program, restricting student enrollment in Calculus I may result in students never passing Calculus I who otherwise might have. Furthermore, there is a disproportionately frequent placement of underrepresented minorities into remedial and precalculus courses, which amplifies for these students the importance of a quality precalculus program.

Which Placement Strategies Are Currently In Use?

From the Phase I Survey results, we learned that about half of the AS-granting, MA-granting and PhD-granting institutions require mandatory placement tests and that about a third of the BA-granting institutions do so. One might wonder how much the use of mandatory placement tests is driven by logistical needs such as having to assess and support large numbers of students. We can see an interesting pattern in our data for four-year institutions: the larger institutions had a greater tendency to use mandatory placement tests. Across the BA-, MA-, and PhD-granting institutions, mandatory placement tests were required by more than half the institutions with enrollment above the median FTE of our sample; less than 30% of the below-average size sites did. This pattern was reversed for AS-granting two-year colleges, where 48% have mandatory placement policies, compared with 63% of those with below median enrollment (see Table 1).

Table 1: Placement policies by sector and by Full-Time Enrollment (FTE).(Median FTE= 5,818).

	2Y-Coll (AS)	4Y-Coll (BA)	Univ (MA)	Univ (PhD)
Above Median FTE	N = 25	N = 14	N = 19	N = 64
Mandatory Placement	48%	57%	58%	53%
Non-Mandatory Placement	8%	7%	16%	19%
No Placement Test	44%	36%	26%	28%
Below Median FTE	N = 27	N = 45	N = 7	N = 8
Mandatory Placement	63%	29%	29%	25%
Non-mandatory Placement	4%	18%	0%	50%
No Placement Test	33%	53%	71%	25%
Total	N = 52	N = 59	N = 26	N =72
Mandatory Placement	56%	36%	50%	50%
Non-mandatory Placement	6%	15%	12%	22%
No Placement Test	38%	49%	38%	28%

Source: maalongdatafile.

Of those post-secondary institutions that did offer a placement exam, the distribution of what was used is reported in Table 2.

Table 2: Source of placement test.

	2Y-Coll (AS) N = 35	4Y-Coll (BA) N = 29	Univ (MA) N = 17	Univ (PhD) N = 58
Department creation	11%	55%	35%	64%
System-wide creation	3%	10%	0%	9%
Accuplacer	37%	21%	18%	3%
Compass	49%	10%	24%	3%
ALEKS	0%	0%	6%	10%
MAA Maplesoft	0%	3%	12%	5%
ACT or SAT	0%	0%	6%	5%

Note: Due to round-off, percentages may not sum to 100%. Source: maalongdatafile.

There are some clear trends that likely show the differences between institution types in deference to faculty judgment. For instance, the majority of BA- and PhD-granting institutions that use placement tests create their own test. AS-granting two-year colleges and MA-granting universities tend to be public institutions and less selective, which induces the need for an "objective" measure that does not rely solely on the professional judgment of the faculty. Therefore, it is not surprising to see that AS-granting two-year colleges very rarely use a department-made test, MA-granting universities use them about one-third of the time, BA-granting four-year colleges use their own exam more than half the time, and PhD-granting universities construct their own placement exam almost two-thirds of the time. In addition, AS- and MA-granting institutions more frequently depend on Accuplacer, Compass, or ACT/SAT scores (86% and 48%, respectively) than BA- and PhD-granting institutions (31% and 6%, respectively). ALEKS and MAA Maplesoft are less frequently used, with 18% of MA-granting and 15% of PhD-granting universities, but only one of 29 BA-granting four-year colleges and none of the 35 two-year colleges using these tests.

What Are Examples of Effective Placement Strategies?

Effectiveness of a placement strategy is always measured with respect to local conditions and goals. Placement policies can be improved by using *multiple measures* with locally appropriate means of combining them. Success must be defined in the context of *broader student success strategy* and is dependent on the specific local student population. Thus, although the literature can give broad guidelines for the effectiveness of particular instruments in any specific setting, it is essential to *use local data* to continually improve the placement strategy. We describe these strategies next.

Multiple Measures

The literature recommends using multiple measures to complement placement via standardized tests (Scott-Clayton, 2012). Although there are logistical challenges to obtain measures that are not standardized test scores (e.g., high school grades) using such measures improves predictive accuracy. Scott-Clayton (2012) found that the predictive power of Compass and Accuplacer exams is weak for two-year colleges but that the power improved when high school GPA was included in the model.

Table 3 lists procedures and locus of decision for placement in our case studies. It shows that about half of our case study sites, including almost all of the MA- and PhD-granting universities, used multiple measures. Usually these measures served as multiple ways to qualify for placement into Calculus I. Sometimes they were part of a more elaborate analysis. For instance at one site students were able to use their AP and SAT scores to place into one of two levels of calculus, with the option of taking a statewide test to qualify. Relative to the non-selected institutions, in which between one-third and one-half did not offer a placement test (see Table 1), only two of the case studies (BA4 and MA2) did not offer a placement test.

Table 3: Placement procedures and locus of final placement decision at case study sites.

Institution	Mandatory Test	Other Measures	Locus of Final Decision
TY1	State test		State
TY2	Accuplacer	SAT, AP	State
TY3	State test		State
TY4	Compass		District
BA0	MAA Maplesoft		Student
BA1	Department test		Student
BA2	MAA Maplesoft		Department
BA3	Accuplacer		Department
BA4	None	SAT	Department
MA1	ALEKS	SAT	Department
MA2	None	HS Math grades	Student
MA3	Department test		Department
MA4	Compass	ACT	State
PrTI	Department test		Student
PTU	ALEKS	ACT/SAT, HS grades	Department
LPrU	Department test	ACT, AP	Student
LPU1	Department test	ACT/SAT, HS grades	Student
LPU2	State test	AP	Department

Sometimes, the measures were used to make a predictive model for student use. One site created a model to predict students' grades in Calculus I using a linear combination of placement test score, the math ACT or SAT score, and high school GPA. This linear formula led to creating three breakpoints to classify students into precalculus, tentative precalculus, tentative Calculus I, and Calculus I.

Broader Student Success Strategy

A placement decision happens against the backdrop of the advising and support services strategies used in each institution. Chapter 6 discusses in detail the variety of advising and support mechanisms at the different sites. Here we briefly discuss strategies sites use to add flexibility to mandatory placement policies and structure to non-mandatory placement policies.

Adding Flexibility To Mandatory Placement. The sites that had a mandatory placement policy used a cut-off score system. This was the case at the two-year institutions, which had the cut-off scores externally mandated. However, some institutions implemented policies to add some flexibility to what might otherwise be a rigid and inaccurate system.

Several case study sites made the placement decision in an interview consultation with the student. This helped to get a better sense of the student and his or her preparation. This also served to let the students understand that the placement system was for their benefit and not meant to be punitive.

One case study site had a drop back policy whereby until the end of the first month, a student performing poorly in Calculus I could drop back to precalculus. Another site allowed a student to appeal the mandatory placement.

Adding Structure to Non-mandatory Placement. Six of the case study sites allowed students to self-place. In one of these sites the unusual policy stated that any student with four years of college preparatory mathematics could take Calculus I. In the five other sites, students were required (or strongly encouraged) to take a calculus placement test that gives them some evidence of their calculus readiness. At one site, a student may enroll in Calculus I without passing the exam, but this is only done in close consultation with a placement advisor. At another site, precalculus, Calculus I, and Calculus II are scheduled so that students can easily transfer to any of these courses at the start of the term.

Using Local Data

The use of local data at PhD-granting institutions is discussed in more detail in Chapter 11. A placement test and policy are meant to serve campus goals, which range from general goals such as improving the department's passing rate to goals for individual students, such as improving the likelihood that each will succeed in Calculus I and be prepared for the courses for which Calculus I is a prerequisite. Accordingly, department self-evaluation should be aligned with its goals.

At several of the sites, either a dedicated faculty member or a committee periodically monitored passing rates for Calculus I as a way to inform the adequacy of the placement test and its policy. Such data are the easiest to collect and monitor. Collecting data on student persistence into and through those classes for which Calculus I is a prerequisite was less frequent, but observed in departments with an intentional strategy for tracking students (especially those who are not math majors). Such data collection requires more effort. Tracking student performance from precalculus through Calculus I and beyond is also demanding. As the research by Bailey et al. (2010) shows, in order to get a picture of the whole health of the placement strategy, one needs to track the performance and subsequent trajectories of all students who take the placement exam, including those who place out of Calculus I as well as those who place into precalculus. Such tracking might be prohibitive in many institutions.

How Effective Are Specific Placement Tests?

In this section we discuss the apparent effectiveness of the various placement measures used by the institutions in the study: the AP exams, Compass and Accuplacer, ALEKS, MAA Maplesoft, SAT/ACT, and department-made exams. In each section we provide a brief general description of the measure and discuss some of their advantages and disadvantages.

AP Exams

The AP Calculus exams are not intended to serve as placement exams for Calculus I, yet a number of students in our study claimed to have placed into Calculus I through AP exam scores (Table 4). AP Calculus scores were also used in some of our case studies in determining placement. Although the percentages remain small, one can see in Table 4 that as the selectivity of the institution increases, so does the percentage of students placing into Calculus I by AP exam: the AS-, MA-, BA- and PhD-granting institutions respectively had 4%, 6%, 7%, and 17%. These figures also parallel the number of students who had studied calculus in high school. Among the Calculus I students at AS-, MA-, BA- and PhD-granting institutions, the percentage of students who have studied calculus in high school was 22%, 40%, 50%, and 67%, respectively.[1]

Many students did well on the Advanced Placement Calculus exam but still chose to take Calculus I. Among all Calculus I students at PhD-granting universities, 15% had earned a 4 or 5 on the AB exam or a 3 or higher on the BC exam. An additional 11% earned a 3 on the AB exam.

Table 4: Student reported determination of placement.

	2Y-Coll (AS) N = 845	4Y-Coll (BA) N = 1,932	Univ (MA) N = 601	Univ (PhD) N = 8,039
ACT/SAT score	9%	20%	23%	27%
Placement exam	20%	43%	31%	45%
Completion of prerequisite courses	77%	45%	59%	42%
AP Exam	4%	7%	6%	17%
Do not know	5%	15%	10%	10%

Note: Students could select more than one response. Source: maalongdatafile.

There is no uniform policy for the threshold at which AP student performance is considered equivalent to Calculus I for the AB exam and to Calculus II for the BC exam. In a study of 51 colleges and universities, Patterson & Ewing (2013) found that 33 allowed advanced placement, which may or may not have included credit for Calculus I, for a score of 3 on the AB exam, and 17 required a score of 4. For the BC exam, 39 allowed advanced placement for a score of 3, while 9 required a score of 4. The remaining institutions gave advanced placement for a score of less than 3.

While advanced placement usually includes credit for the relevant course, there is a variety of ways of handling this credit. Macalester College is one of a number of colleges and universities that allow advanced placement into the second calculus course for a score of 3 on the AB exam, but a score of 3 does not earn credit for the first calculus course unless the student takes and passes the second course.

The International Baccalaureate Higher Level Mathematics and College Board Advanced Placement Calculus exams are the only national standardized tests that measure the extent to which calculus has been learned in high school[2], and AP Calculus is the only one with published effectiveness data for calculus placement. Patterson and Ewing (2013) report that, comparing grades in the next calculus course and with student populations matched so that they were equivalent[3], students who had received advanced placement because of AP scores outperformed the students who had not skipped the relevant calculus course. For AB Calculus, the improvement was 0.19 on a four-point scale

---

1 Source: maalongdatafile.

2 Another national test that assesses knowledge of Calculus I is the College Board CLEP Calculus exam (see media.collegeboard.com/digitalServices/pdf/clep/calculus_fact_sheet.pdf), but it is only available as a tool to assess calculus taught at the post-secondary level.

3 Propensity matching was done to equalize high school GPA, PSAT scores, and gender, racial, and ethnic distributions. For the AB Calculus comparison, there were 1733 students in each group. For the BC Calculus comparison, there were 750 students in each group.

(A = 4.0, B = 3.0, ...) and 0.17 standard deviations. For BC Calculus, the improvement was 0.23 points and 0.22 standard deviations. These figures update the report by Keng & Dodd (2008), which found similar results for AP Calculus AB and BC. For an overview of the various AP Calculus validity studies with a discussion of their respective strengths and shortcomings see Bressoud (2009).

ACT Compass and College Board Accuplacer

The ACT Compass and the College Board Accuplacer are computer-adaptive tests that are administered online, with the progression of questions based on how students respond. They both have the advantage of providing immediate results. While both tests are often used as placement tests for calculus, they are primarily designed to determine whether or not a student is ready for college-level mathematics. Validity studies published by the ACT and College Board are restricted to how well they predict success in courses at or below the level of college algebra or precalculus (Mattern & Packman, 2009; Westrick & Allen, 2014). This emphasis reflects that the institutions that use these tests most often are those with significant numbers of students who are not ready for college-level mathematics (e.g., two-year colleges). According to the ACT (2013), cut-off scores are set so that students "have approximately a 50 percent chance of earning a B or better and approximately a 75 percent chance of earning a C or better in the corresponding college course or courses" (p. 2).

Compass offers exams that cover pre-algebra, algebra, college algebra, geometry and trigonometry. It is the trigonometry test that is often used for calculus placement. A score of 46 or higher generally indicates that a student has sufficient knowledge of trigonometry to be ready for Calculus I. Accuplacer offers tests in arithmetic, elementary algebra, and college-level mathematics, the last of which includes algebra, exponentials, sequences and series, elementary combinatorics, and simple trigonometry. Westrick & Allen (2014) and Scott-Clayton (2012) document the increased predictive value when Compass or Accuplacer scores are combined with high school grade point average.

ALEKS

Like Compass and Accuplacer, Assessment and LEarning in Knowledge Spaces (ALEKS), is also a computer-adaptive test that is administered online with individually generated questions; precalculus is the highest level at which it tests. Unlike Compass and Accuplacer, ALEKS uses only free response questions. More significantly, ALEKS allows students to return to the exam for reassessment of subject areas that may have been missed before and provides online tutoring to help students self-remediate, with the learning modules primed by the student responses.

ALEKS covers a wide range of mathematical topics from third grade through precalculus. Its largest market is for use in K-12. ALEKS runs on an artificial intelligence engine that was developed, starting in the 1980s, at New York University and the University of California, Irvine, using the theory of Knowledge Spaces (Falmagne & Doignon, 2011). This theory is used to map a mathematical subject area such as the mathematics of Algebra I to a set of items, essentially problem types, and to capture the hierarchical structure of dependence among these items. It is this understanding of the dependence structure of problem types that enables it to drill down and identify the most basic level at which a student is experiencing difficulty. Ahlgren & Harper (2011) and Harper & Ahlgren (2013) discuss the implementation of ALEKS at the University of Illinois as a tool for Calculus I placement and a means of bringing students with deficiencies up to speed so that they are prepared for Calculus I.

MAA Maplesoft

The MAA Maplesoft Placement Testing Suite offers both Calculus Readiness and Calculus Concept Readiness tests. The latter is the only national placement exam intentionally designed to probe student reasoning and conceptual understanding around key ideas needed for Calculus I, ideas that include proportional reasoning, covariational reasoning about functions, function growth patterns, the connection between slope and constant rate of change, average rate of change, function composition and inverses, and the various interpretations of trigonometric functions. It is based on research into student difficulties in calculus that has identified conceptual hurdles to student understanding of the important concepts of calculus (Carlson, Madison, & West, 2010). While MAA Maplesoft is administered by computer with multiple versions of each exam, it is not computer-adaptive. The questions are fixed. MAA has provided a booklet on the use of MAA Maplesoft with guidelines for local validation of its results (MAA, 2010).

SAT and ACT Math Scores

It is very tempting to use SAT or ACT scores for placement because most entering students have already taken one of these tests, and there is no additional cost to the college or university. The problem is that neither is designed to serve as a placement test or to assess particular mathematical skills. Famously, the University of Illinois' decision to switch from ACT scores to ALEKS for Calculus I placement was in part motivated by the negative correlation between ACT scores and performance in Calculus I (Ahlgren & Harper, 2011). In 2010, the Board of Governors of the MAA endorsed the following as part of their statement on College Placement Testing:

> College admission tests such as the SAT or ACT measure students' general readiness for college, whereas placement tests seek to measure students' knowledge and skills that are prerequisite for specific entry-level college mathematics courses. Nationally administered tests such as SAT and ACT measure a broad range of quantitative skills, and this measure is often too general to distinguish between readiness for entry-level mathematics courses such as college algebra, trigonometry, precalculus and calculus. (p. iii)

Department-Made Exams

The advantage of using a department-made exam is that it can be customized to the topics and areas that the faculty judges to be important. The disadvantage is that it can be difficult to gather sufficient data to assess whether the exam is valid and reliable. The test makers are almost always working on intuition. The most common departmental assessment of the effectiveness of placement exams is to see how students perform in the class into which they were placed.

Mathematics departments are unlikely to have the will and resources to perform a detailed analysis of their exams and items. However, we list here some basic notions from test development theory that may give test creators ideas for study and improvement. Developers of standardized tests are concerned that their tests are reliable (test takers get consistent scores on different test occasions), valid (they measure what they are trying to measure), and unbiased (performance is solely due to content mastery).

Item analysis theory is concerned that the test as a whole discriminates between students of different aptitudes. Thus, the test needs questions with a spread of difficulty (as measured by the percentage of students who give a correct answer) with some easy and some hard questions mixed in with the middle difficulty questions.

A more subtle issue is item discrimination (how success on an item correlates to success on the overall exam). If item success is poorly (or even negatively) correlated to success overall, the item should be discarded. A common simple measure is the discrimination index of a problem, which is computed by taking the difference between the number of students in the top quartile who got the item right and the number of students in the bottom quartile who got the problem right, and dividing this difference by the number of students in a quartile. A rule of thumb is that a discrimination index of less than 0.20 is unacceptable.

Conclusion

First, whatever placement policy is chosen, it must be monitored continually. This includes looking at correlations between placement scores and grades in Calculus I. It is also useful to compare students who score near the cut-off score: Does sending those students just below the cut-off score to precalculus reduce the likelihood that they will complete Calculus I? Possible confounding factors (e.g., personal or non-academic reasons for dropping a course) could be identified via surveys and focus groups of students who do not return or drop the Calculus I course.

Second, multiple measures can significantly improve the predictive power of any placement procedures. As mentioned in the section on Compass and Accuplacer, both of these exams provide better predictive value when combined with high school GPA. Even just combining SAT or ACT math scores with high school transcript information, as done by Sonnert & Sadler (2014), produced a model with reasonable predictive power (a pseudo-R^2 of 0.216, which means that their model predicts about 22% of the variability in performance in Calculus I).

Finally, it makes no sense to have a policy in place that directs certain students to precalculus if precalculus is, in fact, a dead end for most of the students who take it.

References

ACT. (2013). What are the ACT college readiness benchmarks? *ACT Research and Policy Information Brief.* Retrieved December 29, 2014 from www.act.org/research/policymakers/pdf/benchmarks.pdf.

Ahlgren, A. & Harper, M. (2009). Assessment and placement through Calculus I at University of Illinois. *Notices of the AMS*, *58*,1460–1461.

Bailey, T., Jeong, D. W., & Cho, S. W. (2010). Referral, enrollment, and completion in developmental education sequences in community colleges. *Economics of Education Review*, *29*(2), 255–270.

Bressoud, D. M. (2009). AP Calculus: What we know. *Launchings.* Retrieved December 29, 2014 from www.maa.org/external_archive/columns/launchings/launchings_06_09.html.

Calcagno, J. C. & Long, B. T. (2008). *The impact of postsecondary remediation using a regression discontinuity approach: Addressing endogenous sorting and noncompliance.* National Bureau of Economic Research (working paper No. 14194). Retrieved December 29, 2014 from www.nber.org/papers/w14194.

Carlson, M., Madison, B., & West, R. (2010). *The Calculus Concept Readiness (CCR) instrument: Assessing student readiness for calculus.* arXiv preprint. Retrieved December 29, 2014 from arxiv.org/abs/1010.2719.

Falmagne, J. C & Doignon, J. P. (2011). *Learning spaces: Interdisciplinary applied mathematics.* Berlin: Springer-Verlag.

Harper, M. & Ahlgren, A. (2013). *Detecting concepts crucial for success in mathematics courses from Knowledge State-based placement data.* arXiv preprint. Retrieved December 29, 2014 from arxiv.org/abs/1312.1127.

Herriott, S. R. & Dunbar, S. R. (2009). Who takes college algebra? *Primus.* *19*(1), 74–87.

Hsu, E., Murphy, T. J., & Treisman, U. (2008). Supporting high achievement in introductory mathematics courses: What we have learned from 30 years of the Emerging Scholars Program. In M. Carlson-& C. Rasmussen (eds.), *Making the Connection: Research and Teaching in Undergraduate Mathematics* (pp. 205–220). Washington, DC: Mathematical Association of America.

Jarrett, E. (2000). *Evaluating persistence and performance of 'successful' precalculus students in subsequent mathematics courses*, unpublished M.S. Thesis, Texas Tech University.

Keng, L. & Dodd, B. G. (2008). *A comparison of college performances of AP® and Non-AP student groups in 10 subject areas* (College Board Research Rep. No. 2008-7). New York: The College Board. Retrieved September 4, 2014, from research.collegeboard.org/rr2008-7.pdf.

Martorell, P. & McFarlin Jr., I. (2011). Help or hindrance? The effects of college remediation on academic and labor market outcomes. *The Review of Economics and Statistics, 93* (2), 436–454.

Mathematical Association of America (2010). *Placement test program user's guide.* Retrieved December 29, 2014 from www.maa.org/sites/default/files/pdf/ptp/ptpguide.pdf.

Mattern, K. D. & Packman, S. (2009). *Predictive validity of Accuplacer scores for course placement: A meta-analysis.* College Board Research Report #2009-2. Retrieved December 29, 2014 from research.collegeboard.org/publications/content/2012/05/predictive-validity-accuplacer-scores-course-placement-meta-analysis.

Patterson, B. & Ewing, M. (2013). *Validating the use of AP® exam scores for college course placement* (College Board Research Rep. No. 2013-2). New York: The College Board. Retrieved September 4, 2014, from esearch.collegeboard.org/sites/default/files/publications/2013/7/researchreport-2013-2-validating-AP-exam-scores-college-course-placement.pdf.

Scott-Clayton, J. (2012). *Do high-stakes placement exams predict college success?* (CCRC Working Paper No. 41). New York: Teachers College. Retrieved September 4, 2014, from ccrc.tc.columbia.edu/media/k2/attachments/high-stakes-predict-success.pdf.

Sonnert, G. & Sadler, P. M. (2014). The impact of taking a college precalculus course on students' college calculus performance. *International Journal of Mathematical Education in Science and Technology*, *45*(8), 1188–1207. Retrieved from www.tandfonline.com/doi/abs/10.1080/0020739X.2014.920532.

Thompson, P. W., Castillo-Chavez. C., Culbertson, R. J., Flores, A., Greeley, R., Haag, S., Lawson, A. E., Rose, S. D., and Rutowksi, R. L. (2007). *Failing the future: Problems of persistence and retention in Science, Technology, Engineering, and Mathematics (STEM) majors at Arizona State University.* Report prepared and submitted by the Provost's Freshman STEM Improvement Committee. Retrieved February 27, 2015, from pat-thompson.net/PDFversions/2007FSICfinalreport.pdf.

Westrick, P. A. & Allen, J. (2014). *Validity evidence for ACT Compass® placement tests (ACT* Research Report Series. No. 2014(2)). Iowa City, IA: ACT Research Report Series. Retrieved September 4, 2014, from www.act.org/research/researchers/reports/pdf/ACT_RR2014-2.pdf.

Chapter 6

Academic and Social Supports

Estrella Johnson, *Virginia Tech*
Kady Hanson, *San Diego State University*

In a review of the higher education research literature on student success, Kuh, Kinzie, Buckley, & Hayek (2006) list a number of academic and social supports commonly available to students. These supports include: freshman orientation, transition courses and first-year seminars, peer learning communities, advising, tutoring, supplemental instruction, study groups, summer bridge programs, study skills workshops, mentoring, student-faculty research, and senior capstone projects. Such academic and social supports have the potential to support students in a variety of ways. In addition to providing students with increased instructional time through course and content tutoring, academic and social supports also can help incoming students transition to college and help students navigate a path towards success (Kuh, Kinzie, Schuh, & Whitt, 2005). However, as Kuh et al. (2006) caution, "simply offering such programs and practices does not guarantee that they will have the intended effects on student success" (p. 57).

To understand how such supports influence student success, it helps to observe that many of these programs are targeted toward—or at least applicable to—first-year college students. This emphasis on first-year students is of particular significance as research has found again and again that "involvement, or what is increasingly being referred to as engagement, matters and it matters most during the critical first year of college" (Tinto, 2006, p. 4). Therefore, as we investigated the academic and social supports available to Calculus I students, we were not only interested in the supports available, but also in how these supports engaged students and fostered student community.

Data and Methods

Our investigation progressed through three sets of data, each analyzed with different goals. First, we examined survey data from both the selected and non-selected institutions. When analyzing the survey data, we focused on the availability and usage of two main student supports: tutoring centers and office hours. Second, we used data from our site visits to the 18 selected institutions in order to develop descriptions of the various student support programs offered to Calculus I students. This analysis focused on interviews with instructors and support personnel as well as internal documents from support centers. Finally, we used student focus group interviews to better understand the impact of these support programs on students' Calculus I experiences.

Here we present results from these three rounds of analysis. In the first section, we discuss findings about tutoring centers and office hours from the national survey data. In the second section, we provide specific examples from our selected institutions of how they implement the five types of support: tutoring centers, office hours, college or university wide support programs, special course options, and transfer assistance. In our last section, we turn our attention to the positive learning environments that these support programs help foster for Calculus I students at the selected institutions.

A View from the National Survey

We begin with descriptive and comparative statistics about two of the most common forms of student support—tutoring centers and office hours. The data for this analysis come from both course coordinators and students who responded to survey questions regarding the availability and frequency of use of these two supports[1]. Overall, the analysis of our survey data suggests that selected and non-selected institutions are quite similar with regards to these two forms of student support.

Of the 18 course coordinators from the selected institutions, 13 of them responded to the survey question "Does your department, college, or university operate a mathematics tutoring center available to Calculus I students?" All 13 (100%) of these respondents indicated that they do have a tutoring center. Of the 150 course coordinators from the non-selected institutions, 105 provided an answer to this question, with 102 (97%) indicating that they do have a tutoring center. In other words, we found that selected and non-selected institutions were equally likely to have a tutoring center.

At institutions where course coordinators indicated having tutoring centers, there was no reported difference between the type of staff employed in the tutoring center staff at selected and non-selected institutions. The course coordinator survey provided five classifications for tutoring: tutoring by undergraduate students, tutoring by graduate students, tutoring by paraprofessional staff, tutoring by part-time mathematics faculty, and tutoring by full-time mathematics faculty (see Table 1). None of the intra-category comparisons were significant at the .05 level (e.g., selected and non-selected institutions were just as likely to offer tutoring by full time mathematics faculty). Undergraduates were the most common staff in the tutoring centers, closely followed by graduate students.

Table 1: Frequency and percent of different types of tutoring center staff by status of institution.

	What services are available to students in the Tutoring Center?				
	Tutoring by undergraduate students	Tutoring by graduate students	Tutoring by para-professional staff	Tutoring by part-time mathematics faculty	Tutoring by full time mathematics faculty
Non-selected (N = 102)	91 (87%)	35 (33%)	28 (27%)	23 (22%)	31 (30%)
Selected (N = 13)	12 (92%)	4 (31%)	2 (15%)	1 (8%)	2 (15%)

Note: Respondents could select more than one option.

In terms of student usage of tutoring centers, we found no significant differences in either course coordinator reports of student usage or student reports of frequency of usage. When asked to respond to the statement "Students in Calculus I take advantage of the tutoring center," 10 of the 13 (77%) course coordinators from the selected institutions either *Agreed* or *Strongly Agreed* with this statement, whereas 86 of the 102 (85%) courses coordinators from the non-selected intuitions *Agreed* or *Strongly Agreed*. Similarly, no differences were found in student responses to the question: "How often do you visit a tutor to assist with this course?" (Possible options: *Never, Once a month, A few times a month, Once a week, More than once a week*, see Table 2).

---

1 The file used to perform the analysis in this section includes two institutions that initially served as pilots for the site visits and later completed the survey. See Hsu, Mesa & The Calculus Case Collective (2014).

Table 2: Student reported frequency of tutoring.

	How often do you visit a tutor to assist with this course?				
	Never	*Once a month*	*A few times a month*	*Once a week*	*> Once a week*
Non-selected (N = 3,344)	58%	12%	12%	10%	8%
Selected (N = 1,055)	59%	11%	13%	9%	8%

Finally, there were no student reported differences on how often students at selected and non-selected institutions visited office hours. On the end of term survey, students were asked: "How often do you visit your instructor's office hours: Never, Once a month, A few times a month, Once a week, More than once a week?" (see Table 3).

Table 3: Student reported frequency of visiting office hours.

	How often do you visit your instructor's office hours?				
	Never	*Once a month*	*A few timesa month*	*Once a week*	*> Once a week*
Non-selected (N = 4,087)	50%	23%	16%	7%	6%
Selected (N = 1,243)	50%	22%	17%	7%	4%

In summary, we found no statistical differences in the number of institutions providing tutoring centers, the composition of tutor center personnel, or in the reported frequency of students visiting the tutoring centers or attending office hours. Nationally, mathematics tutoring centers are very common. However, about 60 percent of students reported that they never visited the tutoring center and 50 percent of students reported that they never went to office hours.

Descriptions of Student Supports

We now turn our focus to our qualitative data collected at the 18 selected institutions. This will enable us to investigate how the student supports at these institutions function, and how (or if) these supports promote student success. In this section we provide an overview of the different types of supports offered at each of the selected institutions. We next provide a description for each form of support. Then, in the next result section, we turn our attention to the impact of these supports on student success.

To determine the types of support selected institutions offered, we first examined the summary documents, the "Facts and Features," that were created for each institution. These documents contained information about student support programs, centers, and policies. Using these documents, we were able to group the supports into five main categories: tutoring or learning centers, office hours, college or university support programs, special course options, and transfer assistance. Table 4 shows the supports offered by each institution. We then analyzed the pertinent interview transcripts and internal documents to build a description of how these supports function and what services they provide for students. We begin with the two forms of student supports offered at all 18 of the selected institutions: tutoring centers and office hours.

Table 4: Forms of support offered at institutions selected as case studies.

	Tutoring/Learning Center	Office Hours	College/University Programs	Special Course Options	Transfer Assistance
LPrU	✓	✓	✓		
LPU1	✓	✓	✓	✓	
LPU2	✓	✓	✓	✓	
PTU	✓	✓			
PTI	✓	✓	✓	✓	
MA1	✓	✓		✓	
MA2	✓	✓			
MA3	✓	✓			
MA4	✓	✓			
BA0	✓	✓	✓		
BA1	✓	✓	✓		
BA2	✓	✓			
BA3	✓	✓	✓		
BA4	✓	✓		✓	
AS1	✓	✓			✓
AS2	✓	✓		✓	
AS3	✓	✓			✓
AS4	✓	✓			✓

Note: MA, BA, and AS refer to the institution type based on the highest degree in mathematics granted by the institution: MA-granting universities, BA-granting four-year colleges, and AS-granting two-year colleges. The PhD-granting universities are differentiated by type, with LPrU = Large Private University, LPU = Large Public University, PTU = Public Technical University, and PTI = Private Technical Institute.

Tutoring Centers

While only 13 of the 18 course coordinators at the selected institutions reported having a tutoring center on the survey, all of the 18 institutions offered Calculus I tutoring. The discrepancy may be a result of tutoring centers not always being housed within mathematics departments. Of our 18 selected institutions, 11 offered tutoring through the mathematics department, one offered tutoring through college level programs, and 11 offered tutoring through institution level programs (four had tutoring through both the mathematics department and through institution level programs and one offered tutoring through both the mathematics department and a college level program). Here we describe two comprehensive mathematics tutoring centers: one at a small public AS-granting two-year college and the other at a large private PhD-granting university. Key features of these programs, along with positive features of tutoring centers that we found at other selected institutions, will then be summarized at the end of this section.

Tutoring at AS2. At AS2 the mathematics lab is funded, in part, by the college's Academic Foundations Department. The Academic Foundation Department provides "college prep" courses and "Learning Labs" for writing, mathematics, adult education, reading, and English as a second language. The manager of the mathematics learning lab is a faculty member in the Academic Foundations Department and is also an adjunct faculty member in the mathematics department.

The manager of the mathematics lab is responsible for overseeing everyday functions, handling the budget, hiring new employees, and tutoring students, as time allows. The lab employs three types of tutors: undergraduate students, graduate students from local universities, and professional tutors. When first hired, every tutor receives training on the basic functioning of the mathematics lab. Tutors are also able to ask for assistance from the manager if they become uncomfortable about any mathematical topic. Throughout the semester, if the manager sees problems arise, she schedules an in-person meeting or uses email to discuss the issue with the individual tutor.

The mathematics lab is equipped with two large whiteboards, with 50 to 75 chairs located throughout the room. Also included in the mathematics lab are about 35 computers, all with software that students might need for their lab assignments. The center is open five days a week from six to 11 hours per day, and typically serves from 50 to 100 students per day. Students can visit the center for one-on-one tutoring, group study sessions, or just to study and work on homework. For group study sessions, three or more students can make a reservation to have a tutor, or the manager, assist them with a review of a topic or a common assignment. It is fairly common for Calculus I students to request study groups. As the manager explains:

We help with everything. One thing I will say is that I personally do a lot of calculus study groups in here by request, not because of something special on my part. A lot of students here request me to do their calculus study groups and so I do that a lot. (AS2)

Because the manager of the mathematics lab is also an adjunct faculty member of the mathematics department, she is able to communicate with other mathematics faculty members about what she sees in the mathematics lab. For instance, the manager may be able to identify certain topics or concepts that appear difficult for students in the study groups. In such cases, she sometimes emails members of the mathematics department explaining how the students are thinking about the problems and issues on which they need more clarification. There also is informal communication between the manager and the calculus instructors. This is usually in the form of hallway conversations, where she shares common questions students have had for their homework and lab assignments.

Tutoring at LPrU. At LPrU, the math lab is funded through the dean's office and is run by an executive committee made up of one full-time administrator and four executive tutors. The executive tutors are student-tutors that have been promoted. Two of the executive tutors are "head tutors," one for upper-division mathematics courses and one for lower-division mathematics courses. Head tutor positions exist to help train other tutors on concepts and problems that arise each week. They are also in charge of keeping track of the courses covered in their division, scheduling reviews and providing assistance in any way the mathematics lab can for those courses. There are a total of 50 to 60 tutors and they can choose to work from 10 to 20 hours a week. The tutors can work for the mathematics lab from one to four years.

The physical space of the mathematics lab is divided by mathematics courses (e.g., a section for Calculus I and a section for Calculus II). The lab is open from 9:00 am until 8:00 pm, and offers exam review and drop-in tutoring. The lab actively invites students to exam review sessions, emailing all the students in the course to inform them of the date and time. If students are interested in drop-in tutoring, they put their name on a sign-up sheet and list the problem with which they need help. Students often reported using the tutoring center as a place to do homework, even if they were not there specifically for tutoring services.

Because students sign in for help with individual problems, the mathematics lab is able to collect detailed records that they then use to inform staffing and tutor training decisions. For instance, the mathematics lab knew that in the winter semester of 2011, tutors helped students with more than 47,500 questions; in fall of 2006, during week 13, there were more than 121 questions answered from 3:30 pm to 4:30 pm. The executive committee uses these data to inform staffing and scheduling decisions. Additionally, because the committee knows which questions students usually ask the executive committee is able to identify important areas of tutor training.

There is a weekly training meeting every Monday throughout the semester. During the meeting, the tutors are given problems that students have identified as especially challenging. This allows the tutors to be prepared for the students who come in during the week. Additionally, these training meetings include modules on tutoring methods. During these lessons they discuss various tutoring topics and how to apply them in the mathematics lab to help the students. The topics covered include communication and listening skills, critical thinking, and test anxiety. In the summer of 2012 the College Reading and Learning Association recognized the mathematics lab as a certified tutor-training program.

Interesting Ideas for Established Tutoring Centers
Here we present a summary of interesting and promising ideas we identified at various tutoring centers at the selected institutions. As opposed to the detailed descriptions presented above, these excerpts are presented as possible add-on services and ideas for already established centers.

Late Night Tutoring at BA1. The Student Success Center at BA1 offers late night tutoring. On Monday and Wednesday nights from 10:00 pm to 12:00 am, two senior mathematics majors work as tutors in a common area of one of the freshman residence halls. Students work in this common area on homework assignments and exam reviews, while the tutors circulate the room, helping students with their questions.

Faculty Office Hours Held in Tutoring Centers at BA1. In addition to the late night tutoring offered by the Student Success Center, the mathematics department at BA1 also runs a small tutoring center. Strong undergraduate students and full-time faculty members staff this drop-in tutoring center. All full-time faculty have to schedule one of their office hours in the tutoring center. During this hour the faculty members work as tutors, answering questions and working with students. This requirement is an effort to help increase faculty-student interactions outside of the classroom.

Study Groups at AS2. A group of three or more students can request a study group session. During study group sessions, a tutor will stay with the group for about an hour. Students may request a study group for homework assignments, lab assignments, and test reviews. As described by a student: "It's extremely helpful because ... instead of going to math lab and having a tutor come up to you if you raise your hand, you get personal attention for about an hour or so."

Data Collection used for Training and Scheduling Decisions at LPrU. At LPrU, students write down the specific homework problems with which they need help. The executive committee uses this list to compile a collection of problems for which students often ask questions, and identify times during the semester that are particularly slow or busy. The list of challenging questions is used to help prepare tutors during their weekly training sessions, while the usage rates are used to help inform tutor scheduling.

Office Hours

It is not particularly remarkable that at each of the selected institutions Calculus I instructors were required to hold office hours. However, at some selected institutions, we found examples of what we saw as non-standard office hours. We include descriptions of what students said were effective ways that their teachers encouraged them to visit office hours.

Open Door Policy. At several of the selected institutions, instructors made themselves available to students any time they were in their offices. For instance, at MA4 many of the instructors talked about being available to students outside of office hours on a daily basis. At other selected institutions, this openness and willingness to help students became a departmental norm to the extent that some instructors even volunteered to help the students of other mathematics instructors. Two students described such an atmosphere at MA1:

Student 1:   Always an open door during their office hours ... If you stop by and they're there, then
              they'd help you.

Student 2:   I think they all just live here basically.

Student 1:   I'll stop any math teacher I see in the hallway; I'll say "you have to help me".

Student 2:   Yeah, that's right.

Student 1:   Even if it's not for their class.

These informal open door policies were not always restricted to physical offices. During normal working hours several students talked to instructors and teaching assistants who utilized email, screen capture software, and even text messaging to help students as questions arose. An instructor at AS1 typified this availability, where students discussed email and teacher availability as important resources.

I'll email him on Sunday and in about a half an hour he emails back with the answer and how to work the problem and on Sundays, holidays. And he comes in on Fridays and donates about three to four hours of his own time to help students in the morning. (Student, AS1)

Extended Office Hours. The most time-demanding office hour requirement we found was at AS3. At this college, Calculus I instructors held office hours anywhere from 7 to 12 hours per week. Most students saw the number of hours as a benefit, as it gave them more time to work one-on-one with their instructors. Also, extended hours gave students more options if they had classes that interfered with some of the office hours. Students used office hours to work on homework or ask questions about the lesson taught in class. Some students attended office hours every day to avoid getting behind on the material. However, we found that only four of the 14 AS3 students who answered a question about office hour attendance on the end of the term survey indicated that they attended office hours at least once a month. The other 10 students indicated that they never attended office hours. Across all institutions in our sample, 50 percent of students indicated that they attend office hours at least once of month[2]. So, as Kuh et al. (2006) warned, it appears that just extending hours is not enough to increase student office hour attendance.

Office Hours Held in Tutoring Center. As previously discussed in the tutoring center subsection, Calculus I instructors at BA1 were required to hold one of their office hours in the department's tutoring center. Faculty members at BA1 felt that one of the main benefits of this policy was that it encouraged faculty-student interaction outside of the classroom:

> *I do think that we sort of go out of our way to really try to get students involved in actually interacting with faculty outside of class … I think we try to get at—reach out and make sure they understand that that's part of what they're going to be doing here is not just interacting in class, but outside of class. I think those things helped tremendously over the years.* (Coordinator, BA1)

Encouraging Students to Attend Office Hours. Some instructors at the selected institutions took very direct approaches to getting students into office hours. At MA1 students discussed an instructor who actively monitored students during class and, if she had reason to believe that a student needed more help, she would intervene immediately.
> *She can tell just by facial expressions if you don't understand the material within class. So sometimes when class is dismissed she'll keep a certain student and say "you need to come to my office hour right now". Like, she'll know if a student needs help but doesn't want to ask for it, she'll pull them out to give them the help.* (Student, MA1)

Another example of an instructor strongly encouraging students to come to office hours came from BA0. This instructor required students to come to his office hours in order to collect their exams. Perhaps unsurprisingly, 32 of the 51 students from BA0 who answered a question about office hour attendance on the end of the term survey indicated that they attended office hours at least once a month. Additionally, 18 of those students reported visiting office hours more than once a month. Therefore, this policy appears to encourage students to come to office hours more frequently than exam retrieval alone would require. In fact, as a student from BA0 describes, this policy is used by the instructor to check in with his students and discuss how they are doing in the course.

> *After we have tests he makes you come to his office to pick up the tests and he'll spend like 5 to 10 minutes with every student from at least his Calc I and Calc II classes, I know. Just like going through the tests and then evaluating the grade you got on the test as well as sometimes what you have in the class. Especially at the university level, I think that's pretty hard to come by.* (Student, BA0)

College or University Support Programs

Seven of our 18 selected institutions had institutional support programs that went beyond tutoring. These services included: tutoring, supplemental instruction, personal counseling services, summer bridge programs, and early academic advising. Some of these programs specifically targeted first year students, with extra attention given to those that exhibit risk factors. In all we found the following support services offered by our case study institutions:

- Monitoring of at-risk students
- Peer mentoring programs

---

2 It is important to note that the survey was given out the year prior to the site visits. Therefore, the students that participated in the focus group interviews are not the same students who filled out the survey.

- Tutoring for specific content areas
- Tutoring for study skills and academic preparation
- Early alert system for instructors to report struggling students
- Summer-bridge programs
- Supplemental instruction
- Connecting students to resources and support programs

Here we detail four of the most comprehensive support programs we found in our case study institutions, those at BA1, LPrU, BA0, and LPU2.

BA1—Student Success Center. The Student Success Center offers a broad spectrum of supports for struggling students. The center is run by the Associate Vice President of Student Affairs and is funded with a grant from the parents' association. The center is located in the first year residence area of campus, and students either seek out assistance on their own or are recommended to the center through an academic warning system. In the most recent year, a third of the students at BA1 had visited the student success center[3], with 190 students receiving one-on-one tutoring during the spring semester. The number of students receiving one-on-one tutoring through the center was increasing. Midway through the semester of our site visit, they had already provided tutors to more than 350 students (with mathematics and science being the subjects most commonly requested).

At any point during the semester, an instructor at BA1 can initiate an academic warning through the center's online system. Instructors are encouraged to submit academic warnings for patterns that include poor attendance, a drop in grades, poor test results, or behavioral changes or problems. Once the instructor initiates an academic warning, the student receives an email from his or her instructor and a follow-up email from the center. The email from the center explains that it provides both academic and personal counseling services and that all assistance is confidential. Services offered through the center include free one-on-one tutoring, late night tutoring, time management counseling, personal and academic counseling, and some preliminary academic advising.

The two main academic supports for calculus students are late night tutoring and one-on-one tutoring. Late night tutoring in one of the residence halls is held three nights a week from 10:00 pm to 12:00 am, two nights dedicated to mathematics and the third to biology and chemistry. During the mathematics tutoring, students gather in a main area of a freshman residency hall and senior mathematics majors circulate the room answering questions. This program was envisioned to be a "just in time" support. As described by the director of the center, "even if they don't have a questions, it's a great place to do your homework because, if a question comes up at 11 o'clock at night, there's nobody to call, so … tutoring works really well."

LPrU—First Year Experience. LPrU started a program ten years ago called the First Year Experience, which helps incoming first year students transition smoothly from high school to college. As part of this program, the housing department places pairs of roommates into the same sections of courses they both pre-register to take. This is, in part, intended to facilitate dorm study groups. The first year experience also runs a mentoring program. First year students are grouped together based on major and assigned a mentor. The mentor's responsibilities include learning about the students, attending social events with them, and providing support for common difficulties first year students experience, such as time management and the transition from high school to college. Although every first year student student is assigned a mentor, they may opt out of the mentoring program.

BA0—First Year Resource Center. BA0 has a first year resource center that identifies students who are at risk during their first or second year, and tries to connect those students with campus resources which may be able to help them. During the 2012–2013 school year, the First Year Resource Center communicated with more than 500 students, more than 50% of the freshman class (exact numbers on how many of these contacts involved Calculus I specifically were not provided). The focus and goal of the First Year Resource Center is first year student retention. As described by the director of the center:

---

3 BA1 currently has about 4,500 full-time students.

The First Year Center was put into place in 2001 with that sole... intention. It was like, "What can we do to help freshmen become sophomores?" So ... all of our efforts are just about trying to help with that transition.

The center utilizes a two-pronged approach toward first-year retention: monitoring, outreach, and advising for at risk students, and first-year workshops for all incoming freshman. Initially, incoming freshman may be flagged for a number of at risk indicators, including low high school GPA, low high school GPA paired with high SAT scores, low SAT scores, out-of-state residency, non-Catholic religious affiliation (BA0 is a Catholic University), undeclared major, and a first-choice university preference that was not BA0. Depending on their risk factors, these students either receive early support or are monitored through their first year. For instance, BA0 has a significant number of students from Hawaii. For these students, the center tries to intervene early, before the fall weather sets in. This intervention may include informing students of Hawaiian restaurants in town and directing them toward the warm, sunny buildings on campus.

For other students with risk factors, the center may decide to wait until there is an indication that a student needs assistance. At any point during the semester, instructors can email the center if a student does poorly on an exam or is missing class. The center will reach out to these students, connecting them to tutoring for specific courses (e.g., the mathematics tutoring center or the writing assistance center) or to an academic coach to help with broader study and academic skills. Finally, at the beginning of the spring semester, the center compiles a list of freshmen that have a GPA below 2.0, and places them on academic probation. These students are required to work with a student mentor during the spring semester. The student and the mentor meet at least once a week and discuss why the student struggled the previous semester (e.g., study skills, organization, motivation, or conceptual difficulties).

Along with identifying and helping at risk students, the freshman resource center also runs a workshop that all freshmen attend during the fall semester. The workshop sessions are one hour each week for the first eight weeks of the semester. The first two weeks are taught during orientation and are focused on how to communicate with different people around campus, such as new roommates or faculty members. As the weeks progress, the workshops cover topics designed to help students adjust to their new college surroundings. They discuss everything from the logistics of registering for classes and meeting with your advisor, to the different study and time management skills needed for college. The decision to run a freshman workshop during the first eight weeks of the semester aligns with research suggesting that during these weeks students are forming first impressions of their new environment and determining if they belong (Hossler et al., 2006); the timing therefore is key to retention.

The workshop sessions are taught by upperclassmen who have gone through an application process and whom the director, assistant director, and the coordinator of the Freshman Resource Center all have agreed to hire. There are about 30 to 35 workshop leaders, with approximately a third of them returning leaders from the previous year. After being hired, the workshop leaders go through a four-day training just before freshman orientation begins. Once the workshops begin, leaders meet with the director one-hour a week to discuss the topic each will be teaching that week. Some of the workshop leaders are also chosen to become a mentor for certain "at risk" students later on in the semester.

LPU2—Student Support Program. LPU2 has a university support program run by the Student Affairs Office. This program offers mathematics and science tutoring, a summer bridge program to help transition incoming freshmen, and mathematics and science workshops offered throughout the academic year. The primary goal of this program is to help students from historically under-represented populations. This includes students from educationally disadvantaged high schools, low socio-economic backgrounds, and first-generation college students.

To help ease the transition from high school to college, the Student Support Program offers a summer bridge program. The summer bridge program serves approximately 150 students annually. Students who choose to participate in the bridge program live on campus for four weeks prior to the beginning of the fall semester. During these four weeks, students take two courses. One is an educational policy course designed to look at the achievement gap in higher education and educational policies that have been implemented to address achievement gap issues. The second is a project-based mathematics and science course utilizing real world applications. Students who choose to attend the summer bridge program receive priority enrollment for all the services offered by the Student Support Program. However, in exchange for priority registration, they are required to participate in the relevant mathematics and science workshops offered during their freshman year.

The Student Support Program is responsible for multiple mathematics and science workshops that are offered throughout the school year. It offers workshops for all levels of mathematics, physics, and chemistry. Priority enrollment is given to students who participated in the summer bridge program, and then enrollment is offered to all students. Each fall the workshops serve between 1,500 and 2,000 students, with 150 of those students coming from the summer bridge program. The workshops take place once or twice weekly throughout the semester, and are structured as a group-learning classroom giving students a chance to study difficult concepts and work collaboratively with other students. Workshops are led by student tutors, who are required to take a 4-unit, 10-week tutor training. During the workshop, the tutors are expected to follow the pace and the content of the course that they are assisting.

Special Course Options

Across the selected institutions we found many examples of optional courses and registration policies available to Calculus I students. These include supplemental instruction, policies that reduce some of the penalties for starting Calculus I and then realizing that precalculus would have been the better choice, and Calculus I sections that offer additional instructional time.

Supplemental Instruction. BA2 offers an optional course that runs parallel to Calculus I and provides supplemental instruction. Students who scored on the borderline for Calculus I on the mathematics placement exam are strongly encouraged to take this course. Additionally, Calculus I instructors can recommend that students add this course if they notice students struggling in the first few weeks of class. Over the last five years, BA2 has found that this course has improved pass-rates (C– or better) for at-risk engineering students. Before they began offering this course, only 42% of these students were able to complete Calculus I with a C- or better. That number has risen to 68% when these "at-risk" students enroll in both Calculus I and the supplemental instruction course. This is a 1-credit course, typically with 12 to 20 students, and is taught by a faculty member who is also teaching Calculus I. During the weekly class meetings students are encouraged to ask questions about specific homework problems or concepts that they did not understand in class. The instructor answers questions and students are given worksheets for extra practice.

MA1 has a student instructor (SI) program that assists gateway classes, such as Calculus I. Most instructors of these gateway courses have the option of using student instructors who work with them. When an instructor's DFW rate is noticeably high, they will be assigned an SI. Instructors can have their assigned SI be involved in their course as much or as little as they like. Some instructors handpick past students who they know are strong mathematically and have them help with instruction as well as running the classroom. SIs can also schedule separate help sessions, based on their availability and the availability of the students. This provides students with another venue to ask questions and receive tutoring if needed. SIs are usually hired for two semesters and can follow instructors from Calculus I to Calculus II. Calculus I students at MA1 spoke very highly about their SI and the SI program in general:

> *I could relate to him [the SI], 'cause we're both going for engineering, so he helps out a lot. `Cause he knows Calc I, it's a rigorous course and it's a must have if you want to be an engineer... So he's always hitting it on me saying, "Oh, you need to pass this or you're not going to get Calc II".* (Student, MA1)

Drop-back and No-Penalty Policies. BA4 has a policy for dropping back that assists in the placement of incoming students. Students are placed into Calculus I based on their SAT scores, but BA4 has implemented a policy that allows students who feel they have been placed too high or are not doing well in the course to drop down to a precalculus course. The students have about a month to determine if they want to stay in Calculus I or to drop back. The department schedules precalculus courses at the same time as every Calculus I course. This ensures that students will be able to enroll in Precalculus without scheduling conflicts.

At PTI there are two institutional policies allowing students to take courses they desire, rather than a course they have been placed into. First, PTI has no prerequisite system. This means that students may enroll in any course they are interested in taking, regardless of their previous coursework. In relation to this policy, PTI also has a no-penalty policy, which eliminates all D and F grades and replaces them with a No Record grade (NR grade). Students can receive an NR grade by either dropping a course prematurely or earning below a 70% for the course. This system allows students to challenge themselves and take intellectual risks without being penalized. Students are allowed three NRs per year.

Stretched-Out Calculus. Academic terms at PTI usually last 7 weeks. However, there is an option to take Calculus I over two terms (14 weeks). This is referred to as "stretched-out" Calculus I. Students can either register for this course before the term starts or transfer into it from a 7-week Calculus I section. The stretched-out Calculus I course serves fewer students than the traditional 7-week course; typically there are only two sections of stretched-out Calculus I each with 35 students. The students who choose to enroll in the stretched-out Calculus I course tend to have a weaker mathematical background, and to be more comfortable with the pacing of a 14-week course. Students do not get penalized for opting into stretched-out Calculus I. They receive the same number of credits as for the regular calculus course and, because there are four 7-week terms during the academic year, students opting into stretched-out calculus can remain on schedule to graduate in four years. This stretched-out version is also offered for students in precalculus and Calculus II.

At LPU1 there is a university program that is a part of the admissions process. As a part of this program, the university offers a separate section of Calculus I for underrepresented students who are identified as "at risk." Lecturers teach this section, which runs for the same number of weeks as the traditional Calculus I course but for longer sessions (50% more time). The students in this "University Program Calculus I" have the same assignments as the rest of the Calculus I sections; however, unlike the other Calculus I sections at LPU1, students receive grades and feedback on their homework assignments. The course itself is not a remedial version of Calculus I; it is designed to give more instructional time in the classroom for students who may need that extra time.

Transfer Assistance

Transfer assistance was a feature of associate degree-granting institutions. All four of the AS-granting two-year colleges offered some transfer support for students transitioning to other institutions. However, only one of the selected institutions, AS4, had a Transfer Center and a dedicated Director of Transfer. The Transfer Center at AS4 sees 225 to 300 students a semester, with multiple visits from each student. In addition to advising students, the director also organizes a student workshop with more than 30 colleges and universities from across the state. This workshop is intended to give students the opportunity to talk to many different representatives about their career and transfer options.

More frequently we saw that in all the institutions, calculus instructors used their professional connections and knowledge of universities in their states to help students navigate and prepare for transferring. For instance, at AS3 there is informal communication between the dean and the surrounding institutions. When there are specific questions about transfer, the dean at AS3 can initiate face-to-face meetings, phone calls, or video conferencing with individuals at the local colleges and universities. AS3 also has the advantage of being in a state where there is legislation to support students transferring from AS-granting two-year colleges to other colleges and universities. It is state law that, when the students have the equivalent of an associate's degree, all universities must accept all units as transferrable. Therefore, whenever possible, students have their credits packaged into an associate's degree before transferring, which makes the process seamless.

Fostering Community

To better understand not only what supports are available, but also how these supports are contributing to student success at the selected institutions, we looked at transcriptions of student interviews. During our analysis of these interviews, we identified instances in which students either described or discussed a support that was available to them. By looking across the student interviews from the selected institutions, we began to understand the importance of the academic and social networks for student success. Students at many of the selected institutions discussed a strong community for Calculus I students. At 12 of the 18 selected institutions, students described a collaborative atmosphere surrounding Calculus I. Attributes of these positive learning environments included space for students to work together, proximity to other calculus students, encouragement and high expectations, and available and invested teachers. Here we provide descriptions of these four attributes, including student testimonials and examples of specific aspects of support systems contributing to this atmosphere.

Space for Students to Work Together

Students from almost every institution talked about working together with other students. Not surprisingly, providing a dedicated space for students to work together helped facilitate these interactions. This space was not limited to the tutoring center: students also routinely gathered in common areas (such as hallways and atriums), the library, and dedicated study halls:

> *So you just go in there [the common room], and there's always six kids sitting, on their laptops doing physics or math or whatever. Even if they're not in your class, they can help you, because we're learning the same things, so it's really helpful.* (Student, PTI)

> *I can walk into the math lab, and I can sit down with someone from a different class, and I can do my homework with them.* (Student, LPrU)

> *I always go to the library and find people working on calculus and just sit down, work with them. If I have a problem I'll ask them if this looks right or something.* (Student, AS3)

One of the ways in which institutions provided a space for students to work together was by adding tables outside of instructors' offices, in front of Calculus I classrooms, and in dorm common areas. This struck us as a simple, low-cost, and straightforward way to foster community. Furthermore, bringing tutoring services to areas where students already gather (e.g., late night tutoring at BA2) increases the likelihood that students will use these services. For example, a study by Hossler, Kuh, & Olsen (2001) found that high-risk students were almost twice as likely to make use of tutoring services when they are offered in their dorm hall, as opposed to other campus locations.

Proximity to Other Calculus Students

When students were asked where they go when they need help, many students at the PhD- and MA-granting institutions described using their dormitory roommates as resources. As one female student from PTU expressed, "we're our own support systems is what I find, because when the teacher is not there, we can only teach ourselves." One way in which such student-to-student support systems were fostered was through proximity, including students living in the same dorm with other Calculus I students, roommates being placed into the same Calculus I section, and institutions with a technical focus.

> *Well, all the people... in my class, in [instructor's] class, live near each other so someone will just be like "okay like group review, [dorm] floor be there, 7 pm." So I know that people do group study, they use the math lab, there are a bunch of flyers for like individual tutors and stuff and you can go online and get that.* (Student, MA3)

> *I have a roommate too who's in the same classes that I am, so we work together, so if we have a problem, we just ask each other.* (Student, LPrU)

> *I think there's probably something about it that you're here at [PTU] with a set of like-minded students who are focused on engineering or science or math or something ... So you have immediate help that you can go to that's right down the hall, across the street, your roommate.* (Student, PTU)

Some of these student experiences were the result of the type of institution that the student attended, as we can see in the comment from the PTU student. However, we did find policies that were specifically designed to support dorm room study sessions. For instance, at LPrU, part of the Freshman Experience program is a registration system that tries to place students in the same dorm into the same classes. Another policy that might support this sort of student interaction would be basing dorm assignments on intended major or college. As Hossler et al., (2006) found, such "thematic communities" have the potential to raise GPAs, second-year persistence rates, and levels of engagement in educationally purposeful activities.

Encouragement and Expectations

While many of the students at our selected institutions stated that they worked together on a regular basis, it was not always clear how this norm became established. When students did describe how they started working together, they often attributed it to their instructor's encouragement and stated expectations:

> *I think right at the beginning they beat it like a dead horse where they just literally kept saying, "Work with other people."* (Student, LPrU)

At AS1, a pair of students described how the instructor not only encouraged students in the same course to work together, but also helped create an environment where students across the calculus sequence helped each other:

Student 1:   [The Calculus I instructor] tells all of his other Calculus II and Calculus III students, if one of us would ever ask for help, they can try to help as best they can, and they will sometimes.

Student 2:   So we're out to help each other.

In addition to instructors, there were also policies that encouraged students to work together. This includes the group study policy at the AS2 tutoring center, where a group of three or more students can request a tutor to work with them for an hour on homework assignments and test reviews. Additionally, just having common homework assignments and tables dedicated to Calculus I students at the LPrU mathematics lab encouraged students to work together.

Available and Invested Instructors

In many of the student focus groups, students identified their instructors as their number one support. Positive attributes discussed by students include availability, proactively helping students, and caring for students. Here we share statements that illustrate the powerful effect these instructors had.

> *I would say she does care a lot, I mean, any professor that pulls out a student that she knows is failing or struggling and she pulls them out and... says "you, I'm going to take you, I'm going to hold your hand to my office hours," that's a pretty caring teacher I would say.* (Student, MA1)

> *I think it's an interesting mix of all the different factors. As [the student] said, the honor code has a lot to do with it, the lifestyles that we choose to live here, as well as just the quality of the love expressed by the professors. You know, like right before the tests, what they'll always say to you is, "How well do you need to do for me to be proud of you? I want you to do your very best, that's all you need to do." I'll be prepared for the exam but he really instills in me a sense of personal responsibility because I want to represent him well.* (Student, LPrU)

> *If he [the teacher] notices your grade is slipping or anything or if he thinks you could have done better on a test or something, he'll talk to you about it and make sure that everything is okay and there's no problem with your understanding. Like I said, he builds a relationship with every person.* (Student, BA0)

With all the outside services and support programs available for students, it is easy to overlook the importance of the Calculus I instructor as the main support for students. Classroom interactions are the main source for student-to-student and student-to-teacher interactions, and they often determine if and how students will interact within the larger institutional support system. As Tinto (2006) explains, "the classroom is, for many students, the one place, perhaps only place, where they meet each other and the faculty. If involvement does not occur there, it is unlikely to occur elsewhere" (p. 4).

Conclusion

Higher education research has found that students are more likely to persist in college when they are integrated into both a social and an academic community (Tinto, 1997). The extent to which a student has integrated into a social community can be understood in terms of the richness in peer-to-peer interactions and faculty-student interactions, whereas indications that a student is integrated into an academic community include academic progress, satisfaction with intended major, and a clear understanding of the academic expectations at their institution (Fox, Zakely, Morris, & Jundt, 1993; Kuh et al., 2006; Kuh, Vesper, & Krehbiel, 1994; Tinto, 1997). Such integration is particularly important in the first year of college, when attrition is more likely to happen, as "nearly half of all leavers depart before the start of the second year" (Tinto, 1997, p. 167). Analogously, one would expect that students are more likely to persist in STEM related fields when they have strong academic and social connections in the STEM community. Furthermore, because students' first-year experience plays such a critical role, it follows that social and academic integration within students' first-year STEM courses, such as Calculus I, is of particular importance for STEM-intending students.

Student support services have great potential for facilitating both social and academic integration. With all five of the student supports we identified, academic integration can certainly be understood as an important goal. Tutoring centers, office hours, freshman orientation, and first-year experience programs are all designed to help students make academic progress and understand how to be successful within their courses and chosen major. However, in analyzing the student focus group interviews, the social integration component of these supports appeared to be an important factor in how they were helping students. Tutoring centers, supplemental instructions courses, first-year experience programs, and even office hours were described as providing opportunities for student-to-student interactions. Most importantly, at the selected institutions, students were taking advantage of these opportunities. Further, this happened across all four institutions types. For instance, at PTU, a residential, PhD-granting, technical university, one student explained, "we are our support system." While at AS2, an urban, commuter, associate's-granting institution, 14 out of the 16 students in the focus group were regularly meeting outside of class—including one group of students that reserved a study room in the library two or three times a week to work together. It is this sort of student engagement and involvement that has been found to be the single most important factor in student retention during their first year of college (Tinto, 2006). It appears that our selected institutions have successful Calculus I programs at least in part because of the social and academic integration they are able to facilitate through their student support services.

References

Fox, L., Zakely, J., Morris, R., & Jundt, M. (1993). Orientation as a catalyst: Effective retention through academic and social integration. In M. Lee Upcraft, R. H. Mullendore, B. O. Barefoot, & D. S. Fidler (eds.), *Designing successful transitions: A guide for orienting students to college* (Monograph No. 13) (pp. 49–59). Columbia, SC: University of South Carolina, National Resource Center for the First-Year Experience.

Hossler, D., Kuh, G. D., & Olsen, D. (2001). Finding (more) fruit on the vines: Using higher education research and institutional research to guide institutional policies and strategies (Part II). *Research in Higher Education, 42*(2), 223–235.

Hsu, E., Mesa, V., & The Calculus Case Collective (2014). *Synthesizing measures of institutional success.* (CSPCC-Technical Report #1). Washington DC: Mathematical Association of America.

Kuh, G. D., Vesper, N., & Krehbiel, L. (1994). Student learning at metropolitan universities. In J. C. Smart (ed.), *Higher education: Handbook of theory and research*, (Vol. 10, pp. 1–44). New York: Agathon.

Kuh, G., Kinzie, J., Buckley, J., & Hayek, J. (2006). *What matters to student success: A review of the literature.* Commissioned report for the National Symposium on Postsecondary Student Success. Washington DC: National Postsecondary Education Cooperative.

Kuh, G. D., Kinzie, J., Schuh, J. H., & Whitt, E. J. (2005). *Student success in college: Creating conditions that matter.* San Francisco: Jossey-Bass.

Tinto, V. (1997). Colleges as communities: Taking research on student persistence seriously. *The Review of Higher Education, 21*(2), 167–177.

Tinto, V. (2006). Research and practice of student retention: What next? *Journal of College Student Retention: Research, Theory and Practice, 8*(1), 1–19.

Chapter 7

Good Teaching of Calculus I

Vilma Mesa, *University of Michigan, Ann Arbor*
Helen Burn, *Highline College*
Nina White, *University of Michigan, Ann Arbor*

As indicated in Chapter 2, the analysis of student survey data revealed that student responses to questions about instructor characteristics factored into three clusters: Good Teaching, Technology, and Ambitious Pedagogy. Of these three, only Good Teaching had a positive effect on the change in students' attitudes towards mathematics (a composite of three outcomes: mathematics confidence, enjoyment, and persistence).

In this chapter, we further analyze the data collected in the study to understand better what the construct means. We seek to answer the question: What are the features of good teaching that are revealed through student responses, interviews with faculty and administrators, and classroom observations in the institutions participating in the CSPCC study?

The chapter is organized into four sections. We start with a brief description of how good teaching has been conceptualized in the literature. We next describe the sources of data and the analysis we performed to answer our question. Following this, we present our major finding—namely, that good teaching in this study has three components: Classroom Interactions that Acknowledge Students, Encouraging and Available Faculty, and Fair Assessments. After describing these components, we conclude with suggestions for institutions, departments, and faculty about using this information to infuse changes in their practice.

Good Teaching in the Literature

There is a strong body of research dedicated to the identification of features of teaching that are important for various aspects of students' experiences in college. For example, in a now classic study, Chickering & Gamson (1991) identified the following seven principles of good practice in undergraduate education:

1. Student-faculty contact.
2. Cooperation among students.
3. Active learning.
4. Prompt feedback.
5. Time on task.
6. High expectations.
7. Respect for diverse talents and ways of learning.

Chickering & Gamson (1991) identified these principles via surveys of large numbers of students in various types of post-secondary institutions and a variety of disciplines. Their work was seminal because the operationalization of these principles allowed further research that investigated the impact of these practices on students' college experiences. More current work has provided evidence that high expectations, specifically the use of active learning (e.g., via inquiry-based learning), result in positive affective and cognitive gains among undergraduate students (Kuh, 2008; Kuh, Kinzie, Buckley, Bridges, & Hayek, 2007). Likewise, having high aspirations for student learning, setting clear expectations for student performance, and establishing standards for holding students accountable have been highlighted as key elements that faculty need to consider in their pedagogy (see, e.g., Hassel & Laurey, 2005; Tagg, 2003). Rendon (1994) has advocated for the use of validation activities (e.g., calling students by name, working one-on-one, praising students, encouraging students to see themselves as capable of learning, and providing encouragement and support) as important for "transformational changes in students, accompanied by an increased interest and confidence in their capacity to learn" (as cited in Kuh et al., 2007, p. 67). Notice the recurring themes across these works: active engagement and high expectations.

Other researchers indicate that knowledgeable and enthusiastic instructors who also encourage students to express their views through discussion and invite them to interact with others inside and outside of class help build a positive classroom atmosphere that is conducive to learning (Angelo & Cross, 1993; Pascarella & Terenzini, 2005), which in turn results in better dispositions towards learning. Providing timely feedback that is both supportive and corrective, and that includes individualized instruction as needed, has been shown to make a difference in students' learning (Angelo & Cross, 1993; McKeachie & Svinicki, 2006). Finally, and perhaps more importantly, using challenging, novel, meaningful, and stimulating activities and assignments influences students' growth and satisfaction (e.g., Strauss & Volkwein, 2002), which is conducive to positive attitudes towards learning.

While this literature has not differentiated these principles by disciplinary orientation the mathematics education literature adds other features to these ideas of good teaching. For example, the K-12 mathematics education literature on high-quality teaching has emphasized the importance of giving students tasks of high cognitive demand (Henningsen & Stein, 1997). Such tasks require students to engage with mathematical content in ways that go beyond using known facts in standard procedural ways, and instead pose questions for which the students have to generate new connections and find the required knowledge (Stein, Grover, & Henningsen, 1996). Students of teachers who consistently use tasks at the higher level of cognitive demand show significant gains in standardized tests (Silver & Stein, 1996), and teachers who are recognized as exemplary teachers are more likely to use high-cognitive demand tasks in their teaching and in their assessments than teachers who are not exemplary (Silver & Mesa, 2011; Silver, Mesa, Morris, Star, & Benken, 2009). The literature in undergraduate mathematics education has documented that inquiry-based approaches to the learning of mathematics has a positive impact on affective gains, especially for women and minority students (Laursen, Hassi, Kogan, & Weston, 2014; Rasmussen & Kwon, 2007; Stephan & Rasmussen, 2002).

Thus there are features in this literature that point to characteristics of the instructor, to characteristics of the engagement of students, and to characteristics of the tasks that students are asked to work on. This literature informed the design of the surveys and of the interviews we used to collect data in the CSPCC study. As we will see, the analysis of the data we collected partially supports some of the ideas found in the literature. We present next a brief note on the methods of analysis for this chapter.

Methods and Limitations

We had a variety of sources at our disposal: student, instructor, and coordinator surveys collected during the first phase of the study; interviews with faculty, administrators, and staff; focus groups with students; and observations of Calculus I teaching at the 18 institutions selected in the second phase of the study. Using the full data set from the surveys (N = 3,448[1]) we conducted a factor analysis using the 22 survey items identified by Sadler and Sonnert as defining good teaching (see Chapter 2). Three factors emerged: Classroom Interactions that Acknowledge Students, Encouraging and Available Faculty, and Fair Assessments (see Table 1).

---

1 The file used to perform the analysis includes data from students from two pilot institutions that were later included as part of the study. See Hsu, Mesa, & The Calculus Case Collective (2014).

Table 1: Mean, standard deviation, and reliability of each of the good teaching factors.

Factor (Survey items included)	N	Mean[a] (SD)	Cronbach α
Classroom Interactions that Acknowledge Students (e.g., presented more than one method for solving problems, asked questions to determine if I understood what was being discussed, listened carefully to my questions and comments, allowed time for me to understand difficult ideas, helped me become a better problem solver, provided explanations that were understandable; discussed applications of calculus, frequently asked for questions; prepared extra material to help students understand calculus concepts or procedures, (–)made students feel nervous during class)	3,448	4.48 (.954)	0.918
Encouraging and Available Instructor (e.g., encouraged students to enroll in Calculus II, (–) discouraged me from wanting to continue taking Calculus, acted as if I was capable of understanding the key ideas of calculus, made me feel comfortable in asking questions during class, encouraged students to seek help during office hours, was available to make appointments outside of office hours if needed, showed how to work specific problems, made class interesting)	3,448	4.78 (.766)	0.788
Fair Assessments (e.g., assignments completed outside of class were challenging but doable, my Calculus I exams were a good assessment of what I learned, my exams were graded fairly, my homework was graded fairly)	3,439	4.56 (.921)	0.714

Note: a. Average of the items and average across all available data. Items measured on a scale from 1-6. Negative items, marked with (–), were rescaled.

Although the survey data analysis is revealing, a main limitation is that the data are self-reported—as are the data used in the studies conducted in the higher education literature reviewed at the beginning of the chapter. In our case we also had low response rates in several of the institutions and over-representation of the PhD institutions in the survey data. These sampling issues make it difficult to rely solely on the survey data, which is why we sought to corroborate some of these trends with the information gathered during the in-depth site visits to the selected institutions. Thus, we augmented the factor analysis with concrete examples, seeking to understand in more detail how participants expressed each of these features of good teaching. A potential issue with the case study data is that we visited institutions about two years after the survey data were collected. The students to whom we spoke were different from those who responded to the surveys. In some cases, we also talked with a different group of faculty and administrators. We believe, however, that this is a strength of the design, as it helps us understand the stability of the responses over time.

We drew from data collected during Phase Two of the CSPCC study to illustrate these factors. We began with analyzing institutional documents produced by each team that synthesized major key features of each of the institutions visited (henceforth "Facts and Features documents"). We then analyzed the student focus groups looking for confirming and disconfirming evidence for these three features, using at least one focus group transcript from each of the institutions visited (N = 20) attending mainly to questions about their instructors, their class interaction, and their assessments. Finally, we analyzed 72 reflective memos that drew on evidence from various record-keeping logs used by observers during our classroom observations in the project (see White & Mesa, 2012). We summarized the trends in responses to 13 interview questions[2] that spoke directly about classroom interactions and encouraging and available instructors.[3]

---

2 There were 916 responses to the 13 questions. Of these, 71 (8%) were not included in the analysis because they were empty, ambiguous, or non-interpretable. For more details refer to Sümer and Mesa (2014). The full analysis included 1,252 comments.

3 There were no questions regarding assessment in the observation protocol and we explicitly requested to observe lessons in which no examinations were to be administered. A copy of the questionnaire is available through the MAA (see www.maa.org/cspcc).

Good Teaching in the CSPCC Data

The 22 items in the good teaching factor clustered into three main factors, which we call Classroom Interactions that Acknowledge Students, Encouraging and Available Instructor, and Fair Assessments (Table 1), because of the types of items that made up each factor. We discuss them next, listing first the survey items that clustered in each and then providing corroborating data from institutional documents, student focus groups, and classroom observations.

Classroom Interactions that Acknowledge Students

The survey items that clustered in this factor refer to specific actions that occur inside the classroom and that describe how teachers and students relate to each other. This factor mainly includes things teachers do to encourage student participation: they present more than one method for solving problems and help students improve their problem-solving skills; they ask questions to gauge students' understanding, but they also listen to questions, comments, and they invite students' questions and comments. These instructors also prepare extra explanations and additional materials, and talk about applications of Calculus I.

Out of the 12 Facts and Features documents that described classroom interaction and instruction, lecture was the predominant form of interaction in nine of them, although in eight cases the lecture was combined with other forms of interaction: small group work, individual work, and student presentations. The variety in the interaction is important because lecture tends to be characterized in the literature as a form of instruction that discourages classroom interaction. We note that 14 out of 16 institutional reports that addressed classroom size described it as small, with 30 to 35 students. Only two institutions had lectures of over 200 students with small recitation sections of 30 students. Small class sizes are more conducive to having interaction in the classroom, which may explain these observations.

Data from the student focus groups also suggest that lecture with many questions was the norm in these courses. Students of all teachers indicated that their instructors lectured during some portion of the lesson and they labeled the lectures as "interactive." In interactive lessons students were allowed and encouraged to ask questions and their teachers responded to their questions thoroughly, making sure they understood the answers, as expressed by a student in a bachelor's granting institution:

> It's more interactive though. It's not just blah, blah, blah; I mean when I came to college for math I expected that math teachers would be really boring. [My professor] isn't boring, but at the same time like we don't have some crazy, frizzy-haired mathematician or anything. (BA1[4])

In nearly half of the institutions (7 out of 18), there were instructors who included more interactive forms of engagement, sending students to the board, doing interdisciplinary projects, or working in groups during class:

> My teacher will lecture for like a couple minutes and the stuff he lectures seems really vague to me ... and then he'll hand out a worksheet for everyone to do and if [we] have a question [we] can ask it. (TY2)

Students recognized that having smaller classes made it easier to get to know their teachers, and that taking classes in large lecture halls limited the amount of interaction. Yet even in these large classes, their teachers made sure that students participated:

> I think for the most part, it's hard to be interactive with a massive lecture hall, but he took the time to wake you up or to make sure that you would understand things. And he would prompt you with questions if you needed it. So I guess there was a degree of interaction between the professor and the students. (LPU2)

We also corroborated these impressions in our classroom observations. The observers reported that the atmosphere was such that it encouraged students to ask questions. Indeed, in very few classes did the observers say that students did

---

4 We refer to the type of institution (MA, BA, TY) and the internal identification of the institution (a number between 0 and 4). We refer to the PhD-granting universities as LPU (Large Public University) 1 or 2, LPrU (Large Private University), PTU (Public Technical University), or PTI (Private Technical Institute).

not ask questions (7 out of 65[5]). They mentioned that the level of student questioning seemed adequate, with students asking for clarification about procedures or requesting justifications for the work. Pacing is also germane to making it possible for students to feel at ease in a lesson. Observers indicated that the pace of the class seemed very reasonable (53 out of 69) and that this pace was such that students could participate and seemed comfortable following the presentation.

The analysis further suggests that the most popular interaction form in the classes was an exchange known as IRE/F, which describes a three-turn pattern of speech: Initiation, in which the instructor asks a question; Response, in which a student provides a short answer to the question, and Evaluation/Feedback in which the teacher judges the answer as correct or incorrect or gives more information to the student (Cazden, 1986; Hicks, 1995-1996). These are short exchanges that may occur at a fast pace in any given lesson. In addition, observers noted the use of questions during the lecture that were meant to elicit more information from the students. IRE/F questions and other questions in the lecture were reported in 43 of 65 observations. Sharing in pairs or quiet exchanges among students was observed in 16 observations, whereas group work or student presentations were infrequently mentioned (only four times each).

Although students may participate via IRE/F interactions, in general they were not observed making contributions to content delivery, although such contributions did occasionally occur, such as when students presented their own solutions to problems or provided detailed answers to questions (eight observations each). In only three cases did the observers note that students actually guided the content of the class. In 13 cases observers said that students did not make any contribution to content delivery. These figures confirm that lecture, guided by the instructor, is a primary form of interaction in the classrooms observed.

These observations indicate that, when teaching, the majority of the observed teachers created an environment that encouraged students' participation via questions, with interesting examples, and opportunities to correct mistakes. Students of those teachers indicated that the lessons observed were fairly typical. Thus, although lecturing dominated the content delivery, there was interaction between the instructor and the students; this interaction was mainly directed by the teacher and involved few students each time. Students participated both by asking questions and responding to questions posed by the instructor. Group work or student presentations on problems that were not from the homework were not very commonly observed.

Encouraging and Available Instructor

The survey items that clustered around this factor (see Table 1) refer specifically to the perception students had that their instructors encouraged them to continue taking Calculus II, and invited them to seek help during office hours, making themselves available outside of office hours as needed. This factor also includes perceptions that the instructors acted as if students were capable of understanding the material, made them feel comfortable in asking questions during class, and showed how to work specific problems. This factor captures the perception that teachers care about students' learning, that they believe in students' abilities, and that they see students as capable of taking more calculus courses.

The analysis of the Facts and Features documents provided more details about how this factor was perceived by participants. Out of 15 Facts and Features documents that explicitly mentioned instructors, seven characterized them as caring, available, flexible, and seeking to maintain high expectations. We also note that, for the most part, faculty assigned to teach Calculus I wanted to teach the course or were rigorously trained (in the case of teaching assistants or visiting professors) to engage in the specific pedagogy that was supported by their institution.

Eleven out of 12 Facts and Features documents that mentioned faculty status indicated that Calculus I was taught by full-time or tenure-track faculty only, with the majority being at baccalaureate and two-year institutions. The 2010 CBMS statistical report indicates that the percentage of all sections of mainstream Calculus I taught by full-time faculty was 53% for four-year institutions and 90% for two-year institutions (Blair, Kirkman, & Maxwell, 2013, p. 18). It appears that in the selected institutions the proportion of Calculus I sections taught by full-time faculty was possibly above the 2010 figure. Because full-time faculty are more likely to be on campus than adjunct faculty, this availability might be playing a role in the importance of this aspect of good teaching. However, further analysis would need to be performed to understand better the interaction between faculty status and the characteristics of the instructors described in this factor.

---

5 There were 74 observation documents, but not all the observers answered all questions. The reader will notice the fluctuation of the available data in the reporting.

Students in focus groups eloquently described how their instructors were encouraging and available. In all the institutions we visited, students said that the Calculus I faculty made them feel that they were capable of working through difficulties, and sometimes went out of their way to assist them when they needed help. For example, one student at a bachelor's granting institution said:

> Well, I never wanted to go to the board and I went up one time and I actually knew what I was doing, so I felt better that I knew the material that we were learning. He expects us all to understand it and I think he knows that we all can do it. (BA4)

Likewise, students described instructors' availability, and patience dealing with them:

> In my class mostly he's on top of things. I'm kind of slow sometimes—it takes me a little longer to get it, but he understands. If you need help outside of class he'll make time for that. (LPrU)

Observers described a positive atmosphere in the classroom in which teachers were encouraging, asking for more questions, making sure the whole class was on the same page or pausing to wait for a response. The majority of the observers (51 out of 65) described the observed lessons as "interesting" because of the teacher (energetic, friendly, justified steps in a novel way). They also described the students as spellbound by the instructors, and indicated that the content was original or included challenging problems. Although tangential to being available, these observations do suggest that in most cases the observed faculty behaved in ways that made the students feel at ease, which might be interpreted by the students as encouraging and trusting in their capacity to do challenging work.

Fair Assessments

This feature of good teaching refers to students' rating of the challenge of the assignments completed outside of class and how doable they were. In addition it speaks about students' perceptions that their Calculus I exams were a good assessment of what they learned and that both exams and homework were graded fairly. We called this factor Fair Assessments.

The Facts and Features reports suggested that faculty had more latitude in assigning and designing homework and quizzes than in designing exams. Indeed, in 11 of 18 institutions the final exams were common or had questions that were required for all students taking Calculus I. However all faculty were consulted on the contents of the common exams.

The student focus group data corroborated that students felt their exams were fair. By "fair" students meant that they were rarely surprised in the exams. That is, the instructors would give them as much information as possible to make sure they were ready and prepared. This information came in the form of homework (the homework was usually described as harder than the examples given in the lecture) and quizzes; students also relied on exams done in previous years and attended review sessions. Students knew what to expect:

> The exams are like the homework problems, there are no surprises. There's past exams online, so if you go through past exams and stuff it kind of helps you because you're prepared for like the types of story problems. They're not going to be exactly the same, but you're prepared for what kind of material you're going to be tested on. (LPU1)

This did not mean that the exams or assessments (including homework) were easy. Quite the contrary, students found them challenging. In all institutions, students indicated that although the exams were not surprising, the faculty constructed or contextualized them in ways that forced students to show they understood the material. Memorization alone was not useful:

> In the last test we had to put the limit definition in our own words and we couldn't use like formal definitions. If we tried to put the formal definition she wouldn't accept it. (TY3)

Another way in which instructors increased the challenge of the exams was by making them cumulative:

You can't just memorize. My teacher mixes and matches the problems, the solutions, you have to think all the way back to chapter 1. (MA3)

In general, we note that faculty in selected institutions had an important say in the assessment of the courses, both in terms of homework and quizzes but also in terms of designing exams or making contributions when they were common.

Implications

Good Teaching is a construct identified by Sadler and Sonnert (see Chapter 2) that contributed in our identification of institutions that had positive changes in students' attitudes toward math (a composite of three of our outcomes: mathematics confidence, enjoyment, and persistence). In this chapter we have delved deeper into understanding the components of good teaching using the data we collected from students, faculty, and administrators, corroborating some of those with research literature. Our analysis reduced 22 survey items defining good teaching into three factors: Classroom Interactions that Acknowledge Students, Encouraging Instructors, and Fair Assessments. These factors are under the control of the instructors. They can provide concrete elements that can be used by instructors and departments to improve practice or to evaluate it.

The definition of good teaching described in this chapter, as coming from the voices of students, administrators, and instructors, combines a mixture of three elements, all related to what the instructor does in the classroom, with students, and with the mathematics. Good teaching involves, first, a teacher who is encouraging of students' efforts to learn and who is available to answer their questions and to support them in their learning; second, a class environment that fosters interactions geared at eliciting students' participation as a mean to promote mastery and understanding of the material; and third, tests and assignments that are perceived as fair. These features are not novel. They have been documented in the literature on good practice in teaching, and they are present in the institutions we selected for our case studies.

We propose that departments support the following five practices related to good teaching of Calculus I:

1. Create a positive atmosphere in which the instructors encourage students to ask questions.
2. Maintain a positive attitude towards students' mistakes.
3. Keep reasonable pacing of the lecture to ensure all students are on the same page, with time for individual, pair, or group work.
4. Set high standards and clear expectation that all students can meet.
5. Have availability to answer student questions and respond to students needs.

In this list it is worth noting that Practices 1 to 4 add to what the literature says about good practices in teaching, because they are centered on the actual calculus lessons we observed. Practice 5 is not novel (it was already identified by Chickering & Gamson, 1991). As stated earlier, these five practices are under direct control of the instructor. Even though most of the instructors in our study delivered lectures, they were nonetheless able to have lectures that were interactive, with many exchanges between students and instructors, and had a reasonable pace that allowed students to understand the material. The exchanges were quick, in the form of short questions and answers, and involved more than a handful of students. This work that faculty do in classrooms corroborates the crucial importance of teachers in creating an environment in which students can learn Calculus I through interaction with the material.

In the selected institutions we visited, most of the administrators explicitly indicated that their calculus program was successful because of their instructors, as opposed to other features that they could mention, like the use of technology, or the small class size. Our analysis has underscored the importance of getting the best instructors into the Calculus I classroom. If student interest in taking more mathematics hinges on the quality of the experiences in the classroom, the everyday contact with a knowledgeable, caring, and supportive teacher, then departments should ensure that this is the case. For Calculus I, the teacher may be the student's most important resource. As such, investing in faculty development and in hiring high quality instructors would be of paramount importance.

In addition to hiring and supporting instructors, this study suggests that departments and institutions may need to consider class size and assigning full-time faculty to the teaching of calculus. Small class size enables faculty to create a classroom environment in which students interact and their interactions are valued, thus facilitating the exchanges that help students engage with the material. As a bonus, smaller classes allow faculty to get to know students personally and encourage them to stick with their mathematics regimen, as the personal connection can create personal accountability. Assigning full-time faculty can also foster such relationships because they are more likely to be available for students than part-time faculty.

In all, our take home point from the analysis of good teaching is that the instructor and what she or he does in the classroom matters for students. It is an old time truth that continues to be corroborated today.

Acknowledgments. We thank Murat Sümer and Justin Tompkins who contributed to the analysis of the data reported in this paper.

References

Angelo, T. A. & Cross, P. K. (1993). *Classroom assessment techniques: A handbook for college teachers* (2nd ed.). San Francisco, CA: Jossey-Bass.

Blair, R., Kirkman, E. E., & Maxwell, J. W. (2013). *Statistical abstract of undergraduate programs in the mathematical sciences in the United States. Fall 2010 CBMS Survey*. Washington D.C.: American Mathematical Society.

Cazden, C. (1986). Classroom discourse. In M. C. Wittrock (Ed.), *Handbook of research on teaching* (pp. 432–463). New York, NY: Macmillan.

Chickering, A. W. & Gamson, Z. F. (1991). Seven principles for good practice in undergraduate education. *New Directions for Teaching and Learning, 47*, 63–71.

Hassel, H. & Laurey, J. (2005). The dea(r)th of student responsibility. *College Teaching, 53*(1), 2–13.

Henningsen, M. & Stein, M. K. (1997). Mathematical tasks and student cognition: Classroom-based factors that support and inhibit high-level mathematical thinking and reasoning. *Journal for Research in Mathematics Education, 29*, 514–549.

Hicks, D. (1995–1996). Discourse, learning, and teaching. *Review of Research in Education, 21*, 49–95.

Hsu, E., Mesa, V., & The Calculus Case Collective (2014). *Synthesizing measures of institutional success. CSPCC-Technical Report #1*. Washington, D.C.: Mathematical Association of America.

Kuh, G. D. (2008). *High impact educational practices: What they are, who has access to them, and why they matter.* Washington, D.C.: American Association of Colleges & Universities.

Kuh, G. D., Kinzie, J., Buckley, J. A., Bridges, B. K., & Hayek, J. C. (2007). *Piecing together the student success puzzle: Research, propositions, and recommendations*. San Francisco: Jossey-Bass.

Laursen, S., Hassi, M. L., Kogan, M., & Weston, T. (2014). Benefits for women and men of inquiry-based learning in college mathematics: A multi-institution study. *Journal for Research in Mathematics Education, 45*(4), 406–418.

McKeachie, W. J. & Svinicki, M. D. (2006). *Teaching tips: Strategies, research, and theory for college and university teaching* (12th ed.). Boston: Houghton Mifflin.

Pascarella, E. T. & Terenzini, P. (2005). *How college affects students: A third decade of research.* San Francisco: Jossey-Bass.

Rasmussen, C. L. & Kwon, O. N. (2007). An inquiry-oriented approach to undergraduate mathematics. *Journal of Mathematical Behavior, 26*, 189–194.

Rendon, L. (1994). Validating culturally diverse students: Toward a new model. *Innovative Higher Education, 19*(1), 33–51.

Silver, E. A. & Mesa, V. (2011). Highly accomplished teachers of mathematics and effective instructional practice: Probing the intersection. In Y. Li & G. Kaiser (eds.), *Expertise in mathematics instruction: An international perspective* (pp. 63–84). New York: Springer.

Silver, E. A., Mesa, V., Morris, K., Star, J., & Benken, B. (2009). Teaching for understanding: An analysis of mathematics lessons submitted by teachers seeking NBPTS certification. *American Educational Research Journal, 46*, 501–531.

Silver, E. A. & Stein, M. K. (1996). The QUASAR project: The "revolution of the possible" in mathematics instructional reform in urban middle schools. *Urban Education, 30*, 476–521.

Stein, M. K., Grover, B. W., & Henningsen, M. (1996). Building capacity for mathematical thinking and reasoning: An analysis of mathematical tasks used in reform classrooms. *American Educational Research Journal, 33*, 455–488.

Stephan, M. & Rasmussen, C. L. (2002). Classroom mathematical practices in differential equations. *Journal of Mathematical Behavior, 21*, 459–490.

Strauss, L. C. & Volkwein, J. F. (2002). Comparing student performance and growth in 2- and 4-year institutions. *Research in Higher Education, 43*(2), 133–161.

Sümer, M. & Mesa, V. (2014). *Analysis of questions from the Post-Observation Questionnaire: Characteristics of Successful Programs in College Calculus.* Ann Arbor, MI: University of Michigan.

Tagg, J. (2003). *The learning paradigm college.* Bolton, MA: Anker.

White, N. J. & Mesa, V. (2012). *Description of Observation Protocol for Characteristics of Successful Programs in College Calculus* [unpublished manuscript]. School of Education. Ann Arbor, MI: University of Michigan.

Chapter 8

Beyond Good Teaching

The Benefits and Challenges of Implementing Ambitious Teaching

Sean Larsen, *Portland State University*
Erin Glover, *Oregon State University*
Kate Melhuish, *Portland State University*

Ambitious Teaching is the label Sadler and Sonnert attached to a collection of instructor characteristics addressed in the CSPCC survey (see Chapter 2). These characteristics include the use of group projects, the inclusion of unfamiliar problems both in homework and on exams, requirements for students to explain how they arrived at their answers, and a decreased reliance on lecture as the primary mode of instruction. A factor analysis revealed these to be highly correlated and independent of a second group of instructor characteristics that were labeled as Good Teaching (Chapter 7). Note that characteristics included in the ambitious teaching factor are consistent with instruction that is often referred to as *active learning* or *student-centered instruction*.

Lampert, Beasley, Ghousseini, Kazemi, & Franke (2010) define ambitious teaching as teaching designed to meet the ambitious learning goal of developing conceptual understanding, procedural fluency, strategic competence, adaptive reasoning, and productive dispositions proposed in the National Research Council's *Adding it Up* (Kilpatrick, Swafford, & Findell, 2001). Lampert and colleagues argue that this kind of teaching necessarily involves actively engaging students by having them share and refine their reasoning through interaction with their instructor and classmates. In this chapter we will use the term ambitious teaching in two ways. When we discuss the CSPCC survey results, we use this term in the same way as Sadler and Sonnert defined it in Chapter 2, in reference to their factor analysis of the survey. All other uses of the term ambitious teaching should be understood to be a reference to instructional approaches consistent with Lampert et al.'s notion of ambitious teaching. While these two uses of this term are not identical, the characteristics of the label as used by Sadler and Sonnert are broadly consistent with Lampert et al.'s construct so that there should be no confusion.

Analyses of the survey data indicate that lecture continues to be the predominant mode of instruction in Calculus I across the country. This is true despite the fact that better approaches to teaching and learning are well documented. Based on their meta-analysis of 225 studies, Freeman et al. (2014) argued that active learning has been empirically validated as a preferred approach to teaching. Student-centered instruction has been shown to support conceptual learning gains (e.g., Kogan & Laursen, 2013; Kwon, Rasmussen, & Allen, 2005; Larsen, Johnson, & Bartlo, 2013), diminish the achievement gap (Kogan & Laursen, 2013; Riordan & Noyce, 2001; Tarr et al., 2008), and improve STEM retention rates (Hutcheson, Pampaka, & Williams, 2011; Rasmussen, Ellis, & Bressoud, 2014; Seymour & Hewitt, 1997).

The purpose of this chapter is to provide a pragmatic discussion about ambitious teaching. Drawing on the research literature and the CSPCC project, we will discuss the potential benefits of incorporating aspects of ambitious teaching in Calculus I instruction and the challenges related to successfully implementing and sustaining such ambitious teaching practices.

We will start by summarizing some relevant results from the CSPCC national survey. First we will characterize the extent to which students (from both the national sample and the schools selected as case study institutions) reported experiencing ambitious teaching practices. Then we will summarize the findings from two studies that examined connections between ambitious teaching practices and outcomes. One of these studies examined connections between ambitious teaching and changes in student attitudes and beliefs, while the other examined connections between ambitious teaching and students' intentions to continue on to Calculus II.

These findings are mixed and we will devote a section to understanding the findings. This discussion will motivate a brief review of the educational research literature, which will focus both on the reported benefits of ambitious teaching and findings related to the challenges involved in implementing and sustaining such practices.

We will then turn our attention back to the CSPCC project and discuss what we have learned from our case studies regarding ambitious teaching. Specifically, we will present in some detail two important examples of ambitious teaching that emerged from our case study research. First we will discuss a long running program of ambitious Calculus I instruction that dates back to the calculus reform movement of the 1990s. Then we will discuss an ongoing project to innovate Calculus I instruction to including technology-supported ambitious teaching.

Results From The CSPCC National Survey

The CSPCC national surveys included questions about what kinds of instruction students received. It also included questions designed to track changes in students' intention to take Calculus II, and changes in their confidence in mathematics, enjoyment of mathematics, and interest in mathematics (see Appendix A). This section will describe two independent studies using the CSPCC survey data to examine relationships between ambitious teaching and outcomes (retention and changes in attitudes and beliefs). First we will present a basic analysis of the survey data that characterizes the extent to which students reported ambitious teaching both nationally and at the selected case study institutions.

Characterizing the extent to which students reported ambitious teaching

At the end of their Calculus I course, students from the sampled institutions were asked to rank the frequency of various pedagogical activities. Over 5,500 students completed end of term surveys (see Hsu, Mesa, & The Calculus Case Collective, 2014). Students at selected and non-selected institutions reported that lecturing was frequently occurring in their classes, with *Very Often* as the most popular response. In fact, as we see in Figure 1, the percentage of students selecting a response strictly increases as responses choices move from *Not at All* to *Very Often*. This trend was consistent both nationally and at selected schools.

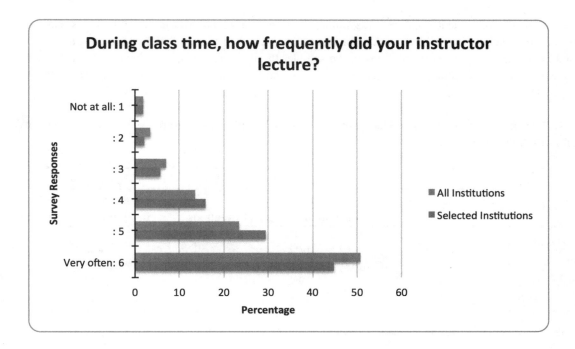

Figure 1: Percentage of students reporting levels of lecture frequency at all institutions (N = 5,565) and at selected institutions (N = 1,221).

Questions about activities associated with ambitious teaching revealed a different pattern of responses. Figure 2 reflects students' responses on the frequency of working with other students during class time. *Not at all* was the most common response nationally (29%); however, high frequencies (5 and 6) were the next most reported options. At selected institutions (N = 1,220), only 19% of students selected *not at all*. This proportion was significantly ($z = 9.36$, $p < .01$) smaller than the proportion (33%) of students selecting *not at all* from non-selected institutions (N = 4,338).

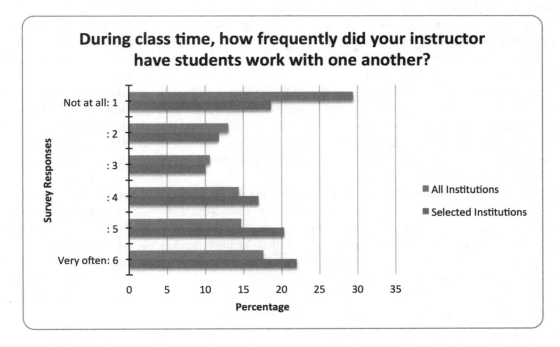

Figure 2: Percentage of students reporting levels of collaborative work frequency at all institutions (N = 5,558) and at selected institutions (N = 1,220).

The frequency of student responses was similar for three other ambitious teaching activities, class time spent on working individually on problems, asking students to explain their thinking, and whole-class discussion, for the selected institutions and all the institutions in the sample. In all cases, the selected schools typically had a higher percentage of students selecting *Frequently or Very Often* and fewer students selecting *Not at All or Not very Often* (see Table 1).

Table 1: Percentage of reported class time spent on ambitious teaching activities for selected institutions (N = 1,221) and all institutions (N = 5,554).

	Not at All or Not very Often		*Frequently or Very Often*	
	Selected Institutions	All Institutions	Selected Institutions	All Institutions
Work individually on problems or tasks	17%	26%	45%	39%
Explain thinking	19%	26%	44%	40%
Whole-class discussion	32%	37%	36%	34%

Note: The students were asked to rate the frequency of the activities on a 6-point Likert scale, (1: *Not at All* through 6: *Very Often*)

While lecture was prevalent at both selected and non-selected institutions, the comparison of ambitious teaching activities suggests that calculus programs at selected institutions tend to have instructors integrating ambitious teaching to a higher degree than in the rest of the institutions in our sample. These results may also suggest that integrating some ambitious practices even while using a significant amount of lecturing, might be a good move for any.

Ambitious Teaching: Changes in Attitudes and Beliefs and Intention to Switch Out

Sonnert and Sadler's analysis of our survey data (see Chapter 2) revealed that good teaching (see Chapter 7) had a positive impact on the composite of change in student attitudes (confidence, enjoyment and desire to take more mathematics) and that ambitious teaching had a small negative impact on that composite.

Rasmussen and Ellis (2013) pursued a complementary analysis to identify the characteristics of students who indicated an intention to take Calculus II at the start of the term, but who changed their intention at the end of Calculus I (called *switchers*) or maintained their intention to continue on to Calculus II (called *persisters*). Their analysis considered the connections between good teaching and ambitious teaching and the students' decision to switch or persist. They found that ambitious teaching practices were associated with lower switcher rates. More specifically, when high levels of ambitious teaching were coupled with low levels of good teaching, only 12% of students switched (compared to the 14% overall national percentage of students who switched). And when high levels of ambitious teaching were coupled with high levels of Good Teaching, just 7% of students switched. These findings suggest that there is some promise in using a combination of good teaching and ambitious teaching if the goal of improving student attitudes and beliefs and student persistence.

Ambitious teaching by itself did not appear to be related to positive changes in the composite of student attitudes in the survey. As we detail in the following section, this finding is consistent with prior research. Educational research that attempts to relate ambitious teaching to changes in student attitudes and beliefs must overcome significant methodological challenges. In particular, it is extremely challenging to characterize attitudes and beliefs in useful ways and then develop valid measures that are aligned with these characterizations. In the case of the CSPCC survey, our measures of attitudes and beliefs are quite rough, incomplete (only confidence, interest, and enjoyment are included), and are self-reported. So it might be premature to assume that ambitious teaching has a negative impact on students' attitudes and beliefs, without considering other potential explanations.

It is also worth noting that the changes in student attitudes and beliefs that were studied in the CSPCC survey only partially address changes in students' productive disposition, one of the five strands of mathematical proficiency described by NRC's *Adding It Up* (2001). Ambitious teaching is meant to support also conceptual understanding, procedural fluency, strategic competence, and adaptive reasoning (NRC, 2001). Our inconclusive findings may suggest that implementing ambitious pedagogies successfully is challenging. In the remainder of this chapter, we will draw on the research literature and use the CSPCC case studies to discuss the potential benefits of ambitious teaching, the challenges of implementing it, and the factors that can support overcoming these challenges.

What Does The Research Literature Say About Ambitious Teaching?

As indicated by the meta-analysis reported by Freeman et al. (2014), the research literature supports the idea that ambitious teaching can have significant benefits in terms of student learning. The literature suggests that there is a complex relationship between ambitious teaching and non-cognitive outcome variables. In this section, we will briefly review the research literature regarding ambitious teaching. First, we will discuss the potential benefits reported in the literature. Then we will consider some of the challenges involved in realizing these benefits. Finally, we will consider what kinds of things support implementing and sustaining ambitious teaching practices.

Lampert et al. (2010) argue that ambitious teaching necessarily involves actively engaging students by having them share and refine their reasoning through interaction with their instructor and classmates. Freeman et al. (2014) suggest that it is possible to see benefits with a variety of types and levels of ambitious teaching. A meta-analysis of 39 studies in multiple STEM fields found that small-group learning had a positive impact on achievement, persistence, and student attitudes (Springer, Stanne, & Donovan, 1999). More specific to calculus, a number of studies have examined the impact of the "reform calculus" that emerged in the 1990s, which emphasized conceptual understanding and applications, often with the use of technology to facilitate this focus. These studies have consistently found that students from reform courses developed stronger conceptual understanding and were more likely to persist in STEM fields while showing little or no negative impact on procedural fluency (Chappell & Killpatrick, 2003; Hurly, Koehn, & Ganter, 1999; Joiner, Malone, & Haimes, 2002).

The literature is less clear regarding connections between ambitious teaching and non-cognitive outcomes (including attitudes and beliefs). Smith & Star's (2007) review of the literature noted that studies tended to focus on achievement, with studies focused on non-cognitive outcomes being less common and less carefully conducted. In particular, they noted that researchers do not define carefully terms such as "beliefs," "attitudes," and "perceptions;" and the findings from these studies are mixed. For example, consider two studies focused on reform calculus. On the one hand, Bookman and Friedman (1998) found that early in their experience with reform calculus, students disliked it, but that one and two years after their reform calculus experience these same students more strongly felt that they understood how mathematics was used compared to students who were taught in the non-reformed courses. On the other hand, Brown (2000) found that students' reaction to the Harvard Consortium Calculus became more negative when the program was scaled up to all sections. One promising (and more well-defined) finding is Hofer's (1999), who found that reform calculus students had more sophisticated beliefs about mathematics than students taught in the non-reformed courses. In their own study, focused on transitions in which students experienced changes in their educational experiences, Smith & Star (2007) found that the transition from high school to college had a large impact on student achievement (in terms of grades) while transitions from reform to traditional instruction (or vice versa) did not. They also examined interaction between achievement and students' dispositions. They reported that "achievement and disposition were positively related dimensions of students' mathematical experience (at least as they move between traditional and reform programs), but that relationship was modest in strength and defied simple or uniform description" (p. 28). Smith & Star argued for a more sophisticated conceptualization of outcomes that recognizes that students who experience similar changes in achievement (e.g., a drop in test performance) may react in a variety of ways affectively.

The complexity inherent in students' reaction to ambitious teaching is likely one of the things that makes it challenging to implement and sustain a transition to ambitious pedagogical practices. However, the challenges a teacher engaged in ambitious teaching will encounter go beyond dealing with possible pushback or other negative reactions on the part of students. A hallmark of ambitious teaching is engaging students with cognitively demanding tasks, and the research suggests that the teacher has an important role in keeping students engaged at a high level. For instance, Henningsen & Stein (1997) identified a number of teacher behaviors that supported high levels of student mathematical engagement including scaffolding, modeling high-level performance, and consistently pressing students to provide meaningful explanations.

The significant effort needed to successfully engage in ambitious teaching is not the only factor that can inhibit reform initiatives. Woodbury & Gess-Newsome (2002) found that teachers' perceptions of the necessity for change had a significant impact on their responses to messages about reform initiatives. If teachers were not dissatisfied with the current instructional approach, they were unlikely to embrace changes. In addition to this critical factor, five other factors were identified as influencing teachers' reaction to, and enactment of, change. These were, "(a) a departmental culture of sharing, (b) teachers' sense of autonomy, (c) teachers' professional development experiences, (d) the nature of reform messages and messengers, and (e) teachers' views of themselves in relation to the reform movement" (p. 777). Of course initiating a transition to ambitious teaching is only a beginning. Sustaining such a change presents its own challenges. Coburn, Russell, Kaufman, & Stein (2012) note that sustaining innovations in instruction requires teachers (and others) to make continual adjustments to new conditions. They found "that teachers with a solid grasp of reform-related instructional strategies are able make adjustments that maintain high-quality instruction," (p. 165). Further they found that sustainability was supported by social networks that were characterized by strong ties, in-depth interaction, and high levels of expertise.

In summary, the research literature supports the notion that ambitious teaching can have important benefits for students in terms of their conceptual understanding without hindering their procedural understanding. While the literature does include some positive findings relating ambitious teaching and student attitudes, the impact of ambitious teaching on non-cognitive outcomes is a complex issue that requires more study. The role of the teacher is of course central. Engaging in ambitious teaching is a challenging endeavor for any instructor and faculty are unlikely to embrace such a challenge if they are satisfied with their current teaching. Finally, the sustainability of shifts to ambitious teaching depends upon the existence sufficient supports for teachers.

Ambitious Teaching in the CSPCC Case Studies

The research literature suggests that ambitious teaching can have important benefits. The literature also makes it clear that ambitious teaching can be challenging to implement and sustain. In this section, we examine the two most robust examples of large-scale ambitious teaching that we encountered in our case study site visits. The first is an established program that has been ongoing for two decades and the second is a newer initiative, but one that continues a tradition of technology-related instructional innovation at the institution. We begin each subsection with a brief overview of each calculus program and an explanation of why we consider it to exemplify ambitious teaching. These descriptions will be followed by a discussion of how these aspects are viewed by the participants in the program. This discussion will include the perceived benefits and challenges of engaging in these practices, as well as insights into what characteristics of the institution and calculus program support the success of these ambitious pedagogical practices.

Sustained Ambitious Teaching: The Case of Large Public University 1

Large Public University 1 (LPU1) is a large public institution serving more than 44,000 students with 26,000 full-time undergraduate students. At the time of the interviews, 53 sections of Calculus I were taught in the fall by 48 instructors, who were mostly graduate students. The current approach to Calculus I at LPU1 can be traced back to the early 1990s reform movement. For more than two decades, the department has been focusing on conceptual understanding and student engagement. Calculus I is taught in small sections (of approximately 32 students) using the Harvard Consortium Calculus text (Hughes-Hallet, 2012). The graduate students who teach calculus are called Graduate Student Instructors (GSIs) and have autonomy over their in-class instruction, but are encouraged to feature small-group work. All students take common midterms and a common final. Homework is also common, with students doing online homework that is procedurally focused and team homework problems that are conceptually focused. The GSIs participate in a robust training program that includes instruction in the ambitious teaching practices that characterize the program. Training is used to explain the benefits of the ambitious practices and to provide practical instruction in implementing them. Each semester, one of the GSIs helps to coordinate the course. This GSI coordinator is responsible for writing some of the team homework problems and conducting classroom observations of new GSIs.

How is the teaching ambitious? The Calculus I program at LPU1 includes a number of ambitious pedagogical practices that are consistent with the aims of the Harvard Consortium text used by all instructors. There is an emphasis on having students routinely explain their thinking: they provide extensive explanations on team homework assignments and brief explanations regularly on conceptually focused exams. In addition to the collaboration on team homework problems, students worked in small groups during class time (with the amount of time devoted to group work varying by instructor).

What do the participants have to say about these ambitious pedagogical practices? One of the things that stood out from our site visit to LPU1 is how consistent the various participants were in identifying the primary characteristics of the Calculus I program. Administrators, instructors, and students all described group work, an emphasis on conceptual understanding, and a consistent requirement for students to explain mathematics and their own thinking. For example, in the following interview response, we see the GSI coordinator describe the emphasis on applications and the insistence on having students write explanations:

They're problems that involve explaining, a lot of explaining. So... they'll be something like, "Oh this weird phenomenon happened." "Why is this going on?" or something like, "Your friend tells you that this can't possibly be right because of this, why is your friend wrong?"... So there are a lot of things where it's checking that they're really understanding. Making them explain things really thoroughly.

Thus, the team homework problems presented students with a real world situation and asked them to discuss its relevant mathematical aspects. They were required to use calculus concepts to address the problems and provide detailed explanations to go along with the procedures they used to solve the problem. Such problems serve to connect the mathematics to areas of interest to students in applied disciplines like engineering, and also provide a way to assess students' understanding of the concepts rather than merely their ability to select and execute procedures. In the following two quotes, we see students at LPU1 confirming the emphasis on applications and on writing explanations:

It's not just memorizing the formulas. It's mostly applying them. It's difficult to do. In my high school we didn't, it was just like memorizing and applying. Here it's much more different.

Being the person who actually has to write the explanation stuff, it's a total pain, but I understand why they're trying to make you do it because they want you to really understand it.

Both comments evidence the students' perception that these aspects of the course make it more challenging and time-consuming. The students consistently felt that their calculus course was more challenging than their high school calculus course or the college calculus courses their friends were taking at other institutions:

I have friends who are taking Calc I at other colleges and they show me like the hardest problem on their test and I'm like, really? Like that's not even close to any of the problems that we ever have to do. It's so easy.

The participants we interviewed were also consistently positive about the Calculus I program and its benefits. There was a near consensus that the program was well suited for developing strong conceptual understanding of calculus and for preparing students to succeed in future science and engineering courses. The engineering advisor at the institution indicated that the conceptually focused curriculum was "a very good curriculum for training engineers" because it focused on "quantitative reasoning, understanding the concepts and not just knowing mechanics." The course coordinator pointed out that a major benefit was having "the opportunity to hear where they're confounded or confused or have a little misinterpretation or understanding." One of the students, referring to small group work, pointed out that it is mostly beneficial "because you get to see different students answer the problems in different ways, ways in which you are not used to. Different ways help you learn the problem better." So while there were aspects of the program that some participants had negative or mixed feelings about (students felt team homework required excessive explaining, the administration desired greater participation from tenured faculty, and instructors expressed mixed feelings about group work during class), the participants were consistently of the opinion that the methods used by the program were effective. The following quote from a GSI offers some clues why the program continues to be successful and to be perceived as successful by the participants:

> We go through a week of training before we become a GSI and it's stressed to us that this is sort of [LPU1] philosophy. This is how we've run our course in the past, and it's been really successful, and it's a good idea to use this group work in your teaching. I think most people get sold on it, and they don't really question it because it does really seem like it's really effective.

This comment alludes to both the success of the program's training component and the fact that the program enjoys established stability and a documented record of success. In the following section, we will argue that these factors go a long way toward explaining the ongoing success of the program in sustaining ambitious teaching practices.

What is supporting or constraining these ambitious pedagogical practices? This case is particularly important and interesting because some rather ambitious practices have been institutionalized and the program has resisted a number of challenges over the years.

Challenges from the institution's administration have focused on the cost of the small sections. Multiple participants (e.g., GSIs, instructors, and the department chair) argued that the small class sizes were absolutely essential. The associate chair was teaching a large lecture section of pre-calculus at the time we interviewed him. He noted that, "I barely know any of them. I can't tell you anything about their intellectual capabilities unless I have the person and the spreadsheet and ...That's not how it's supposed to be."

Nevertheless, the program has sustained ambitious teaching practices for over two decades. Based on our interviews, we identified a number of factors that may explain this sustained success. Perhaps the most important one is that the faculty took steps to use locally collected data to assess the success of the program and that the data documented success in supporting students' development of conceptual understanding of calculus.

The success of ambitious teaching of a course depends primarily on the instructor. In this case, the instructors are almost exclusively graduate student instructors, many in their first year of graduate school. The GSI trainer and the department chair both noted that the graduate students' teaching evaluations are at least as good as those of senior faculty members. Although this might be explained because students might relate better to GSIs who are closer to their own ages, the students of these GSIs were just as successful in demonstrating conceptual understanding as measured by the Calculus Concept Inventory (CCI, Epstein, 2007) as the faculty teaching the course. The former course coordinator, who used the CCI to evaluate the calculus program in the face of challenges from administrators said,

> I was scared spitless. I really was. You know, what if we fall on our face? I mean, we'll find out something we don't want to know, but I thought, well I don't know what else to do right now.

In fact, the results were strikingly positive, and she noted that one of the findings was the that "the new guys, the brand new grad students, did just as well as the more experienced."

The success of the graduate students is likely due in part to the GSI training, which appears to be successful both in terms of articulating the key characteristics of the program (so that the GSIs know what it is they are supposed to do in their classrooms) and selling these characteristics as essential. This job of selling the program is of course made easier by the fact that the GSI trainer (and other mentors) can point to the study using the CCI to argue that the program does indeed support students' conceptual understanding. This success is also helpful in defending the program against pushback on the part of students and administrators alike. The former course coordinator was clearly aware of the need to convince the students of the benefits of the program and that in order to do this, she needed to "sell it to our instructors first … And if they believe in it you'll find many fewer complaints [from the students]."

As the GSI quotes suggest, the trainer has been successful in selling the program to the instructors; likewise, our interviews with students suggest that the students are convinced of the quality of the program as well and that they realize that they are taking a challenging calculus course.

Takeaways from the case of ambitious teaching. It should be noted that a department wishing to build a program similar to the one detailed will need to consider that the LPU1 program has been in place for over two decades. In its current state, the program enjoys much of the same inertia that is typical of traditional programs. At this institution, ambitious teaching is now normative and new teachers are expected to engage in these practices because that is how Calculus I is done there. However, considering the program in light of the research literature, there are some actions that could be taken by any department interested in establishing a similarly ambitious approach.

First, the program needs to set up a structure that would support ambitious practices—small classes with instructors who felt ownership of their classrooms. The associate chair argued that it was important for graduate students to teach their own classes rather than serve as recitation leaders saying, "I think when you give a teacher their own class and they're responsible for making sure they learn enough to actually pass the darn exam it changes the game a lot."

Second, the department needs to take steps locally to assess and document the existence of the kinds of increases in conceptual understanding that the research literature has linked to ambitious teaching. This documentation of success provided leverage to acculturate new instructors and resist pushback from students and administrators alike.

Third, the department will need to institute a robust training program for all instructors that sells the program to the instructors, makes the expectations clear, and supports the instructors in meeting those expectations, for the whole time they teach the course. Chapter 10 discusses in details the features of the GTA training program used in LPU1.

Technology-Supported Ambitious Teaching: The Case of Private Bachelors Granting University

Private Bachelors-Granting University (BA1) is a private university serving approximately 8,000 students on a large campus situated in a suburban area. There are 12 tenured or tenure track faculty in the mathematics department who typically teach three or four classes per term. BA1 has a long history of testing and adopting innovative teaching practices with strong support from the department chair and deans. The current department chair's belief is that, "If somebody's got an interesting idea, we can find some money and let them try their interesting idea."[1] When the CSPCC project team conducted the case study visit, half of the calculus sections were being "flipped." This means students were required to watch lecture videos outside of class and then spend their class time working on problems and discussing their solutions in small groups of two to four students. The department was moving towards flipping all of the Calculus I sections for subsequent terms. Instructors had control over how they ran their classes, but the course was coordinated and there was a common final exam. Additionally, some common questions were used on midterms to allow the department to assess the success of the flipping project. Except for one section, all Calculus I sections were taught by full-time tenure-track faculty. All Calculus I sections were capped at 30 students; the flipped classrooms were capped at 24. Two of the 10 instructors teaching the Calculus I courses at the time of our site visit were mathematics educators and one of them was spearheading the flipped calculus study. Technology-supported teaching included online video lectures and various types of technology used to give demonstrations (e.g., graphing calculators and Maple), quickly assess student understanding (clickers), or share student work with the class (iPads and AppleTVs).

How is the teaching ambitious? BA1 is a case of an institution and more specifically a department with a history of active involvement in technology-related instructional innovation. Much of this innovative work is used to support active learning including group work, student presentations, whole-class discussions, and challenging tasks.

What do the participants have to say about these ambitious pedagogical practices? The instructors we interviewed indicated that the goal of technology-supported innovation was to increase student engagement. One instructor stated that his "main purpose of doing a lot of technology now is to get students involved in class." By flipping the classroom so that students view the lectures outside of class, instructors gain time for group work during class. One of the benefits of this in-class work is that it provides an opportunity for instructors to interact with students and assess students' understanding of the mathematics. One instructor noted that this kind of instruction also helped students to assess their own understanding, saying that, "By having them do the work in class, with their peers and with my support as needed, they get a real chance to test their understanding of the material that they've watched on the video or read in the book."

---

1 At the time of our data collection this institution, like many others across the country, was dealing with a severe budget shortfall.

Instructors at BA1 also increase student engagement by using iPads to project student solutions during whole-class discussions. A student noted that, "interacting with other students … you get everyone's idea and then you kind of form your own and develop it." This student's instructor (in a separate interview) made a similar point stating that giving students a chance to present their work allows them to, "clarify their thinking, sharpen their thinking, and communicate their thinking in a way that makes sense to a group of people. So I think that also helps deepen their understanding."

The technology-supported innovation at BA1 is also used to facilitate engagement in challenging tasks, including application problems, in order to deepen students' conceptual understanding. One instructor observed that moving the exposition about definitions and procedures to the online videos freed up time in class to get students "to think more deeply about problems, make connections, think in a more abstract way and solve more complex problems." These problems include application problems, which the dean of engineering observed to be a strength of the calculus program saying, "I think its strength is the application. That's the way we look at it from engineering. There are lots of examples done in the classroom to link concepts to what the students do." The calculus students also noticed this emphasis on conceptual understanding. When a group of students were asked how their instructor engaged with their small groups, they reported that their teacher did not often answer their questions directly but rather replied with questions, "so you have a deeper understanding of the concept that you're doing."

Of course, there were students and instructors alike who expressed slightly negative reactions to some of the technology-supported ambitious teaching at BA1. For example, some students expressed frustration with members of their small groups. While one student in a focus group interview reported that "I turned around to my partner and he basically helped me and from there I knew what I was doing," another said, "We sit there, we kind of look at each other and then we just do it on our own anyways." The dean of engineering related some mixed feedback he had received from engineering students about the flipped calculus initiative:

> I heard from students about flipping the classroom... and they are very happy about it, they are really doing well and excited and whatever. I also heard from some that we should be [telling them] in advance that this is a flipped class because, as you know, some students learn by discovery, some students learn by imitation.

Overall, our interviews at BA1 revealed that the participants (students, instructors, and administrators) considered the Calculus I program to be quite successful. While some professors were hesitant to flip their own calculus sections before the evidence of impact had been established, the faculty was committed to exploring ways to increase student engagement.

What is supporting or constraining these ambitious pedagogical practices? The department chair noted the department had been, "refurbishing classrooms with tables, round tables, where the focus will be on students working in groups." This supported the instructors who wanted to have appropriately sized groups to use the technology in effective ways. One instructor noted that, "I think the calculus instructors kind of agree that two or three [students] seems to work best because … the students will be working over the iPads." Changing the layout of the classrooms was an important factor in supporting group work and using technology in the classroom. This was one way that the financial support provided by an internal grant was helpful in establishing the technology-supported innovation.

However, instructor buy-in is much more important to supporting and scaling up innovation than monetary support. The course coordinator noted that department-wide instructional changes were questioned before adoption. He noted that, "it's not that they're unwilling to make changes, but they have to be convinced and that's often not an easy thing to do." We saw evidence of this in two of our interviews with instructors. One instructor said, "I haven't decided yet on whether I want to make the investment to do that. I'd have to feel there was a payoff." Another instructor said,

> If the department adapts [flipping], or adopts it as the mode of teaching here, it's something that I would pick up, but it's not where I come from. As to what I think, just maybe for lack of evidence, I haven't seen that it works better than what I'm doing.

As noted by Woodbury & Gess-Newsome (2002), the research literature reports that innovation depends on instructors seeing the need for change. The department at BA1 is collecting local data on student understanding (shared questions on midterms and common exams) in order to document whether the flipping initiative does indeed provide a better learning experience for students. In this way, the department is taking steps to answer skeptical instructors' reasonable questions about whether the change is worth the investment of time and energy. This important issue was not lost on the students either. For example, one student reported that students were avoiding an instructor's class because, "they had a teacher that was flipping, but didn't want to be."

We see this requirement of a perceived need for change in remarks of the department chair (also a Calculus I instructor at the time of the case study visit), who felt that something needed to be done with their calculus program, believing that all students in the class should be engaging with the mathematics:

> *The reason I wanted to flip was maybe part of the concerns. I felt like I could reach 75% of the class, but there was 25% of the class that were just sitting there, not responding to me, and could get by. They'd smile, they were happy, but they were not doing well in the course. I wanted to do something, and I thought we needed to do something, where we could get a little bit more interaction with everybody and make sure everybody's doing the work.*

Instructors who were dissatisfied with the level of student engagement during class initiated the flipped calculus innovation. However, there were also instructors that were satisfied with their instruction and were not sold on flipping. One of these instructors said, "there's always going to be compromise, but so far, every time we've done something that's common across the board, we've had discussions." This kind of collegial formal (and informal) communication was important for moving the innovation forward while ensuring that all of the faculty felt respected and included. That the department had a supportive faculty that shared ideas, were flexible, and were willing to communicate about instructional innovations enabled the department's tradition of technology-based instructional innovation. A number of instructors we interviewed spoke about the culture of the department and indicated its importance in supporting instructional innovation. One instructor noted that, "It's the collegiality. I think that's partially what makes it so successful, is that there are no real competing agendas here. And there's a lot of sharing of material and there's a sharing of ideas." This kind of culture also supports the constant refinement that the research literature suggests is necessary to sustain instructional innovations. The department chair said of the faculty,

> *It's a big part of their identity as a math department, that they are good successful undergraduate teachers, and that they're engaged in sort of tweaking and revising their teaching work over time to get better and better at it.*

Instructors at BA1 devote time to craft their instruction in order to best support students, in part by incorporating various technology-supported instructional innovations. This work is further supported by the university faculty development center. In interviews, instructors shared a common sentiment that learning new technologies was challenging, but was supported by the faculty development center. The dean of the College of Arts and Sciences noted that, "almost anything that goes on at the [faculty development center], the faculty that are in there teaching others are over-represented by mathematicians." The calculus instructors at BA1 were not simply consumers of professional development; they were leaders in sharing ideas about technology-supported instructional innovation.

Takeaways from this case of ambitious teaching. The largest contributing factor in the success of the calculus program at BA1 is the level of commitment to teaching by instructors and the department culture they create. Instructors were initially dissatisfied with the level of student engagement in Calculus I classes. This dissatisfaction motivated initiatives to innovate instruction (at an institution with a history of technology-supported instructional innovation) in order to increase student engagement. The department faculty see themselves as good undergraduate mathematics teachers and this identity motivated them to continually refine their instruction to produce high levels of engagement, incorporating ambitious teaching practices that include engaging students in group work, having students solve non-routine and application problems, and asking students to share and explain their thinking. The collegial nature of the mathematics department supports instructors both in spearheading innovation initiatives and in collecting local data to evaluate the impact of those initiatives (in order to provide colleagues with information needed to determine whether they should buy in). Finally, the mathematics faculty is able to get the most out of the institution's faculty development center by being active leaders in the center.

Discussion

The research literature and the results from the CSPCC project suggest that ambitious teaching practices are exactly that—ambitious. Teaching practices that move away from traditional lectures to incorporate active learning experiences (e.g., facilitating small-group collaboration, pressing students to explain their thinking, engaging students in solving non-routine problems, and conducting whole-class discussion) are ambitious in that they are meant to support lofty educational goals including the promotion of deep conceptual knowledge and active student engagement with mathematics as well as the development of sophisticated views about the nature of mathematics. They are also ambitious in the sense that they require substantial institutional supports and advanced knowledge, skills, and beliefs on the part of instructors. The benefits of such strategies can be significant, but institutions and instructors should be aware of the challenges of implementing such strategies and the conditions needed to address these challenges. The BA1 flipped calculus project and the LPU1 small-section active learning model are two examples of committed systemic efforts to incorporate ambitious teaching into calculus instruction. The BA1 flipped calculus initiative is a newer innovation, but one that continues a tradition of technology-supported efforts to increase students' engagement with mathematics. This case sheds light on what it takes to get a new innovation up and running at scale. The LPU1 program is a stable one that first emerged at the beginning of the 1990s calculus reform movement. It is a case that demonstrates that it is possible to institutionalize ambitious teaching in Calculus I. It is also a case that suggests programmatic practices that support and sustain a calculus program featuring ambitious teaching. These two cases and lessons from the literature provide a good foundation for any institution interested in revitalizing its own calculus program through the use of ambitious teaching practices.

References

Bookman, J. & Friedman, C. (1998). Student attitudes and calculus reform. *School Science and Mathematics, 98*(3), 117–122.

Chappell, K. & Killpatrick, K. (2003). Effects of concept-based instruction on students' conceptual understanding and procedural knowledge of calculus. *Problems, Resources, and Issues in Mathematics Undergraduate Studies, 13*(1), 17–37.

Coburn, C., Russell, J., Kaufman, J., & Stein, M. K. (2012). Supporting sustainability: Teachers' advice networks and ambitious instructional reform. *American Journal of Education, 119*(1), 137–182.

Epstein, J. (2007). Development and validation of the Calculus Concept Inventory. In *Proceedings of the Ninth International Conference on Mathematics Education in a Global Community* (vol. 9, pp. 165–170). Charlotte, NC.

Freeman, S., Eddy, S., McDonough, M., Smith, M. K., Okoroafor, N., Jordt, H., & Wenderoth, M. P. (2014). Active learning increases student performance in science, engineering, and mathematics. *Proceedings of the National Academy of Sciences, 111*(23), 8410–8415.

Henningsen, M. & Stein, M. K. (1997). Mathematical tasks and student cognition: Classroom-based factors that support and inhibit high-level mathematical thinking and reasoning. Journal for Research in Mathematics Education, *28*(5), 524–549.

Hughes-Hallet, D. (2012). *Calculus single variable*. Hoboken, NJ: John Wiley & Sons.

Hofer, B. (1999). Instructional context in the college mathematics classroom: Epistemological beliefs and student motivation. *Journal of Staff, Program & Organization Development, 16*(2), 73–82.

Hsu, E., Mesa, V., & The Calculus Case Collective (2013). *Synthesizing measures of institutional success* (CSPCC-Technical Report #1) Washington, DC: Mathematical Association of America.

Hutcheson, G., Pampaka, M., & Williams, J. (2011). Enrollment, achievement, and retention on "Traditional" and "Use of Mathematics" pre-university courses. *Research in Mathematics Education, 13*(2), 147–168.

Hurley, J., Koehn, U., & Ganter, S. (1999). Effects of calculus reform: Local and national. *American Mathematical Monthly*, *106*(9), 800–811.

Joiner, K., Malone, J., & Haimes, D. (2002). Assessment of classroom environments in reformed calculus education. *Learning Environments Research*, *5*(1), 51–76.

Kogan, M. & Laursen, S. (2013). Assessing long-term effects of inquiry-based learning: A case study from college mathematics. *Innovative higher education*, *39*(3), 183–199

Kwon, O. N., Rasmussen, C., & Allen, K. (2005). Students' retention of mathematical knowledge and skills in differential equations. *School Science and Mathematics, 105*(5), 227–239.

Lampert, M., Beasley, H., Ghousseini, H., Kazemi, E., & Franke, M. (2010). Using designed instructional activities to enable novices to manage ambitious mathematics teaching. In M. K. Stein & L. Kucan, L. (eds.) *Instructional explanations in the disciplines* (pp. 129–141). New York: Springer.

Larsen, S., Johnson, E., & Bartlo, J. (2013). Designing and scaling up an innovation in abstract algebra. *The Journal of Mathematical Behavior*, *32*(4), 693–711.

National Research Council (NRC) (2001). *Adding it up: Helping children learn mathematics.* J. Kilpatrick, J. Swafford, & B. Findell (eds.). Mathematics Learning Study Committee, Center for Education, Division of Behavioral and Social Sciences and Education. Washington, DC: National Academy Press.

Rasmussen, C., & Ellis, J. (2013). Who is switching out of calculus and why? In Lindmeier, A. M. & Heinze, A. (Eds.). *Proceedings of the 37th Conference of the International Group for the Psychology of Mathematics Education, Vol. 4* (pp. 73-80). Kiel, Germany: PME.

Riordan, J. & Noyce, P. (2001). The impact of two standards-based mathematics curricula on student achievement in Massachusetts. *Journal for Research in Mathematics Education*, *32*(4), 368–398.

Seymour, E. & Hewitt, N. M. (1997). *Talking about leaving: Why undergraduates leave the sciences* (Vol. 12). Boulder, CO: Westview Press.

Smith III, J. & Star, J. (2007). Expanding the notion of impact of K-12 standards-based mathematics and reform calculus programs. *Journal for Research in Mathematics Education*, *38*(1), 3–34.

Springer, L., Stanne, M., & Donovan, S. (1999). Effects of small-group learning on undergraduates in science, mathematics, engineering, and technology: A meta-analysis. *Review of educational research*, *69*(1), 21–51.

Tarr, J., Reys, R., Reys, B., Chávez, Ó., Shih, J., & Osterlind, S. (2008). The impact of middle-grades mathematics curricula and the classroom learning environment on student achievement. *Journal for Research in Mathematics Education*, *39*(3), 247–280.

Woodbury, S. & Gess-Newsome, J. (2002). Overcoming the paradox of change without difference: A model of change in the arena of fundamental school reform. *Educational Policy*, *16*(5), 763–782.

Chapter 9

Calculus Coordination at PhD-granting Universities: More than Just Using the Same Syllabus, Textbook, and Final Exam

Chris Rasmussen, *San Diego State University*
Jessica Ellis , *Colorado State University, Fort Collins*

Most PhD-granting universities offer many sections of calculus each semester. These sections tend to be taught by a wide range of instructors, including visiting faculty, postdocs, adjunct lecturers, graduate students, as well as ladder-rank faculty (tenure track or tenured). The tremendous variation in who is teaching calculus makes for a situation where different students taking calculus the same semester at the same university may not be taught the same core material. This is particularly problematic with calculus because it is a fundamental prerequisite for subsequent courses in science, technology, engineering, and mathematics (STEM). Moreover, how the content is covered may vary considerably, which can affect what students actually learn, even if the same content is being covered and assessed. For these two reasons, the need to ensure that consistent core material is taught and the need for high quality instruction, coordinating calculus makes sense.

Each of the five PhD-granting universities that were identified as having a successful calculus program had a well-established system for coordinating Calculus I. We use the term "system" to highlight that the coordination went beyond surface level features, such as a common syllabus, textbook, and final exam. Instead, the system of coordination involved leveraging these and other features by key faculty to initiate and sustain a community of instructors working together to create rigorous courses and high quality instruction. What we learned from the five case studies is that it is not the existence per se of a common syllabus, textbook, and final exam, but rather something more nuanced in which both coordination and instructional independence are valued.

In this chapter we describe the systems of coordination at the five selected PhD-granting universities. We derive our findings from an analysis of 92 interviews with instructors, administrators, and students for a total of more than 95 hours of audio recordings. After transcribing and coding (see Appendix A), we focused on all the codes related to coordination, and from those developed a strong understanding of the coordination systems at each institution. Through grounded analysis (Strauss & Corbin, 1998), we came to understand the more structural components of these coordination systems (such as what is and what is not coordinated), as well as more nuanced components (such as the role of the coordinator, regular meetings that promoted collaboration, and faculty views of coordination). We present in this chapter concrete examples of what aspects are uniform across instructors and how these uniform aspects are enacted, as well as the roles and responsibilities of key faculty, especially the calculus coordinator, in creating a departmental climate in which calculus instruction is a joint endeavor spread across individuals.

Uniform Features at a Glance

In this section we provide a top-level view of what is and what is not uniform at each of the five selected institutions. We offer this information as a quick reference for readers to compare institution type and calculus coordination at their institution to the five selected institutions. However, as we cautioned earlier, the existence of these uniform features is only a small part of the story. Nonetheless, these are the elements one needs to consider to develop or revise a calculus coordination system and hence offer an appropriate starting place before detailing the more nuanced and unique aspects of how the different features are enacted and by whom.

Table 1 summarizes institutional characteristics of the selected institutions: type of institution, Carnegie classification, approximate undergraduate enrollment, length of term, class size, and class schedule.

Table 1: Institutional characteristics.

	Large Public University 1 (LPU1)	Large Public University 2 (LPU2)	Large Private University (LPrU)	Public Technical University (PTU)	Private Technical Institute (PTI)
Institution type	Large public	Large public	Large private	Public technical	Private technical
Carnegie Classification[a]	RU/VH	RU/VH	RU/H	RU/H	DRU
Enrollment	≈ 45,000	≈ 32,000	≈ 40,000	≈ 8,000	≈ 6,000
Term length	15 weeks	10 weeks	15 weeks	14 weeks	7 weeks
Class size	30–40	200 +	200+; 30–40	30–40	30–40
Class schedule	Three 90-minute sessions per week	Three 50-minute sessions and one 50 minute recitation per week	Two formats 1) Large: Three 50-minute sessions and two 50-minute recitations per weeks 2) Small: Five 50-minute sessions per week	Two formats 1) Regular: Three 50-minute sessions and one 50-minute computer lab per week 2) Stretched: 4-50 minute sessions and one 50-minute computer lab per week	Two formats 1) 7 weeks: Four 50-minute sessions, one 50-minute recitation, and one 50-minute computer lab per week 2) 14 weeks: Three 50-minute sessions and one 50-minute lab per week

Note: a. RU = Research University, VH = Very High research activity, H = High research activity, DRU = Doctoral Research University.

As shown in Table 1, the five case study sites are diverse with respect to the institutional context (type of institution, enrollment, and term length) and the calculus course structure (class size and schedule). Nonetheless, as shown in Table 2, there also are similarities across the five institutions. Among all five selected institutions, there were multiple elements of the coordination system that ensured consistency in course content and assessment across calculus sections. The specific measures taken to maintain uniformity in course content and assessment manifested in different ways based on the institution, reinforcing the adage that one size does not fit all.

Reading down each column in Table 2, one can see which features are uniform per institution. Reading across each row one can see the variation across the five selected institutions.

Table 2: Uniform features at a glance.

	Large Public University 1 (LPU1)	Large Public University 2 (LPU2)	Large Private University (LPrU)	Public Technical University (PTU)	Private Technical Institute (PTI)
Course Schedule	Common syllabus with text section covered and pacing	Common syllabus with text section covered and pacing	Common syllabus with topics covered and learning outcomes	Common syllabus with text section covered and pacing	Common syllabus with topics covered
Homework	Common online and common written homework	Common written homework, no online homework	Common online and common written homework	Common online homework, written homework not common	No common online or written homework
Exams	Two common midterms and common final	Two common midterms and common final	Three common midterms and common final	Two common midterms and common final	Common final only
Exam Grading	Exams and final graded using a common rubric	Exams and final graded using a common rubric	Exams and final graded using a common rubric	Exams and final graded using a common rubric	Final graded using a common rubric
Quizzes	No common quizzes	Four common quizzes	No common quizzes	No common quizzes	No common quizzes

In order to encourage uniform content coverage, every institution required a common textbook across calculus sections and a common syllabus that specified topics or text sections to be covered. To encourage uniform pacing, four of the five institutions also linked the topics covered to a weekly schedule or to the common weekly homework.

Four institutions had common online homework, common written homework, or both. Additionally, the midterms and exams were common across sections at four of the five PhD-granting institutions. The Private Technical Institute (PTI) was the institution with less uniformity among content and assessment. At this institution, which has 7-week terms, there was a common syllabus with topics covered, but pacing was not specified, neither online nor written homework was common, and the only common assessment was the final exam. Instructors still benefited, however, from periodic meetings that brought them together. At all five of the selected institutions, the common exams were graded using a common rubric to ensure consistency across sections. The existence, number, and content of quizzes were left to the discretion of the instructor at four of the five selected institutions. The Large Public University 2 (LPU2) had uniform, weekly quizzes based on the homework. These were used in place of grading the common, written homework.

Variations in Calculus I Programs

In addition to showing the uniform features of the five selected institutions' Calculus I programs, Table 1 also highlights the variety in the Calculus I programs themselves: term lengths range from 7 to 15 weeks, enrollment ranges from around 6,000 to nearly 40,000, classes range from 30 students to over 200, and some institutions offer multiple types of mainstream Calculus I courses. These variations in the Calculus I programs combined with the widespread implementation of systems of coordination highlights the utility and applicability of coordination among a variety of institutional contexts.

The CSPCC study was restricted to mainstream Calculus I courses, and at three of the five case study sites we saw two versions of mainstream Calculus I. Both technical institutions, PTU and PTI, offer two formats of mainstream Calculus I based on students' calculus placement, with one section for students whose placement criteria indicated insufficient calculus readiness. Instead of requiring these students to enroll in precalculus, they offer a format of mainstream Calculus I at a slower pace that integrates practice with algebraic skills into the calculus material. At PTU, this "stretched-out" format includes an additional weekly 50-minute meeting, and at PTI the course lasts for two of the seven-week sessions. At both institutions these courses appeared to help students who would otherwise have been tracked into precalculus succeed in Calculus I. Research focused on the effects of such variations in Calculus I indicates that calculus courses that integrate precalculus concepts can close the achievement gap between students who had taken calculus in high school and those who had not (Doerr, Staniec, & O'Neil, 2012; Keynes & Olsen, 2000; Klingbeil, Mercer, Rattan, Raymer, & Reynolds, 2004).

One other notable variation was Calculus I class size, even within the same program. LPrU offers both a large lecture-recitation format and a small class format. The large class typically has over 200 students, and meets in a lecture hall three times a week for 50 minutes and in small recitation sections, which are taught by a graduate student twice a week for 50 minutes. The small class typically has 30–40 students, meets five times a week for 50-minute class sessions, and is taught by faculty or a graduate student instructor. The majority of students enroll in a large lecture-recitation format, as the small class format is offered in the late afternoon and evening to accommodate part time students or those with family or work commitments during the day. LPU1, PTU, and PTI all taught Calculus I in a similar small class format. LPU2 on the other hand, used only the large lecture-recitation format.

System of Coordination and the Role of the Course Coordinator

One thing of note from the previous section is the high level of consistency among the five institutions regarding what aspects of calculus instruction are uniform, even while the institutions themselves vary considerably. While each individual aspect of coordination is important, a more powerful net effect is achieved when the individual aspects are combined in a system of coordination. Systems, however, do not run by themselves. They need to be designed and overseen by faculty who enact and are part of the system. At each of the five institutions we visited there was a central person, the calculus coordinator, who organized and oversaw the implementation of the uniform aspects of calculus instruction.

There are several essential characteristics of the position of the coordinator that cut across the five institutions. For institutions that either have a coordinator or are considering creating such a position, the following lessons learned from the five case studies will be valuable .

At each institution the calculus coordinator held a semi-permanent position. It was not a rotating committee assignment, but rather was viewed as a significant assignment that included some teaching release. This is a nontrivial commitment of resources, indicative of the value that these departments placed on delivering high quality undergraduate instruction.

The background of the coordinator varied from a top research mathematician, to a teaching professor, to a well-respected lecturer with a master's degree in mathematics education. In our discussions with the coordinators it was clear that, regardless of their academic background or research priorities, each was knowledgeable about different instructional approaches. Further, other faculty members saw the coordinator as a respected and vital member of the department.

While the highest degree and the extent to which the coordinator engaged in research varied across institutions, a common feature of all coordinators was their disposition toward their role. They viewed themselves as resources and facilitators rather than as owners of the calculus program or authorities on how to teach. This is important because it promoted a sense of shared responsibility and aligned with the faculty expectation of pedagogical autonomy.

Perhaps even more important in terms of lessons learned are the concrete actions that the coordinators take to promote a climate where calculus was community property. By "community property", we mean that the calculus program was not under the control of a single individual (although the coordinator was certainly a key player); instead it was a joint endeavor spread across individuals. In the next section we describe the concrete actions the coordinators took that helped support calculus as community property.

Concrete Actions Taken by the Course Coordinator

A core action the coordinator takes is to convene regular meetings of calculus instructors. At some of the case study institutions these meetings were held biweekly and at other institutions they were held less frequently (two or three times per term as well as over email). The meetings responded to the needs and priorities of the participants, focusing on practical issues of delivering course content and assessing student learning. The following list is what instructors and the coordinators told us they do in these meetings:

- Compare progress on coverage and express concerns over pacing.
- Discuss what topics should be emphasized or de-emphasized.
- Tell others about difficulties their students are having.
- Share ideas for problems to give and ways to explain ideas or engage students.
- Write and vet items for the common exams.
- Develop grading rubrics and grade exams.

As noted in the introduction, a primary motivation for coordinating calculus instruction is to ensure that core material is taught, to create consistency across sections, and to promote high quality instruction. Certainly the meetings with calculus instructors go a long way in addressing these needs. Side benefits of such meetings include developing a shared sense of what is valued for students to learn, contributing to a department climate that values teaching as well as research, and fostering trust and open lines of communication among colleagues. This last benefit aligns well with research that examines the effect of social networks in initiating and sustaining change (Daly, 2010).

Meeting regularly with colleagues about issues of teaching, learning, and assessment is fairly uncommon in undergraduate mathematics departments, especially at research-intensive universities. It is therefore striking that all five of the selected mathematics departments had faculty who were willing to participate in these meetings. We also note that very few, if any, of the faculty we spoke with at the selected institutions made use of their Teaching and Learning Center, which is presumably a place where faculty can learn about different instructional approaches, uses of technology, etc. We conjecture that this is because faculty found it more useful to discuss and reflect on issues of teaching and learning when the issues are of immediate and practical concern. This conjecture resonates with literature of K-12 teacher learning, which stresses the importance of professional development that centers on problems of instructional practice that are directly affecting a teacher (Grossman et al., 2009; Kazemi & Hubbard, 2008; Putnam & Borko, 2000).

The faculty stated that the time spent on meetings was a concern. However, the investment paid off because the coordinator did (or facilitated) a number of other concrete things that freed up time for faculty. These other actions were more administrative in nature, in contrast to the previous set of actions, which were more aligned with efforts to support cohesiveness and to build community among calculus instructors. Such actions included:

- Handling the logistics surrounding common exams, from copying exams and reserving the exam room to proctoring.
- Maintaining an online homework site and/or creating written homework.
- Supporting teaching assistants (TAs) to grade homework and/or quizzes.
- Meeting with TAs regarding student issues, teaching concerns, or grading questions.

It is also important to note that these calculus programs are situated within environments with many institutional support systems for students (see Chapter 6), such as TA office hours and tutoring centers, and strong TA training and mentoring programs (see Chapter 10). Thus, students do not rely solely on their instructor for help, and the TAs are well trained to reliably assist in course instruction. This environment further frees up time for instructors to participate in the coordination system while maintaining their other academic responsibilities.

Coordinator as Choice Architect

Coming from a behavioral economist viewpoint, Thaler & Sunstein (2008) offer an insightful perspective on how people can be nudged into making particular decisions, ranging from what to choose for lunch to what retirement plan to enroll in. A central construct in their thesis is that of *choice architect*. A choice architect is someone who is responsible for organizing the context in which people make decisions. For example, the person responsible for arranging the way in which school cafeteria food is displayed has the potential to influence the food choices that children make. What should be placed at eye level, french fries or green beans? The power of a choice architect lies in focusing people's attention in a certain direction, and nudging them to make the desired choice, rather than making the choice for them (e.g., offering only green beans).

In the calculus systems of coordination we studied at the five selected PhD-granting institutions, the role of the coordinator shares many of the characteristics of a choice architect described by Thaler & Sunstein. In our analysis we identified the following overlaps in the roles of a choice architect and the various roles of the coordinator

- Makes life easier by setting default options.
- Provides feedback to users.
- Makes mappings easy to understand.
- Provides information about what others are doing.

In the paragraphs that follow we describe each of these roles and give examples of how they are manifested by the calculus coordinator or other central member(s) of the department.

Makes Life Easier by Setting Default Options

One example tendered by Thaler & Sunstein (2008) for this role of choice architect is the decision made by computer manufacturers for screen-saver default settings. A user can go into settings and change the default options (e.g., when the screen saver comes on and how long before the computer locks itself), but doing so takes time and requires the user to take some action. Many computer users have never changed their screen-saver default settings. The manufacturer has made certain decisions for the user that she or he thinks is best (primarily for battery conservation), but the user still has the option to override the default settings. However, users often do not opt to override these default settings because going with the default option makes one's life easier.

We found that the calculus coordinator similarly sets a number of default options for the coordinated sections. The default options include such things as what homework problems are assigned, the exam schedule, the exams themselves (often co-constructed among faculty), pre-made lesson plans (especially for TAs), syllabi including grade distributions for each type of assessment, and rubrics for exam grading. Not all five institutions had the same set of default options, but this list covers the range of what we saw. In our interviews with faculty we learned that the majority of instructors very much appreciated the coordinator taking care of these decisions, while still allowing for pedagogical autonomy, as illustrated in the following excerpts:

> I think the fact that I have freedom and there's plenty of examples to go off of; it's probably the best of both worlds. I can look at what other people are doingand tweak to my own preference. Something that was also very helpful is that they have this [information] posted and it's listed on their main website, even the syllabus telling you roughly how many lectures each section will take. This is great as I'm planning lessons for the first time. (LPU2 Instructor)

> I think [graduate students] usually need a lot of guidance when it comes to teaching their first class. So I think for them, it can really help them to have a schedule, "teach this on this day," and because they don't have to write the midterms all by themselves, that relieves some of the work burden on them. (PTU Instructor)

At each of the five institutions ladder-rank faculty had the option to opt out of the coordinated section. In our cases we found only one instance of a ladder-rank instructor who chose not to teach a coordinated section. In all other cases, ladder-rank faculty were happy to opt in, primarily because it made their life easier and freed up time for them to do their research. Moreover, such default options have the potential to nudge faculty in certain directions regarding what content gets emphasized and assessed.

Provides Feedback to Users

Another role of a choice architect is to provide feedback to users, which then allows a user to take some sort of action. Thaler & Sunstein (2008) describe how digital cameras typically provide users with an image of a shot just after it is taken. This feedback allows the user to make corrective action if need be, such as removing the lens cap or zooming in or out. Low battery warnings and reminders to include the attachment on an email are other examples of how choice architects build in feedback to users. In these examples, there is likely not one single choice architect, but rather a team making decisions about what kind of feedback to provide users and what they hope the user will do with the feedback. A similar situation exists with calculus coordination systems in the case study sites.

For example, at LPU2 historical calculus grade distribution data (e.g., percentage of students receiving an A, B, etc.) are made available to faculty. As illustrated in the following excerpt, this information provides a benchmark that allows instructors, especially new faculty, visiting faculty, and postdoctoral students, advanced notice on the expectations of the department:

> *There's a handbook that they produced for new instructors and new people in the department that has the grade distributions that are typical for the lower-division courses and it's useful. It's nice to know what the standards are at the university. It's good to know what the student expectations are because they hear from their upperclassmen and it's good to know what the department expectations are, so I like it. I feel like the more information the better.* (LPU2 Instructor)

Another source of more direct feedback from the coordinator occurs during the regular meetings of Calculus I instructors. In these meetings instructors typically receive feedback on scheduling, pacing, content emphases, etc. The following excerpt from the PTU coordinator highlights the value of these regular meetings:

> *We meet on a weekly basis, just to talk about what's happening that week, or to start to prepare for an exam… we're having a weekly conversation about what's happening in that class, and you've got faculty and you've got graduate students, and I myself have a master's degree in Math Education … So we have a really nice conversation about what's happening in the class and what we can do to do better, maybe steal somebody else's idea, "I tried this and it worked." I think a lot of that helps.* (PTU Coordinator)

Makes Mappings Easy to Understand

A third role of a choice architect is to help people understand how certain options or structures map onto different outcomes, which in turn improves one's ability to make choices. For example, a doctor functions as a choice architect when she maps out different cancer treatments and their respective benefits and trade-offs. In terms of calculus coordination, we identified one very nice example of such a mapping. At LPrU, the coordinator took several weeks over one summer to cross catalogue all the common homework problems with the learning objectives for Calculus I. This mapping between what the department wanted their students to learn and the opportunities they were being given for learning this content was, according to the faculty we interviewed, very helpful in ensuring that the homework sets included enough problems on what was valued. This mapping was also seen as being useful for individual instructors, as exemplified in the following excerpt:

> *I really like [the mapping between the homework problems and the learning objectives], because it saves me time as I'm preparing my lecture, I do look at the homework and I can see what's going to be important, or what the department thinks is important for the students, so I know how to spend my time in class.* (LPrU Instructor)

Provides Information About What Others are Doing

Lastly, a choice architect provides users with information about what their peers or colleagues are doing. As Thaler & Sunstein (2008, p. 54) point out, "If many people do something or think something, their actions and their thoughts convey information about what might be best for you to do or think." For example, federal judges on a panel are often affected by how their colleagues vote. Assigning college students to particular dormitories and to roommates with the same major can have a big influence on the extent to which students study and hence their success in their courses. People are influenced by what others do, and so an important role of a choice architect is to expose individuals to certain actions of others, thereby influencing their choices.

An example of how choice architects provide feedback about what others are doing is the sharing of historical grade distribution at LPU2. Like the panel of federal judges, being aware of what colleagues are doing in terms of assigning final course grades can influence one's own choices. Another example of this type of choice architect move involves instances when either the coordinator or department chair told faculty about instructional innovations that other departments around the country were doing. One department chair sent out periodic emails with links to or attachments of articles on the effect of different instructional approaches. Faculty were not required to read the articles or to enact the ideas in the articles, nonetheless there is something powerful about providing such information. Knowing what others are doing can make a difference in what one does in one's own classroom. Thus, by providing information about what other Calculus I instructors are doing (locally and nationally), the coordinator or Chair can influence instruction while maintaining a culture of academic freedom.

Conclusion

As previously noted, all five of the selected institutions with more successful calculus programs have a system for coordinating calculus. One question that this might raise for readers is whether or not a coordination system exists at institutions that were not selected. Moreover, how important is a coordination system for a successful calculus program? While the design of the CSPCC study does not allow us to make causal claims, we were able to retrospectively compare selected and non-selected institutions using survey data. In comparison to all the selected Calculus I programs, 84% of the non-selected institutions indicated that they had a common final used for all sections of calculus. In terms of faculty meeting regularly during the term, 60% of coordinators of non-selected institutions indicated that Calculus I instructors do so, whereas all but one of the selected Calculus I programs indicated that instructors meet frequently or sometimes during the term.

While these differences are not large, they suggest that departments that were not selected were less likely to have a common final and were less likely to have regular meetings of the faculty who taught calculus. Having a common final and meeting regularly are two important features of the coordination systems, and one may argue that they support some of the other features. For example, if instructors meet regularly, they are likely discussing issues of pacing, assignments, or exams. These are all features that characterize what coordination systems entail. We next turn to a discussion of what coordination systems do not entail.

Coordination at the five selected institutions does not mean that instructors are tightly controlled. Instead, a better characterization of coordination is what we call *coordinated independence*. Coordinated is synonymous with synchronized or in step. Independence is synonymous with autonomy or freedom, the very notion of which eschews mandated sameness. Coordinated independence is intended to embrace how in-step elements of a calculus program work together with elements that allow for individual autonomy.

We see the notion of coordinated independence as consistent with Henderson, Beach, & Finklestein's (2011) findings regarding institutional change strategies. In their extensive review of literature surrounding STEM education initiatives, they found that among the 191 articles they reviewed, there were four primary strategies encouraged to promote change in STEM instruction: disseminating curriculum and pedagogy, developing reflective teachers, enacting policy, and developing shared vision. Of these, the authors determined that the most ineffective change strategies were those that sought to identify best practice curricular materials and then simply make these materials available to other faculty without supporting them in the implementation, and those that employed top-down policy-making meant to influence instructional practices. In comparison, effective strategies were aligned with the beliefs of the individuals involved or focused on shifting those beliefs, involved long-term interventions, lasted more than one semester, and required understanding a college or university as a complex system and designing a strategy that is compatible with it.

By viewing the coordinators as choice architects, we may consider the strategies they use to promote change (or to continue supporting a working system) within their calculus programs in relation to the strategies articulated by Henderson and colleagues (2011). At first glance, the coordinator's role of providing information about what others are doing may seem to be a change strategy that makes best practices available to faculty—a strategy determined to be ineffective by Henderson et al. (2011). However, fostering widespread implementation of the curricular materials was not the goal of the coordinators. Rather, the coordinators make these curricular innovations known to faculty for the purpose of providing options, one of which was the use of innovative materials. We saw evidence that when such curricular innovations were shared with faculty, some faculty implemented them in their classrooms. This may be due to the other change strategies implemented by the coordinator.

The second change strategy that Henderson et al. (2011) determined to be ineffective was top-down, mandated change. Instead of mandating a coordination system in a top-down way, the coordinator acts within the department, providing options that improve other faculty's abilities to implement the instruction that they prefer. Furthermore, the actions of the coordinator help to foster a community surrounding calculus instruction in which teaching calculus is a joint enterprise, in effect working with or shifting the beliefs of faculty regarding calculus instruction. Another key feature about the coordinator position is that it was not a rotating assignment. This enables the coordinator to develop long term strategies for continued improvement and to develop lasting collaborations. Lastly, the coordinator supports a coordination system, which itself exists within the complex system of calculus instruction.

Lastly, we provide advice for departments that are interested in creating their own system of coordination. A first essential step is to collect data about the successes of the existing calculus program. We refer readers to Chapter 11 for details on what type of data they may want to collect. In addition to collecting data on student success, departments would do well to take seriously the finding of Henderson et al. (2011) that effective change strategies work from the ground up, including those involved in the making and implementing of decisions. Holding department meetings to discuss the advantages and disadvantages of developing a coordination system seems essential to developing faculty buy-in.

References

Daly, A. J. (ed.). (2010). *Social network theory and educational change.* Cambridge, MA: Harvard Education Press.

Doerr, H. M., Staniec, A. C., & O'Neil, M. (2012). Designing for improved success in first-year mathematics. *Proceedings of the 2012 American Society for Engineering Education Annual Conference & Exposition,* San Antonio, TX.

Grossman, P., Compton, C., Igra, D., Ronfeldt, M., Shahan, E., & Williamson, P. (2009). Teaching practice: A cross-professional perspective. *Teachers' College Record, 111*(9), 2055–2100.

Henderson, C., Beach, A., & Finkelstein, N. (2011). Facilitating change in undergraduate STEM instructional practices: An analytic review of the literature. *Journal of Research in Science Teaching, 48*(8), 952–984.

Kazemi, E. & Hubbard, A. (2008). New directions for the design and study of professional development: Attending to the coevolution of teachers' participation across contexts. *Journal of Teacher Education, 59*(5), 428–441.

Keynes, H. B. & Olson, A. M. (2000). Redesigning the calculus sequence at a research university: Issues, implementation, and objectives. *International Journal of Mathematics Education Science and Technology, 31*(1), 71–82.

Klingbeil, N. W., Mercer, R. E., Rattan, K. S., Raymer, M. L., & Reynolds, D. B. (2004). Rethinking engineering mathematics education: A model for increased retention, motivation and success in engineering. *Proceedings of the 2004 American Society for Engineering Education Annual Conference & Exposition,* Salt Lake City, UT.

Putnam, R. T. & Borko, H. (2000). What do new views of knowledge and thinking have to say about research on teacher learning? *Educational researcher, 29*(1), 4–15.

Stake, R. (1995). *The art of case study research.* Thousand Oaks, CA: Sage Publications.

Strauss, A. & Corbin, J. (1998). *Basics of qualitative research: Techniques and procedures for developing grounded theory* (2nd ed.). Thousand Oaks, CA: Sage Publications.

Thaler, R. H. & Sunstein, C. R. (2008). *Nudge: Improving decisions about health, wealth, and happiness.* New Haven, CT: Yale University Press.

Chapter 10

Three Models of Graduate Student Teaching Preparation and Development

Jessica Ellis, *Colorado State University, Fort Collins*

This chapter provides three models for graduate student teaching preparation and development, and example of implementation for each. In this chapter, I use the phrase *graduate student teaching preparation and development* (GTPD) to emphasize that these models go beyond pre-term training in two keys ways: first, they extend into graduate students' roles as recitation leaders or course instructors and second, they prepare graduate students not just for their immediate roles as teaching assistants (TAs), but also for a profession involving teaching. Before describing these three models, I provide an overview of the important roles that graduate students play in undergraduate instruction overall and specifically within the CSPCC study.

Graduate students contribute to undergraduate instruction in two primary ways: as course instructors and as recitation leaders. As course instructors, graduate teaching assistants (GTAs) are in charge of the course just as a lecturer or ladder rank faculty (tenured track or tenured) would be, although they typically lack the experience, education, or time commitment of their faculty counterparts. Graduate students are also frequently employed as recitation leaders, tutors, or graders. Belnap and Allred (2009) found that of the 23 PhD-granting universities surveyed, 35% of the GTAs were the sole instructor for one or two classes, 39% of the GTAs were discussion or recitation leaders, while 25% had other responsibilities such as grading or tutoring[1]. Further, GTAs can be viewed as the next generation of mathematics instructors. Thus, in addition to their immediate contribution to Calculus I teaching, GTAs will contribute significantly to the long-term state of undergraduate mathematics instruction. The teaching preparation and development graduate students receive to prepare them for teaching Calculus I therefore influences both their immediate teaching practices and their long-term pedagogical disposition.

Among the institutions involved in the CSPCC study, graduate students were employed as instructors, as recitation leaders, as tutors in the tutoring centers, and as graders. Of the five doctoral-granting institutions selected for case studies, four employed graduate students in the teaching of Calculus I: two universities mainly employed graduate students as recitation leaders for large Calculus I lectures, while two universities mainly employed graduate students as sole instructors for small sections of Calculus I.[2] Among these four institutions, three distinct GTPD models were used for the teaching preparation and development of graduate students. In this chapter I describe the main features of these three GTPD models, which can be used to inform the creation of a new GTPD program or to help think critically about strengthening an existing program. For each model I answer two questions:

---

1 These percentages do not add up to 100% because institutions could select multiple roles for graduate students.
2 Graduate students were also employed as graders, tutors, and experienced graduate students taught upper-level courses, such as abstract algebra.

1.   What is the guiding philosophy of the model?
2.   What are the structural components of the model?

Additionally, I provide one example from the CSPCC case studies to illustrate what each model may look like when embedded within a specific institutional and departmental context. The three models of GTPD are referred to as: *the Apprenticeship model*; *the Coordinated-Innovation model*; and *the Peer-Mentor model*.

Apprenticeship Model

What is the guiding philosophy of the model?

The primary guiding philosophy behind the Apprenticeship model is the desire to transition graduate students into the role of instructor, both as part of their immediate role as GTAs and as their (potential) future role as undergraduate mathematics instructors. Embedded within this philosophy is the belief that people learning a new profession (who will develop a professional identity surrounding it) must participate in the practices of a profession with growing responsibility. This belief is in line with a situated a perspective in which learning is viewed as the process of engaging a novice in the practices of a profession with legitimate but peripheral participation (Lave & Wenger, 1991). The term "peripheral" indicates that the practices novices are involved in are less central versions of the authentic practices, or are central practices with limited responsibility. As one clinical psychology professor involved in the Grossman et al. (2009) study said when describing how clinical psychologists are prepared, "if you're learning to paddle, you wouldn't practice kayaking down the rapids. You would paddle on a smooth lake to learn your strokes" (p. 2026).

What are the structural components of the model?

The main components of the Apprenticeship model are:

- A three-unit class, inspired by Lesson Study (Lewis, 2004), that takes place during the semester before the graduate student is placed as a course instructor.
- A mentor instructor for whom the mentee acts as a teaching assistant in the class they will be teaching during the semester before the graduate student is placed as a course instructor.
- Weekly course meetings once the graduate student is placed as a course instructor.
- Observations and feedback once the graduate student is placed as a course instructor.

Graduate students are required to participate in a number of teaching development activities, both prior to teaching and while they teach. All new GTAs must attend a one-day seminar led by the mathematics department, with some of this time spent doing practice teaching presentations. During the seminar faculty conduct workshops on topics including pedagogical basics, such as how to write well on the board, as well as more advanced pedagogical topics, such as how to implement cooperative learning. Additionally, all first-year GTAs are assigned a faculty mentor during the orientation session.

In addition to this initial preparation, graduate students must serve as a teaching assistant to a faculty member who mentors them in teaching, and participate in a one-semester course that is based on Japanese Lesson Study (Alvine, Judson, Schein, & Yoshida, 2007).

When serving as teaching assistants to a mentor, graduate students attend the course (typically the same course they will be assigned to teach the following term), help create assignments and assessments, and reflect on class events with the mentor to discuss specific pedagogical decisions. The Lesson Study inspired course involves students in multiple rounds of collaborative lesson development, presenting lessons to one another, giving feedback to one another on these lessons, revising lessons, and delivering the lesson to students. This course is structured to engage graduate students in multiple aspects of being an instructor (preparing and delivering a lesson) with increasing autonomy, while also encouraging graduate students to reflect on their own instruction.

After successful completion of this course and being mentored, graduate students are placed in the classroom as instructors of record. As instructors of record, the graduate students are responsible for most aspects of the course: preparing a course syllabus, preparing for and leading each class, creating assignments, writing quizzes and exams, grading homework and exams, holding office hours, and determining grading scales. Once placed into the classroom as instructors of record, all GTAs are observed by a faculty member and participate in weekly meetings with other course instructors.

Example: Public Technical University (PTU). PTU is a small, public technical institution with approximately 8,000 undergraduates, 20 PhD students, and 15 Master's students. The majority of these graduate students are supported by teaching assistantships. PTU was selected as a case study institution because it had higher than average positive gains in each student success variable reported (increased interest, enjoyment, and confidence in mathematics). It also had a large number of STEM-intending students and a large number of those students who persisted in their STEM intentions after completing Calculus I. In a typical fall semester, there are approximately 270 Calculus I students in 6 classes of 30-40 students, and typically 5-10 new graduate students. These courses are taught by lecturers, tenured or tenure track faculty, and graduate students, and are coordinated by a long-term lecturer who also serves as the TA trainer and is in charge of placement. The coordination includes uniform assignments and exams. GTAs at PTU serve as course instructors for precalculus, Calculus I, Calculus II, and Introductory Statistics. GTAs may also work in the Mathematica Lab. All calculus students spend one day a week in a computer lab working on Mathematica assignments that are coordinated across sections. This is an uncommon assignment for GTAs and is most often used for GTAs who are not ready to teach their own courses after going through teaching preparation.

The GTPD model was developed by the current department chair when he was the director of the graduate program. When he came into the role of Graduate Director, new graduate students had a 1.5-week orientation in the summer where they would give a few practice lectures and have sessions on how to grade, how to facilitate group work, etc. The department chair said of the program:

> *They packed a lot of good information, but it was a week and a half and a lot of them were teaching that first semester. So I participated in that and was just interested, concerned about how well they could really do with that kind of preparation.*

With the support of the chair, the department hired a Director of First-Year Mathematics who developed a course for future graduate student instructors and the mentoring program. Though the person in the role of director of first-year mathematics has changed, the program still relies heavily on the original structure.

Coordinated Innovation Model

What is the guiding philosophy of the model?

The primary guiding philosophy behind this model is that Calculus I should be taught in an innovative and student-centered way, in small, highly coordinated classes. This innovation addresses the approach to the content, which is conceptually oriented and application driven, as well as the pedagogical approach, which includes group work and whole class discussions surrounding students' mathematical activity (rather than the teacher's). The coordination of these classes ensures that students have similar experiences across different instructors. Further, this coordination helps to support the secondary guiding philosophy: that graduate students can be prepared and supported to successfully implement innovative instruction. This model is also motivated by a third, underlying philosophy: that graduate students can be, as Elaine Seymour termed it (2005), "partners in innovation" and that graduate students who are effectively prepared to implement innovative instruction will likely carry these innovative practices into their future roles as undergraduate mathematics instructors.

What are the structural components of the model?

The main components of the Coordinated Innovation model are:

- An intensive five-day seminar that occurs the week before graduate students are placed as course instructors.
- Coordination (see Chapter 9).
- Weekly course meetings once the graduate student is placed as an instructor on record.
- Observations and feedback once the graduate student is placed as an instructor on record.

The Coordinated Innovation model prepares and supports GTAs to teach coordinated sections of Calculus I with a conceptually oriented and student centered approach. The main component of this GTPD is a five-day seminar that takes place the week before the semester begins. It provides multiple opportunities for graduate students to present a prepared lesson and get feedback, and a series of presentations aimed to introduce graduate students to the department's approach to calculus, to explain the rationale for the approach, and to share evidence of its success. Many of the materials are reused year after year, with small additions or changes based on facilitators' experiences and feedback from the GTAs. All first-time GTAs participate in the seminar. After the third day of the seminar, the GTA supervisors make course assignments based on availability and graduate student participation in the seminar, specifically their performance in their practice lessons. Most graduate students are placed as course instructors for Calculus I, while some are placed as instructors for precalculus, Calculus II, or are assigned to be tutors in the calculus tutoring center.

Part of the support that graduate students receive once placed in the role of course instructor comes through the coordination of the course. This coordination encompasses common homework, quizzes, exams, and schedule. Because there are many aspects of teaching that are new to graduate students, having these aspects of the course coordinated by an expert instructor allows them to focus their energy on other aspects of instruction. This can be especially helpful when implementing more innovative instruction.

One component of the coordination that is particularly helpful for supporting novice instructors is weekly meetings. These meetings involve all instructors for Calculus I and the course coordinator. These meetings serve as a place to address class management issues including use of group work or how to address specific content, and function not only as an opportunity to cover the logistics of the week, but also as a venue for discussions about student thinking and difficulties.

An experienced graduate student or faculty member observes all GTAs (new and experienced) at least once each term. The observers give feedback to the graduate student. If issues were noted, these are communicated to the GTA, along with concrete ways to address these concerns. In these cases, additional observations are done.

Example. Large Public University 1 (LPU1). LPU1 has approximately 1,500 students enrolled in Calculus I each fall, and approximately 125 graduate students. Every Calculus I course has 32 students enrolled, and there are approximately 50 Calculus I sections. GTAs teach the majority of these sections (in fall 2012, 35 out of 50 instructors were first year GTAs). The remaining instructors are experienced GTAs and faculty. LPU1 was selected as a case study institution because the calculus program has been recognized in best practices literature as successfully implementing innovative practices. Additionally, the students and instructors responded at high rates to our survey, and in our analyses of these responses we saw that the Calculus I program at LPU1 did not diminish student persistence, enjoyment, or interest in mathematics (as was the case in our nationwide sample—see Chapter 2). All courses are coordinated by a team of three permanent faculty. All Calculus I courses are taught using an Inquiry Based Learning (IBL) inspired instructional method, which emphasizes student discovery, group work, and conceptual understanding (see www.inquirybasedlearning.org for more information). A typical class consists of a 15 minute lecture, followed by students working on related problems in groups of four, followed by multiple groups presenting their solutions. Each session lasts two hours, so this sequence may be repeated a number of times during each class meeting. The course uses the Hughes-Hallett textbook that was designed to emphasize meaning, applications, and problem solving. Calculus II is structured in a similar way, but Calculus III and IV are different in that they have large lectures of 80 or more students and use a different textbook series.

There is a large mathematics PhD program at LPU1. All graduate students are funded through teaching assistantships unless they obtain research funding. Graduate students at LPU1 act as course instructors for precalculus, Calculus I, or Calculus II. These courses have common midterms, a common final, common online homework, common written homework, and a suggested schedule. As the course instructors, GTAs are responsible for creating quizzes and grading exams. Coordinators develop the schedule, homework, exams, and the final.

Peer-Mentor Model

What is the guiding philosophy of the model?

The guiding philosophy for the Peer-Mentor model is that a more experienced GTA is not only capable of preparing and facilitating seminars for GTPD, but that this experience additionally supports interested graduate students in taking a leadership role among the GTAs. Further, that by involving interested and experienced graduate students in the teaching preparation of novice GTAs, this model fosters a community of graduate students around teaching undergraduate mathematics.

What are the structural components of the model?

The main components of the Peer-Mentor model are:

- An experienced GTA who co-designs and implements the teaching development of GTAs.
- A one-day seminar before the GTAs are placed as recitation leaders.
- An ongoing seminar that occurs periodically throughout the semester.

The Peer-Mentor GTPD model prepares and supports novice GTAs to lead recitation sections of Calculus I. It also prepares more experienced GTAs to be local teaching experts in their current role as Senior TAs and in their (potential) future roles as mathematics faculty. The recitation sessions are designed to go beyond a question and answer session, instead providing opportunities for students to work together on more conceptually oriented problems related to the lecture. The main components of the GTPD model are an initial seminar held before new graduate students begin as recitation leaders and ongoing seminars that address specific issues throughout the year (such as creating and grading exams). The seminars are jointly developed by a senior TA and a supervising faculty member. They are lead by the Senior TA. In addition to developing and running these seminars, the Senior TA observes new GTAs' recitation sections, provides feedback to the GTAs, and, in general, serves as a point of contact for the GTAs regarding issues around the teaching of Calculus I.

All new GTAs attend the seminars, which are optional for more experienced GTAs. The first seminar takes place just before the term begins. Its emphasis is to prepare GTAs for the first day of class. The main goal of the first session is to make sure GTAs are comfortable and confident walking into class on the first day. GTAs participate in required seminars during the first semester, and the Senior TA determines other ongoing teaching preparation. These meetings primarily serve to focus TAs' attention on proctoring and grading exams. These meetings also provide an opportunity for GTAs to investigate student thinking by looking at records of students' solutions and discussing how they would grade them.

The Senior TA is supervised by a faculty member but has the freedom to shape many aspects of the GTPD program, including both the frequency and content of the ongoing seminars. The Senior TA is a key position for the Peer-Mentor model, and fosters a different culture than if these tasks were led solely by a faculty member. Experienced and interested graduate students apply for the position of Senior TA, and the supervising faculty and current Senior TA choose the best candidate. Typically, this is a graduate student who has been successful as a recitation leader for multiple semesters, has leadership qualities, and is likely interested in an academic position involving higher levels of teaching (in addition to research). Once the new Senior TA has been identified, he or she assists the current Senior TA as a way of being trained for this position. Thus, every year there is a Senior TA and a Senior TA in training who work together. The Senior TA has no other TA responsibilities outside of his or her role as Senior TA, but the Senior TA in training has full TA responsibilities in addition to training to be the Senior TA.

Example: Large Public University 2 (LPU2). LPU2 is a large public university with approximately 32,000 undergraduates. Due to general requirements, almost all undergraduates take the calculus sequence. LPU2 was selected as a case study institution because it had higher than average positive gains in each student success variable reported (increased interest, enjoyment, and confidence in mathematics), and had a large number of STEM-intending students who persisted in their STEM intentions after completing Calculus I. In a typical fall term, there are about 1,040 students enrolled in mainstream Calculus I intended for STEM majors. Calculus I is taught by visiting faculty and tenured or tenure track faculty. There are typically four sections of fall Calculus I, with between 240 and 320 students. These classes have recitation sections of 40 students led by GTAs and undergraduate teaching assistants. The lecture meets three times a week for 50 minutes and the recitation section meets once a week for 50 minutes. Calculus I is coordinated by a full-time faculty member when it is taught in fall (on sequence), but not when it is taught in winter or spring (off sequence). When it is coordinated, there are uniform assignments and exams across all sections. Tenured faculty can opt out of this coordination (except for the common final) but rarely do so.

At LPU2 both undergraduates and graduate students serve as GTAs for calculus. Their responsibilities are the same, but the Senior TA says that he may "ask a little more of the graduate TA." These responsibilities include running a recitation section of 40 students, grading a portion of the common exams, holding office hours, and, in some cases, holding a review session before an exam. Graduate students are given two recitation sections, and undergraduates are initially given one. If they receive positive student evaluations, an undergraduate may be given two sections in subsequent terms. Graduate students who have finished their course work and are in advanced candidacy are able to be course instructors for off-sequence calculus courses as well as upper division mathematics courses.

Conclusion

In this chapter, I provided three models of graduate student teaching preparation and development and examples of institutions that implement each model. The institutions were selected to be a part of the CSPCC case studies because they were determined to be more successful than comparable institutions. After selecting the institutions, we visited them to understand what about them may have contributed to their success. It is no coincidence that among the four PhD institutions that were selected and that employed graduate students in the teaching of Calculus I (as course instructors or recitation leaders), each of the four implemented one of these GTPD models. Certainly these three models are not the only ways to successfully prepare graduate students to become course instructors or recitation leaders; the models instead represent GTPD models that we observed being successfully implemented and that may prove to be effective if adapted at other institutions. However, these GTPD models do not exist as the only factors likely contributing to the success of the selected institutions. Rather, the GTPD models work in conjunction with other successful factors (addressed in the other chapters of this volume).

For instance, each of the GTPD models was implemented at an institution that had a system of coordination (see Chapter 9). This coordination was mandatory for graduate student instructors and recitation leaders, and supported graduate students to be successful as novice instructors in four key ways. First, the coordination served as a control for the type of instruction students would receive in courses or recitation sections taught by graduate students. Novices should not be expected to succeed in all aspects of teaching, and by having certain aspects of the course outside of their control the department can prevent extreme deviations from expected instruction. Second, the coordination allowed graduate students to focus on specific aspects of teaching (such as how to write clearly on the board, how to engage students, what kinds of questions to ask during class, etc.) instead of having to focus on all aspects of teaching (including choosing homework problems, creating exams, determining grading policies, etc.). Third, the coordination was led by someone in the department who was respected for teaching, and whose decisions for the coordinated elements of the course (such as homework problems and exam design) served as a model to novice instructors. Fourth, the coordination fostered a community around the teaching of Calculus I, giving graduate students a network of people to discuss teaching with.

Graduate students at the selected institutions were similarly supported by their departments by being one of many resources for their students (see Chapter 6 for more about student supports), being part of departments that value good and innovative and ambitious teaching (see Chapters 7 and 8), and teaching undergraduate students who are placed in the highest course in which they can succeed (see Chapter 5). The models presented in this chapter should be viewed as a potential ingredient to a larger recipe for Calculus I success, and these ingredients may be adapted to fit the needs and goals of specific departments.

References

Alvine, A., Judson, T. W., Schein, M., & Yoshida, T., (2007). What graduate students (and the rest of us) can learn from lesson study. *College Teaching, 55*(3), 109–113.

Belnap, J. K. & Allred, K. N. (2009). Mathematics teaching assistants: Their instructional involvement and preparation opportunities. *Studies in Graduate and Professional Student Development: Research on Graduate Students as Teachers of Undergraduate Mathematics, 12*, 11–38.

Grossman, P., Compton, C., Igra, D., Ronfeldt, M., Shahan, E., & Williamson, P. (2009). Teaching practice: A cross-professional perspective. *Teachers' College Record, 111*(9), 2055–2100.

Lave, J. & Wenger, E. (1991). *Situated learning: Legitimate peripheral participation.* Cambridge, England: Cambridge University Press.

Lewis, C. (2004), Lesson study. In L. B. Easton (ed.), *Powerful designs for professional learning* (pp. 135–48). Oxford, OH: National Staff Development Council.

Seymour, E. (2005). *Partners in innovation: Teaching assistants in college science courses.* Lanham, MD: Rowman & Littlefield.

Chapter 11

How Departments Use Local Data to Inform and Refine Program Improvements

Dov Zazkis, *Arizona State University*
Gina Nuñez, *San Diego State University*

The goal of this chapter is to acquaint the reader with the various types of data that can be collected in order to assess and initiate improvement to the efficacy of a calculus program. In what follows we discuss several types of data and how programs in this study used them to identify, plan, implement and assess program improvements. Rather than focusing on the specific data types and resulting program improvements that occurred at each institution, we focus on exemplars of how each data type facilitated improvement efforts. This will give the reader a sense for what types of data he or she may wish to begin collecting at his or her institution and the types of program initiatives that these data may provide impetus for. We cover a wide breadth of data issues and institutional contexts and leave it to the reader to determine which issues and data sources are relevant to his or her institution.

Many of the selected mathematics departments had someone who routinely collected, analyzed, and disseminated data, often from multiple sources. The departments did this themselves and did not rely on the university to do so. The routine collection of data facilitated awareness of the current state of affairs. Data aided departments in identifying and prioritizing areas for improvement, allowing them to develop improvement strategies that targeted these specific areas. These included goals for improvement, plans for how this improvement was to be achieved, and setting tangible benchmarks to assess the efficacy of these plans. It bears mentioning that data are institutionally situated. For example, a Calculus I pass rate that is deemed acceptable at a highly selective engineering school is likely higher than a pass rate at a large public university. This difference in what constitutes an acceptable pass rate is partially accounted for by the consequences of pass rates. At an engineering school, not passing calculus likely means a student's future at that institution is in jeopardy and at a liberal arts college it may simply indicate that the student should switch to a less mathematics intensive major. As such, what a specific measure means about the performance of a program is up to the interpretation of the stakeholders in that program. At a minimum, the longitudinal collection of data provides a record for situating the current state of a program relative to its past performance. This provides a basis for conversations of what the status quo should be relative to its current state and aids in the assessment of what goals are realistically attainable.

Assessing the Status Quo

The majority of selected departments viewed the status quo as something that can and should always be improved upon. These departments thus continually used data to identify and prioritize what aspects of their programs needed to be the foci of improvement efforts. The point we wish to make here is that the simple act of collecting and analyzing data does not in itself cause program improvement. Data collection can become a tool used by departments who are working toward change. It is not intrinsically a motivator for change. In fact, Stark, Lowther, Sharp, and Arnold (1997) found that program improvement efforts are rare and usually occur in response to a strong external catalyst or explicit internal leadership. Without stakeholders who are motivated to make meaningful use of data to direct program improvements, data do little more than describe the status quo. So the collection and analysis of relevant data is a necessary but not sufficient condition for the implementation of targeted continuous improvement efforts.

Specific recommendations for creating a department culture that is receptive to continuous data-driven program improvements are beyond the scope of this chapter. However, in this regard, it bears mentioning that data may be what convinces stakeholders that there is a need for change.

Literature on Program Improvement

A number of prior research has looked at program improvement (Briggs, Stark, & Rowland-Poplawski, 2003; Srikanthan & Dalrymple, 2004; Stark et al., 1997; Tucker, 1996). Here we give a brief overview of this literature as additional information for readers wishing to improve their own programs.

Research relating to effective practices in undergraduate mathematics programs has found that the faculty that implement effective practices usually express a common attitude of not being satisfied with the current program (Tucker, 1996). The practice of assessing and working toward alleviating this dissatisfaction was called continuous program planning by Briggs et al. (2003). Continuous program planning involves the constant examination of a program by its faculty followed by adaptations to features such as curriculum. Such adaptations attempt to bring about positive change for those served. The ongoing focus on program planning allows for adaptations that respond to emerging needs. These are group efforts that are maintainable even with busy faculty schedules because the allocation of dedicated time is a component of the planning. Through this collective responsibility opportunities for improvement frequently appear as described by Briggs et al. (2003, p. 371):

> Departments that actively look for opportunities to experiment and improve find those opportunities fairly frequently. In contrast, departments that take the attitude that "if it ain't broke, don't fix it," tend to discuss revisions as discrete efforts they either are doing, are planning, or are done with.

Briggs et al. (2003) analyzed different departments (from varied institution types: research, doctoral, master's, and associate) selected by their chairs for being attentive to curriculum planning at the program level. This enabled the researchers to identify four criteria used to establish whether a particular program was involved in continuous program planning. We paraphrase these as:

The frequent attention to planning processes.
Awareness and responsiveness to changing needs.
Participation of faculty.
The use of evaluation through gathering relevant information.

This chapter focuses on the fourth of these, which we refer to as attention to local data.

The reason for the particular importance of data in planning and implementation of potential program improvements was highlighted by Briggs et al. (2003, p. 376), who explained:

> When departments fail to bring evaluation into the process, program planning tends to be motivated disproportionately by what excites individual faculty members. In such cases, assumptions about what students want or need are tested only through their subsequent enrollments.

This point was also elaborated by Bowden and Marton (1998, pp. 215-216, 230):

> *To make improvement it is necessary to be aware of the current status. This implies evaluation of some kind,*
> *implicit or explicit. It also implies follow up of evaluation in modifying existing practices. It also makes sense*
> *to engage in follow up of the effects of the changes as a check as to whether the expected improvement has*
> *occurred. An evidence-based approach to quality improvement is required if a university is to attend to both*
> *accountability and improvement. Quality is never attained in an absolute sense; it is constantly being sought,*
> *it is a dynamic process.*

Programs must establish standards and then identify mechanisms to assess those standards in order to plan for improvement in the future. It is not sufficient to simply state that a program is student-centered. Rather, attention to assessment and data collection must be used as evidence that the program is providing quality education to students. Ultimately, the goal is to continuously provide an improved learning experience for students.

The previous literature acknowledges the trend seen at universities and colleges where continuous improvement is a departmental characteristic. Specifically, this body of research indicates the importance of collecting and analyzing local data to direct improvement efforts.

In what follows we elaborate on this research base by discussing tangible data-driven improvement efforts implemented by programs in our case studies. These provide readers wishing to encourage continuous program improvement at their own institutions with palpable examples of what types of program improvements can be fueled by the collection and analysis of local data.

Historical Success Rates as Catalysts for Grading Uniformity

Although some improvement efforts may be lengthy and complicated to implement and assess, in some cases the relatively straightforward collection and distribution of data can be the catalyst for change. This was the case with LPU2's efforts to improve the uniformity of grade assignments across sections.

In most institutions, Calculus I is the mathematics course that serves the largest number of students. This often means that multiple sections are taught concurrently. Additionally there is often an implicit assumption that calculus is one of the few courses that all teaching faculty in a mathematics department can cover. Consequently, in many institutions calculus is the most convenient and thus most often assigned course for temporary non-ladder rank faculty, such as post-doctoral fellows and visiting professors. As was the case at LPU2, this may create a situation in which the largest volume course in the math department is being taught by members of the faculty with the least amount of experience with the institution, its policies, and its standards. In some cases these standards may be quite different from those that the faculty member is familiar with. This may create situations where the temporary faculty members' standards for what constitutes a passing grade and what percentage of students are expected to receive a particular grade are vastly different from institutional norms. This may create situations where comparably performing students enrolled in different sections may end up with vastly different course outcomes.

This is precisely the issue encountered at LPU2. The solution involved keeping and distributing records of grade distributions and passing rates. (Also see Chapter 9 on coordination of calculus as PhD-granting institutions.) The department chair at this institution stated:

> *[the records of grade distributions] mitigate the fact that we do have instructors coming from lots of different*
> *backgrounds and different places, especially people who come from, say, Europe where they have a com-*
> *pletely different culture in terms of grades.*

These records are provided in a visitor and new faculty handbook, which includes data going back several decades and provides a benchmark for faculty without dictating to faculty what specific grades they should assign. The records do not obligate faculty to emulate past grade distributions, although some faculty make attempts to do this. Instead, they allow faculty to be aware of how they compare to past norms and to make informed decisions regarding how much they wish to deviate from them. The coordinator at LPU2 stated:

[New faculty will say] "This is how I want to assign the grades," and I'll say, "That's fine." We like to have the historical data as a guideline, but that's not forced on anybody. That's one of the good things about having a coordinator who knows that. If the visiting faculty are worried that they have to adhere to that it's like, no it's fine.

Distributing records of past grade distributions is a low-cost strategy of encouraging faculty to adhere to past norms regarding grade distributions, without having explicit policies that would interfere with faculty grading directly. Additionally, it is proactive in the sense that faculty are informed of norms before they are violated. This also means that faculty that deviate from norms are aware of the magnitude of their deviations and according to the calculus coordinator this information "pulls [faculty] back to the mean."

In short, providing historical grade data creates a social pressure on instructors to conform to past norms. In this way the data collection and distribution is in itself the solution to the issue of variation in grading. It bears mentioning that LPU2 is a large university that teaches calculus in large lectures. The expected averages of these large section classes are thus fairly stable allowing for the historical data to be used effectively by instructors. This tactic may be less effective in situations that have small classes, since the variability in expected class grade distributions would interfere with instructors' abilities to compare their classes to historical data.

Success in Subsequent Courses

One particularly important measure of whether a course is successful is how well it prepared students for subsequent courses. In two-year colleges in particular data on subsequent courses may be more difficult to acquire because subsequent courses that students feed into are often taught at different institutions. However, when there is a particular institution that students commonly transfer to acquiring such information and using it to inform improvement efforts can be beneficial for both institutions.

When feasible, comparing success rates of students taking the course, but who entered that course via different paths, may be useful to identify systemic problems with either how students are routed through a course sequence, or specific courses that may need rethinking.

The first issue is about placement, which is beyond the scope of this chapter and discussed in Chapter 5. In this section we address the second set of issues, those that center on the courses themselves. These issues are discussed here in the context of one of the case study sites, but are broadly applicable to identifying courses that require improvement.

PTU, a Public Technical University, had been collecting data on students' pass rates and noticed an alarming trend. The students who had AP Calculus credit from high school and thus were taking Calculus II the first semester of their freshman year were outperforming students who had taken precalculus Calculus I at that university prior to enrolling in Calculus II. The data collected indicated that over half of the students who had taken precalculus and Calculus I were receiving D and F grades. This meant that high school AP courses were doing a better job of preparing students than the institution's own precalculus through Calculus I sequence. This observation provided the impetus for precalculus and Calculus I improvement efforts.

Identifying what needs to be improved and implementing effective improvement efforts are separate, yet related issues. Using data to identify the need for improvement efforts requires the availability of data sources for assessing the efficacy of those efforts. However, negotiating what those improvement efforts should look like is not always clear. For PTU, three specific improvement initiatives were implemented to address the poor preparation of students for Calculus II. These were:

1. Integration of the blended learning model in the precalculus course.
2. Changes to how graduate students were trained to teach.
3. Rethinking what topics were covered in Calculus I, so that there was more of a focus on topics needed for Calculus II.

The first of these improvement efforts, blended learning, involves teaching some fraction of content through online sources and then using the in-class time gained to implement non-lecture based classroom activities (e.g., group work) aimed at deepening students' understanding of content. The specific implementation of blended learning used at PTU is beyond the scope of this chapter. What is relevant here is that this model of learning had been previously attempted in the Calculus II course with positive results. So the department had reason to believe a similar initiative would work in precalculus, and it was natural to choose to implement this particular initiative. This illustrates how the department learned from its own culture of self-improvement and treated current improvement efforts as building blocks for future efforts.

The second improvement involved implementing an entire semester training course for all graduate students, who typically were assigned to teach precalculus and to be teaching assistants for subsequent courses. The specifics of this teaching-focused course for graduate students are discussed in more detail in Chapter 10. The identification of the graduate teaching staff, who typically entered their graduate programs with no teaching experience, as possible candidates for improvement initiatives was based on both anecdotal data from these graduate students as well as their teaching reviews. The subsequent data on success rates of precalculus and calculus students as well as the graduate students' interactions within the training course demonstrated the efficacy of this course.

It is often the case that identifying the best path for implementing improvement efforts is far less clear than identifying what needs to be improved. Knowledge of resources available and department culture play an important role in this regard. For example, the implementation of a teaching course for graduate students at PTU was contingent on the availability of a mathematics educator who had experience with similar courses for pre-service teachers and was able to design and implement a course targeted at graduate students. Without the availability of faculty able to design such a course, its creation would likely not have been a viable path toward improving teaching. Thus what improvement initiatives can and should be implemented are contingent on available resources. This includes human resources such as faculty experience and time, as well as physical resources, such as available finances and facilities.

Student and Faculty Generated Data on Teaching Quality

There are two complementary sources for collecting data on teaching quality that we encountered in our case studies. The first, and more common source, involves student end-of-semester ratings of their instructors. All the selected institutions collected such data and some even complemented it with department mandated mid-semester evaluations. The literature on student ratings of instruction has pointed to the complicated relationship between what happens in the classroom and student ratings (e.g., Aleamoni, 1999; Theall & Franklin, 1991). Our selected institutions were not blind to these subtleties and a number of them used comparison to historical norms to situate their interpretations of student rating data. The second source of teaching quality data encountered was faculty observation of other faculty's teaching. Such observations also played an important role in informing where teaching improvement efforts should be targeted. These data both complement and situate student rating data. Faculty observations also provide individual instructors with fairly immediate targeted advice on improving their teaching. We discuss the implementation of each of these data sources as well as how they complement each other below.

Student Evaluations
At LPU2 the student evaluations are, for historical reasons, administered by the student union and made publicly available to any interested party. This means that any faculty member may look up the evaluations of his or her colleagues. In much the same way that sharing grading data created social pressure for instructors to conform to the grading norm, the public nature of teaching evaluations creates a similar pressure to perform as an instructor. One instructor commented:

> There's the very public [teaching evaluations], which you probably know about. And so there's this self-imposed pressure because you know that that's going to be public.

The long-term collection of student evaluations means that reviews that can be expected in particular courses are also public knowledge. Additionally, the public nature of the teaching evaluations identifies which instructors are underperforming according to their students. As such, the department is able to allocate resources to help improve those instructors' teaching. The department chair at LPU2 commented that:

Teaching calculus is much harder than teaching upper-division math courses in terms of getting good student evaluations. Usually [in] our graduate courses, instructors get 100% approval, whereas in calculus we consider anything above an 80% approval rating in a 200–300 student lecture to be good. Anything lower, it gets a little dicey. We have some faculty members who get really low ratings, but we try to work with them. What we do is we send the committee on teaching to take a look and give them feedback and try to help them and incentivize them to work on their teaching.

At this point it is important to mention that we are not necessarily advocating public distribution of teaching evaluations. We have seen cases where student-generated teaching evaluations were used effectively while being distributed only to course coordinators and instructors. Our goal was to illustrate that the communication of these evaluations to relevant parties may be beneficial for teaching outcomes. Limiting who sees them to the instructor of the course may limit their effectiveness as a catalyst for improving teaching quality. In such cases, individual instructors have little in terms of a baseline regarding what his or her colleagues' evaluations mean or what constitutes a "good" evaluation. As such it is difficult for these evaluations to serve as a motivator for instructors to improve their teaching.

In-Class Observations of Teaching

Teaching observations involve experienced instructors observing the teaching of colleagues and providing them with targeted suggestions for improving their teaching. The observations can be particularly useful for new instructors when they occur early in the semester. Issues with instructor classroom control, clarity or unproductive discourse patterns, which might otherwise go unnoticed until end of semester reviews, can be mitigated early via early semester observations.

In our case study, institutions' classroom observations were never punitive. Everyone teaching calculus was observed and received feedback. Teaching was seen as something that everyone, regardless of experience and talent, could improve upon. The observations were an opportunity for an experienced colleague to make suggestions regarding ways to improve teaching. At both LPU2 and LPU1 we learned that in some cases an instructor's teaching did not warrant a follow-up, yet the instructor found the initial observation and subsequent advice useful enough that he or she requested follow-ups to further improve their teaching.

At no institution in our study were observations of teaching used as replacements for student-evaluations of teaching. In fact LPU1, which utilized observation data, also had department-issued mid-semester student review in addition to the end-of-semester institution-issued student review.

There can be a reciprocal relationship between observation and student evaluation data. So for example, observers may help lecturers interpret their students' feedback and link it back to tangible teaching behaviors that they can work on. For example, the following was a reflection of one of the observers at LPU1:

It's really striking how students think you are a bad instructor if they can sense that you're not confident. Even if you're not a bad instructor. … The class visits I went to, none of them stuck out as really good or really bad, but the ones that had lower evaluations seem to be the ones where you could tell the students didn't respect [the instructor] for some reason.

The above excerpt provides an example of how observations aid in the contextualization of student reviews. The observer discusses linking her observation of the instructor's low confidence with student feedback regarding the quality of his instruction. This, in turn gives the instructor a concrete in-class behavior that he or she can attend to with the goal improving teaching. Both student evaluations and faculty observations help individual instructors identify the aspects of their teaching that may need improvement. Using both sources of data in tandem provides richer feedback than would be possible if only one of these sources was used.

Learning Outcomes

In working toward improving a course it is useful for the faculty involved to have a common vision of what specific skills and knowledge students are supposed to gain from taking that course. We refer to these knowledge and skills goals as learning outcomes. The creation of a finite list of learning outcomes allows specific homework tasks, example problems, and lesson plans to be objectively compared to the list. Such a list helps facilitate streamlining a course via the removal of content that does not directly serve the learning goals and may help identify learning goals that are underserved by existing curricular materials. Streamlining is particularly important in Calculus I; at least since the calculus reform movement of the late 1980s, Calculus I has been characterized as a course that often attempts to cover too much in too little time (e.g., Douglas, 1986).

LPrU, a Large Private University, used learning outcomes extensively in an effort to improve Calculus I. At the time of the data collection the introduction of the learning outcomes was a relatively new element being initiated as an institution-wide movement. Though suggested by the institution's administration and affecting all courses, those responsible for calculus enthusiastically adopted the improvement measure. They developed the outcomes and were responsible for the collection of data in regards to the outcomes. During the case study visit, it was evident from faculty that the learning outcomes were seen as an opportunity to identify areas of improvement within the Calculus I course. During the case study visit, the department was collecting data in order to determine how they were meeting, and making progress with, the learning outcomes. Therefore, more results are not available at this time. Yet, this is a clear example of an institution and department not being satisfied with the status quo and working toward improving their program through the use of data. The positive reception of the learning outcomes initiative was a chapter in a long history of data-driven improvement efforts. This history of improvement efforts may have contributed to how receptive faculty were to the learning outcomes initiative.

At this point we wish to emphasize that it may be possible to generate a list of learning outcomes and only superficially align a course with these outcomes. That was not the case here as can be seen by the following quote from a LPrU instructor:

> *[Select staff] spent a few weeks in the summer going through all the homework problems and deciding which ones actually were consistent with their learning goals and which ones should be put in the online homework that they have. So they sat down and thought about their goals and what homework problems led them to it. … It's a big thing that they're really trying to teach the things that the students need and give the students a chance to actually learn it.*

Implementing learning outcomes serves a broader purpose than simply providing local data for the department that may lead to improvement efforts. Prior to the collection of data, the identification of specific concepts and skills (learning outcomes) created a foci and level of standard that all instructors are held responsible for. As such, instructors report using the learning outcomes as a guide for what material to focus on in class because they knew the understanding of the outcomes would be assessed on the common assignments and final exam. One instructor reflects on the guidance that the learning outcomes provided when preparing to teach:

> *I really like having a mapping between the homework problems and the learning [outcomes]. And as we were writing this test in particular, they said, "Pay attention to these learning [outcomes], you want to make sure that your test questions match what we want them to know." That I really like, because it saves me a little bit of time as I'm preparing my lecture. I look at the homework, and I can see what's going to be important, or what the department thinks is important for the students, so I know how to spend my time in class.*

When studying the use of learning outcomes in Calculus I at LPrU, we found that the learning outcomes themselves did not serve as a mechanism for evaluating the content of the course or identifying areas of improvement within the course. Rather, how faculty used the learning outcomes and how the learning outcomes aided in the collection and analyzing of data by creating areas of focus was what made the existence of the learning outcomes important for this department. We found that the learning outcomes served different modes of evaluation at both the course level and instructor level. For example, the coordinated homework assignments and final exams created using the learning outcomes served as a baseline for what all students should learn while taking Calculus I at LPrU, regardless of the instructor. This ensured that instructors had a clear understanding of the content that should be covered.

The students' grades on the coordinated assignments and exams are collected and reviewed by the chair in conjunction with the teaching evaluations provided by the students. The evaluations and exams are designed with the learning outcomes in mind. Collecting this information allows the chair to monitor each instructor's coverage of the learning outcomes both through assessment and students' assessment of the coverage, or lack of coverage, of particular learning outcomes. The chair is then able to address any specific issues with individual instructors. The chair explains:

Here are the learning outcomes, everybody knows where they're at, and you hit them. And if any student says in the teaching evaluation, "I didn't get the learning outcomes," the department chair's going to follow up. ... In a lot of courses, including our calculus courses, we created common final exams, and that takes us a lot farther. Because faculty members know that at the end of every semester, the chair's going to see how their section did on the common final exam.

In short, the establishing of departmental learning outcomes allowed for common assignments to be geared toward these outcomes, for exams to focus on testing them, and for instructors to design instruction that focused on teaching them. These outcomes facilitated the creation of a common vision of what was important for calculus students to know and allowed for assessment of whether students gained this knowledge by the end of the calculus course.

Discussion and Recommendations

We conclude this chapter with reflections on the following three themes, each of which is relevant for institutions interested in refining or starting their local data collection efforts: data collection, storage and analysis; cultivating improvement ideas; and scale and scope of improvement efforts.

Data collection, Storage, and Analysis

Two questions to ask are: "Who should collect the data?" and "What data should be collected and analyzed?" Some of the institutions in our case studies charged the calculus coordinator with data collection. The common features of the people in charge of data collection at these institutions included: being long-term members of the faculty who held the data collection responsibility for a number of years, having a vested interest in the data and program improvement, having the knowledge to collect and analyze data regularly, and having the trust of the faculty to do the job. Someone within a department having these four traits is a good candidate for data collection responsibilities.

In deciding what data to collect, we advise that often faculty have reasonable gut feelings regarding where the shortcomings of their programs lie and what data may back up their speculations. This is always a good place to start. However, easily available data should be collected whenever practical even if it doesn't immediately answer questions faculty are interested in because it may help contextualize data or prove to be useful at a later date. In our discussions with faculty during our case studies it became apparent that improvement efforts often led to additional improvement efforts. The same was true with data collection and analysis. The collection and analysis of data often led to new questions regarding the performance of particular aspects of a program, which then led to more extensive collection of data and more analysis. So in terms of what data to collect and analyze, it may be more important to start efforts then to figure out the breadth of those efforts at the onset.

Cultivating Improvement Ideas

We wish to mention, again, that although data might point to what needs improvement within a program, the nature and implementation of those improvements is less clear. There may be many possible improvement paths available and choosing among these paths in a way that satisfies multiple stakeholders may be a challenge. The sources for improvement effort ideas may be varied; many of the institutions in our study made use of multiple internal and external sources. In regard to internal sources, there are multiple stakeholders involved in a program and improvement ideas may come from any one of them. The stakeholders often only need an opportunity to contribute ideas and the creation of such opportunities are often part and parcel to the process of implementing data driven improvement efforts.

External sources for improvement ideas often require additional efforts on the part of interested faculty. Examples of external sources include, but are not limited to, reading education research or practitioner articles and discussing successful program improvements with colleagues in other departments and institutions. In several of the departments we visited, the course coordinator took the role of locating, selecting, and distributing such information to faculty. However, there is nothing that limits this work to a course coordinator and any interested faculty members may find ideas that can be implemented in their home institutions if they are inclined to look.

Scale and Scope of Improvement Efforts

In this chapter we have discussed several data driven calculus program improvements. Some of these require fairly low effort and mainly involve collecting, compiling, and distributing data to relevant stakeholders. The distribution of historical grade data to promote grade uniformity and the publicizing of teaching evaluations to encourage higher quality teaching were examples of such low effort improvements. Other data driven improvement initiatives, such as the implementation of a full semester teacher training course for graduate students and the extensive use of learning outcomes, involve significantly more buy-in from faculty implementing these changes. The wide variation in the resources involved in improvement efforts discussed in this chapter helps illustrate how varied data driven improvement efforts can be.

It is important at this point to mention that the larger scale improvement efforts discussed here were undertaken within departments that had a history of improvement efforts. From this observation we make two related points. First, large-scale improvement efforts are unlikely to work without the buy-in of the faculty involved. This means that the department culture of the institutions that implemented these substantive changes was receptive to improvement efforts prior to their implementation and had a history of successful data driven improvement efforts. Second, low effort improvements, together with data supporting their success may be catalysts for creating faculty buy-in for improvement efforts as a whole. It is up to the stakeholders in a particular program to evaluate their own needs, their culture, and their capabilities when deciding on the scale and nature of improvement efforts. Focusing first on the low hanging fruit may encourage departments to continue to improve their programs. In reference to the discussion in this chapter, we believe the examples from the "Historical Success Rates" and "Student and Faculty Generated Data on Teaching Quality" sections are instantiations of low hanging fruit. However, as with data interpretation, we believe that what constitutes low hanging fruit is institutionally situated and highly dependent on available resources. Therefore, it is up to stakeholders to determine what data-informed improvement efforts are appropriate for their institutional needs. Every institution has room for improvement, potential data available that can be used to identify where that room for improvement is, and stakeholders that can create and implement data-informed improvement efforts.

References

Aleamoni, L. M. (1999). Student rating myths versus research facts. *Journal of Personnel Evaluation in Education, 1*(1), 111–119.

Bowden, J. & Marton, F. (1998), *The university of learning: Beyond quality and competence in higher education.* London: Kogan Page.

Briggs, C., Stark, J., & Rowland-Poplawski, J. (2003). How do we know a "continuous planning" academic program when we see one? *The Journal of Higher Education, 74*(4), 361–385.

Douglas, R. (Ed.). (1986), *Toward a lean and lively calculus: Report of the conference/workshop to develop curriculum and teaching methods for calculus at the college level* (MAA Notes No. 6). Washington, DC: Mathematical Association of America.

Srikanthan, G. & Dalrymple, J. (2004). A synthesis of a quality management model for education in universities. *International Journal of Education Management, 18*(4), 266–279.

Stark, J. S., Lowther, M. A., Sharp, S., & Arnold, G. (1997). Program-level curriculum planning: An exploration of faculty perspectives on two different campuses. *Research in Higher Education, 38*(3), 99–130.

Tucker, A. (1996). *Models that work: Case studies in effective undergraduate mathematics programs* (MAA Notes No. 38). Washington, DC: Mathematical Association of America.

Theall, M. & Franklin, J. (1991). Using student ratings for teaching improvement. *New Directions for Teaching and Learning, 48*(4), 83–96.

Appendix A
Surveys and Case Studies Methods

Jessica Ellis, Colorado State University, Fort Collins

In this document we provide detailed information on the data collected for this project. There were two phases of the project. Phase 1 consisted of surveys sent to Calculus I students, instructors, and course coordinators. Phase II consisted of case studies at institutions selected based on the survey results. In the following sections, we first give an overview of the timeline of this data collection for both phases, and then discuss the preparation, design, administration, and analysis of each phase.

Timeline

Table 1 illustrates the timeline of this five-year project, consisting of two phases. During Year 1 we prepared the surveys by conducting a literature review and creating a taxonomy of dependent and independent variables. During the spring of Year 2 we designed and piloted the five surveys. The surveys were sent out in fall of Year 2 (2010). During Year 3 we started the analysis of these surveys in order to identify a list of possible case studies; we also designed and administered a follow-up survey for students, and prepared for the case studies data collection. In the spring of Year 4 we piloted the case studies, and collected all the data during fall of Year 4 (2012). We devoted Year 5 to data analyses and dissemination.

Table 1: Timeline of CSPCC project.

Year	Spring	Fall
1 (2009)	Literature review for surveys	Taxonomy for surveys
2 (2010)	Design five surveys (student beginning and end of term, instructor beginning and end of term, course coordinator)	Send surveys
3 (2011)	Analyze surveys; identify case study institutions; design follow-up survey for students	Prepare case studies; design interview and observation protocols; send out follow-up survey to students
4 (2012)	Pilot case studies at four institutions (one per each institution type)	Conduct case studies at 16 institutions (four per institution type)
5 (2013)	Write summaries of case studies (the Facts and Features) and send to each case study site	Analyze and write

Survey Preparation and Design

Five major online surveys were constructed: one for the calculus coordinator, two for the calculus instructors (of which one was administered immediately before the start of the course and the other immediately after it ended), and two for the students in the course (one at the start of the term and one at the end).[1] In addition, instructors reported on the distribution of final grades and were asked to submit a copy of the final exam. As shown in Table 1, one year after the surveys were administered, we administered a follow-up survey to those students who had volunteered their email addresses. No incentives were given for completing the surveys.

The surveys were prepared during the 2009–10 academic year, beginning with a literature review and then proceeding to building a taxonomy of potential dependent and independent variables based on the literature and feedback from experts in the Advisory Board of the project. This was followed by constructing, pilot-testing, and refining the survey instruments, selecting the institutions for the study, and then contacting these universities for their agreement to participate. The survey was restricted to what is known as "mainstream" calculus, the calculus course that is designed to prepare students for the study of engineering or the physical sciences.

For the purpose of analyzing the effect of the Calculus I program, we had six dependent variables, four of which were measured at both the start and the end of the term, as shown in Table 2. For the first three variables, students were presented with the following statements and asked to indicate their level of agreement on a 6-point Likert scale (0 = *Strongly Disagree*; 1 = *Disagree*; 2 = *Slightly Disagree*; 3 = *Slightly Agree*; 4 = *Agree*; 5 = *Strongly Agree*):

- I am confident in my mathematical abilities.
- I enjoy doing mathematics.
- This course has increased my interest in taking more mathematics.

Table 2: Time of administration of dependent variables.

Variable	Start of term	End of term
Confidence	X	X
Enjoyment	X	X
Increased interest		X
Desire to continue studying mathematics	X	X
Intention to continue calculus	X	X
Final grade of C or higher		X

The control variables were of two types: student characteristics (e.g., gender, parental education, race/ethnicity) and academic background (e.g., secondary school experience in mathematics including which courses were taken and what grades were received, score on the Advanced Placement (AP) Calculus exam, scores on SAT and/or ACT college admission exams, year at university, prior mathematics courses at university, and career intention).

The independent variables were selected following a literature review to identify the factors influencing student persistence and achievement in college in general and science, technology, engineering, and mathematics (STEM) in particular. Broadly, these factors pertain to (a) a strong sense of community and self-perception of identity with that community (Seymour & Hewitt, 1997; Tinto, 1998), (b) departmental or institutional supports for learning (Keynes & Olson, 2001), and (c) instructional behaviors that meet students' intellectual needs, promote greater learning and develop student self-confidence (Boaler, 1998; Boaler, Wiliam, & Brown, 2000). We were particularly interested in variables that are amenable to change or manipulation as well as easy and reliable to measure. As shown in Table 3, responses were collected at the student, instructor/classroom, and institutional levels. Once we identified the variables of interest, we developed survey drafts that were piloted with students, instructors, and course coordinators. During these piloting interviews, the interviewee provided feedback regarding any questions that were difficult to understand, redundant, or cumbersome. These interviews helped us to organize, refine, and finalize the surveys.

---

1 Links to the surveys can be found at www.maa.org/cspcc. See also Appendix B for a list of all the variables used.

Table 3: Level of independent variables and time of collection

Level	Variables	Instrument
Student	Beliefs and attitudes about learning mathematics, study habits, level of intellectual engagement with the course, experience with technology (graphing calculators or computer software)	Student Beginning of Term Student End of Term
Instructor	Experience and background; beliefs, attitudes, and interests	Instructor Beginning of Term Instructor End of Term
Classroom	Class size; instructional practices; assessment practices; out of class interactions with students; use of technology including use of web resources; textbook; additional instructional resources	Instructor Beginning of Term Instructor End of Term
Classroom	Student perceptions of instructional practices, use of technology, assessment practices, intellectual community outside of class	Student End of Term
Institution	Placement procedures, technological support, institutional support for students, institutional support for instructors	Coordinator Survey

Survey Data Collection

For the purposes of surveying post-secondary mathematics programs in the United States, the Conference Board of the Mathematical Sciences (CBMS) characterizes colleges and universities into four types determined by the highest mathematics degree that is offered: associate's degree (hereafter referred to as two-year colleges), bachelor's degree (referred to as undergraduate colleges), master's degree (referred to as masters universities), and doctoral degree (referred to as research universities). Because enrollments vary so greatly within each type of institution, CBMS further stratifies these institutions according to the number of full-time equivalent (FTE) undergraduate students. We sampled most heavily at the institutions with the largest enrollments. Not-for-profit colleges or universities were included in the study. As shown in Table 4, we selected 521 colleges and universities; 213 participated in the study. The larger the FTE, the better the response rate.

Table 4: Institutional sampling and response rates.

Institution type	Number of institutions[a]	Sample size (sample rate)	Participant[b] (response rate)	Number of substrata by FTE	Response Rates Range[c]
2Y Coll (AS)	1,121	207 (18%)	54 (26%)	8	17%–42%
4Y Coll (BA)	1,015	134 (13%)	60 (45%)	5	29%–52%
Univ (MA)	181	60 (33%)	26 (43%)	4	33%–54%
Univ (PhD)	197	120 (61%)	73 (61%)	6	46%–88%

Notes: a. As counted by the Conference Board for the Mathematical Sciences. b. Number of colleges or universities that provided data and percentage of the sample that provided data. c. Range of percentages, by substrata, of the sampled institutions that provided data.

The surveys were designed to take between 15-60 minutes to complete, depending on the survey. The Student Beginning of Term survey had a total of 62 questions, the Student End of Term survey 47 questions, the Instructor Beginning of Term survey 35 questions, the Instructor End of Term survey 38, and the Course Coordinator survey 16 questions. Surveys were administered online using SurveyMonkey. In order to maintain a link between the course coordinator survey, instructor survey, and student surveys, the link to the survey was sent to the coordinator, who then sent the link to the surveys to all the instructors in the department, who then sent the link to the surveys to their students.

Representatives from the Mathematical Association of America (MAA) initially contacted the institutions, followed up in order to encourage participation, and followed up to ensure completion of the beginning and end of term surveys. From the 213 colleges and universities that participated in the study, there were 663 instructors and over 14,000 students who responded to at least one of the surveys. We have both start and end of term surveys that are linked to each other for 7,260 of the students. There is complete data (all five surveys completed and linked with each other) for 3,103 students enrolled with 309 instructors at 125 colleges or universities.

Case Study Preparation and Design

The survey results from Phase 1 provided information on which institutions enabled students to be more successful in Calculus I (as compared to other institutions of the same type) per our measures of success. Survey results, however well crafted and implemented, are limited in their ability to shed light on essential contextual aspects related to *why* and *how* institutions are producing students who are successful in calculus. The case studies were therefore designed to address this shortcoming by identifying and contextualizing the teaching practices, training practices, and institutional support practices that contribute to student success in Calculus I. As argued by Stake (1995) and Yin (2003), explanatory case studies are an appropriate methodology to study events (such as current practices in Calculus I) in situations in which the goal is to explain why or how, and for which there is little or no ability to control or manipulate relevant behaviors.

When selecting the case study institutions, we considered (a) how well the institution ranked on the dependent variables when compared to institutions in the same strata, (b) the response rate from students and instructors, and (c) how the reported pass rate among respondents compared to the institution's four or six year graduation rate. This resulted in the selection of four institutions at each of the four institution types, for a total of 16 selected institutions. Additionally, we selected case study pilot institutions based on geographical proximity to each of the four teams. The analyses of the data of two of the pilot institutions led the teams to request their inclusion as successful institutions, for a total of 18 case study institutions. See Hsu, Mesa, & The Calculus Case Collective (2014) for more details on the case study site selection.

Common interview protocols for all 18 case studies were developed in order to facilitate comparison of calculus programs within and across institution type. Specifically, we developed 11 interview protocols: student focus group, instructors, graduate students, graduate student trainer, course coordinator(s), placement, teaching center, learning center, client disciplines, dean, and department chair. The interviews were semi-structured, and in the protocols we developed both questions to be asked of everyone and potential follow-up questions depending on the response. These interview protocols were informed by both the survey taxonomies and the survey findings, and were developed through multiple iterations of creating, piloting, and refining questions. The interviews were developed to last between 30 and 80 minutes, depending on the interviewee. In addition to an interview protocol, we developed an observation instrument informed by the literature. The instrument underwent several rounds of revisions (for more details see White & Mesa, 2012). The observation instrument collected information on classroom interaction, tasks used during lessons, and impressions from observers about the atmosphere, the exchanges between faculty and students, the mathematics, and the connections made within mathematics and to other disciplines.

Case Study Data Analysis

At the completion of each site visit the case study teams created brief summaries of the interviews, identified documents to follow up on, and identified additional individuals of interest to interview (through the institution websites or by contacting individuals that we had interviewed). After collecting, organizing, and reviewing all relevant data, each team then developed a reflective summary that captured much of what was learned about the calculus program, including key facts and features that were identified by both the case study team and the people interviewed as contributing to the success of the institution's calculus program. A more formal three to four page summary report was then developed by reviewing the reflective summary and transcripts and sent to the respective department as part of the member checking process (Stake, 1995).

At the 18 site visits, we conducted 198 interviews with instructors, administrators, and students for a total of more than 250 hours of audio recordings. All interviews were fully transcribed and checked by a second person for accuracy and completeness. In order to manage this vast amount of qualitative data, a tagging scheme was developed to facilitate location of relevant interview excerpts related to 35 different areas of interest (codes). These areas of interest include such things as placement, technology, assignments and assessments, and instructor characteristics. Each interview was first organized into smaller sections, in terms of what we refer to as a "codeable unit." A codeable unit consists, more or less, of an interviewer question followed by a response. If follow-up questions result in a new topic being discussed by the interviewee, then a new codeable unit is marked. Each codeable unit is then tagged with one or more of the 35 codes. The idea is that once all interviews have been tagged with one or more codes, we can then systematically identify all instances in which any interviewee addressed a particular topic area. Once these instances have been located, then a more fine-grained analysis will proceed.

The set of 35 codes was developed by representatives from each of the four different case study teams and consists of a priori codes from the literature and codes for themes that emerged from the reflective summaries. The final set of 35 codes underwent an extensive cyclical process in which representatives from each case study team coded the same transcripts, vetted their respective coding, which then led to refining, deleting, and adding new codes and operational definitions. Two different team members coded each transcript and the two coders resolved any discrepancies.

The chapters within this volume represent some of the key findings that arose throughout these analyses. Specific analytic techniques utilized in each chapter are identified within the chapters, and may draw on quantitative, qualitative, or mixed method approaches.

References

Boaler, J. (1998). Open and closed mathematics approaches: student experiences and understandings. *Journal for Research in Mathematics Education, 29*(1) 41–62.

Boaler, J., Wiliam, D., & Brown, M. (2000). Students' experiences of ability grouping — disaffection, polarization and the construction of failure. *British Educational Research Journal, 26*(5) 631–648.

Hsu, E., Mesa, V., & The Calculus Case Collective. (2014). *Synthesizing measures of institutional success* (CSPCC-Technical Report #1). Washington DC: Mathematical Association of America.

Keynes, H. B. & Olson, A. M. (2000). Redesigning the calculus sequence at a research university: issues, implementation, and objectives. *International Journal of Mathematics Education Science and Technology, 31*(1), 71–82

Seymour, E. & Hewitt, N. M. (1997). *Talking about leaving: Why undergraduates leave the sciences.* Boulder, CO: Westview Press.

Stake, R. (1995). *The art of case study research.* Thousand Oaks, CA: Sage Publications.

White, N. J. & Mesa, V. (2012). *Description of Observation Protocol for Characteristics of Successful Programs in College Calculus.* unpublished manuscript. School of Education, University of Michigan, Ann Arbor.

Yin, R. (2003). *Case study research: Design and methods.* Thousand Oaks, CA: Sage Publications.

Appendix B
Survey Questions and Codebook

Gerhard Sonnert, *Harvard University*
Jessica Ellis, *Colorado State University, Fort Collins*

This is a description of all of the information gathered over the summer and fall of 2010 from the surveyed departments, instructors, and students and combined into the data file maalongdatafile_ANON.csv. Instructions for accessing this anonymous data file can be found at www.maaorg/cspcc.

We present the surveys in the following sections, starting on the given pages. In order to identify the survey to which each variable belongs, we used two-letter identifiers:

1. Student survey from the beginning of 2010 fall term, variables starting with "sp", p. 141.
2. Student survey from the end of 2010 fall term, variables starting with "sq", p.149.
3. Instructor survey from the beginning of 2010 fall term, variables starting with "ip", p. 155.
4. Instructor survey from the end of 2010 fall term, variables starting with "iq", p.160.
5. Coordinator survey, variables starting with "c", p. 166.

The coordinator survey was merged with the instructor surveys using the Coordinator ID (CoordID). The resulting file was then merged with the student surveys using the InstructorID (InstID). A total of 376 students without a matching instructor were merged into the data file by Department ID (MAA_ID).

For each piece of information and question response, the code used in the anonymous data file, maalongdatafile_ANON.csv, is included. The codes for responses to the surveys (e.g., sp13symbcalc) indicate which survey they were taken from (sp = student survey at the beginning of the semester), the question number in that survey (13), and an abbreviation suggestive of the information (symbcalc = question about use of calculator with CAS capabilities).

General Information

Basic identifying information about the institution is also included in maalongdatafile_ANON.csv. The MAA's identifying number for each institution encodes information about the institution type and undergraduate enrollment. The institution type is based on the 2010 Conference Board of the Mathematical Sciences classification of non-profit degree-granting departments of mathematics according to the highest degree (Associate's, Bachelor's, Master's, or PhD) offered by the department. Enrollment is undergraduate FTE. These unique identifiers were replaced in maalongdatafile_ANON.csv with MAA_IDinfo codes as described in Table 1.

Additional identifiers include:

State = Institution state
CoordID = Coordinator ID
InstID = Instructor ID
StudID = Student ID

Table 1: Correspondence of MAA_IDinfo code to MAA ID, institution type, and enrollment.

MAA ID	Institution Type	Enrollment	MAA_IDinfo
30001–39065	2y Coll (AS)		1
10001–10249	4Y Coll (BA)	< 1000	2
10250–10449	4Y Coll (BA)	1000 to 1500	3
10450–10729	4Y Coll (BA)	1500 to 2500	4
10730–10929	4Y Coll (BA)	2500 to 5000	5
10930–11010	4Y Coll (BA)	> 5000	6
11212–11306	Univ (MA)	< 7000	7
11307–11353	Univ (MA)	7000 to 11,000	8
11354–11390	Univ (MA)	> 11,000	9
11011–11071	Univ (PhD)	< 7500	10
11072–11129	Univ (PhD)	7500 to 15,000	11
11130–11169	Univ (PhD)	15,000 to 20,000	12
11170–11185	Univ (PhD)	20,000 to 25,000	13
11186–11211	Univ (PhD)	> 25,000	14

There also are identifiers to indicate the completeness of the responses:

Sresponsetype = Indicator of the type of student's participation.

Values: 1 = Both surveys complete, 2 = Pre- complete 3 = Post- complete, 4 = Pre- partial, 5 = Post- partial

Iresponsetype = Indicator of the type of instructor's participation.

Values: 0 = No Response, 1 = Both surveys complete, 2 = Pre- complete, 3 = Post- complete, 4 = Pre- partial

Cresponsetype = Indicator of the type of coordinator's participation.

Values: 0 = No Response, 1 = Complete survey response, 4 = Partial response

Administrative information includes:

- iCourseCreditHours = Course credit hours.
- iMaxEnroll = Maximum enrollment capacity (not actual enrollment which could be below orover capacity). Coordinators provided data before the course start date.
- iCorabove = Estimated percentage of students, including those who finished the course and who withdrew, who in the past years received a C or above.
- iSectioncount = Section count.

Repeated or Parallel Variables

In some instances, an identical or very similar question was asked on both the pre- and post-surveys for students and instructors. Some questions were posed to both students and instructors. These instances are identified in the codebook. For easy recognition of the variables in question, an "r" is added between the survey signifier and the question number. For example: spr26calc2 on the student pre-survey is repeated on the student post-survey as sqr26calc2. The following is a list of all the repeated and parallel variables used. Full description is given in the sections following.

spr25grade-sqr25grade

spr26calc2-sqr26calc2

spr28c2req-sqr28c2req

spr29confident-sqr29confident

spr29enjoy-sqr29enjoy

spr31intend-sqr31intend

spr32diffic-sqr32diffic

spr33unsuccess-sqr33unsuccess-ipr33unsuccess

spr34success-sqr34success-ipr34success

spr35measure-sqr35measure

spr36choice-sqr36choice

spr37study-sqr37study-ipr37study

spr38calc-sqr38calc-ipr38calc

spr39instruct-sqr39instruct-ipr39instruct

sqr19problems-iqr19problems

sqr19collab-iqr19collab

sqr19discuss-iqr19discuss

sqr19present-iqr19present

sqr19indiv-iqr19indiv

sqr19lecture-iqr19lecture

sqr19ask-iqr19ask

sqr19explain-iqr19explain

sqr20extra-iqr20extra

sqr20homework-iqr20homework

sqr20exam-iqr20exam

sqr20read- iqr20read

sqr22collect-iqr22collect

sqr22quiz-iqr22quiz

sqr24demgraph-iqr24demgraph

sqr24graph-iqr24graph

sqr24demcomp-iqr24demcomp

sqr24comp-iqr24comp

sqr30word-iqr30word

sqr30diff-iqr30diff

sqr31word-iqr31word

sqr31diff-iqr31diff

ipr13prepl-iqr13prepl

Q14 on the beginning term instructor survey is similar to Q30, Q32, Q34, Q36, and Q38 on the end of term instructor survey.

Linearized Variables

Original variables that give brackets of an essentially continuous variable (e.g., hours per week) were redefined into that continuous variable by assigning mean values of brackets and estimating for extreme brackets. These variables have an "l" (ell) attached at the end of their name. (For example: sp57workl from sp57work.)

Missing values are coded as '.' throughout.

Student Pre-Survey (Beginning of Term/Semester)

Q1.   My placement in calculus was determined by (*Mark all that apply*):
sp1sat = My ACT or SAT score
sp1place = My score on a placement exam
sp1prereq = My successful completion of prerequisite courses
sp1ap = My AP exam score
sp1dk = Don't know
            Values: 0 = not selected, 1 = yes, . = none selected

Q2.   sp2sat = Did you take the SAT exam?
            Values: 1 = yes, 0 = no, . = missing

Q3.   sp3satreadscore = SAT critical reading score
sp3satmathscore = SAT mathematics score
            Values: 200 to 800

Q4.   sp4satsubjmath = Did you take the SAT Subject Test in mathematics?
Values: 1 = yes, 0 = no, . = missing

Q5.   sp5subjmathscore1 = SAT Subject Test in mathematics Level 1 score
sp5subjmathscore2 = SAT Subject Test in mathematics Level 2 score
Values: 200 to 800

Q6.   sp6act = Did you take the ACT exam?
Values: 1 = yes, 0 = no, . = missing

Q7.   sp7actcompscore = ACT composite score
Values: 1 through 36
sp7actmathscore = ACT mathematics score
Values: 1 through 36
sp7act_satc = SAT-ACT concordance according to the following:

(144 = 1600) (143 = 1600) (142 = 1600) (141 = 1600) (140 = 1590) (139 = 1580) (138 = 1560) (137 = 1550) (136 = 1530) (135 = 1520) (134 = 1510) (133 = 1500) (132 = 1480) (131 = 1470) (130 = 1460) (129 = 1440) (128 = 1430) (127 = 1420) (126 = 1410) (125 = 1400) (124 = 1390) (123 = 1380) (122 = 1360) (121 = 1350) (120 = 1340) (119 = 1330) (118 = 1320) (117 = 1310) (116 = 1300) (115 = 1290) (114 = 1280) (113 = 1270) (112 = 1260) (111 = 1250) (110 = 1240) (109 = 1230) (108 = 1220) (107 = 1210) (106 = 1200) (105 = 1200) (104 = 1190) (103 = 1180) (102 = 1170) (101 = 1160) (100 = 1150) (99 = 1140) (98 = 1130) (97 = 1120) (96 = 1110) (95 = 1100) (94 = 1090) (93 = 1080) (92 = 1070) (91 = 1070) (90 = 1060) (89 = 1050) (88 = 1040) (87 = 1030) (86 = 1020) (85 = 1010) (84 = 1000) (83 = 990) (82 = 980) (81 = 970) (80 = 960) (79 = 950) (78 = 940) (77 = 930) (76 = 920) (75 = 910) (74 = 900) (73 = 890) (72 = 880) (71 = 870) (70 = 860) (69 = 840) (68 = 830) (67 = 820) (66 = 810) (65 = 800) (64 = 790) (63 = 780) (62 = 770) (61 = 750) (60 = 740) (59 = 730) (58 = 710) (57 = 700) (56 = 690) (55 = 670) (54 = 660) (53 = 640) (52 = 630) (51 = 610) (50 = 590) (49 = 570) (48 = 560) (47 = 540) (46 = 520) (45 = 510) (0 thru 44 = 500)*

*notice that ACT sum scores of 0-44 were all given an SAT value of 500.

This variable contains the combined mathematics and critical SAT scores, if available. If not, the SAT equivalents of the student's ACT scores were included. ACT scores were translated into SAT scores according to a concordance table created by the College Board (1999). This concordance equates the sum of all four ACT subtest to a score on the combined SAT math and SAT critical reading subtests. Note: The writing subtest is not considered in this variable. To fit the values of sp7actcompscore to the scale used, sp7actcompscore was multiplied by 4.

sp7act_satm = SAT math concordance for the ACT math score, according to the College Board (1999).

Q8.   My mathematics courses in high school have prepared me to
sp8nocalc = complete complex calculations without a calculator
sp8word = solve word problems
sp8factor = factor expressions
sp8equat = solve equations
sp8inequal = solve inequalities
Values: 0, 1, 2, 3, 4, 5 (rating scale): 0 = strongly disagree, 1 = disagree, 2 = slightly disagree, 3 = slightly agree, 4 = agree, 5 = strongly agree, . = missing

Q9. The teacher of my last mathematics course in high school
sp9lecture = lectured most of the time
sp9answer = primarily showed us how to get answers to specific questions
sp9group = frequently had us work in groups
sp9challenge = frequently had us solve challenging problems
sp9care = cared that I was successful in the course
> Values: 0, 1, 2, 3, 4, 5 (rating scale): 0 = strongly disagree, 1 = disagree, 2 = slightly disagree, 3 = slightly agree, 4 = agree, 5 = strongly agree, . = missing

Q10. sp10graphcalc = I am comfortable in using a graphing calculator
sp10comp = I am comfortable in using a computer algebra system (e.g., Maple, MATLAB)
> Values: 0, 1, 2, 3, 4, 5 (rating scale): 0 = strongly disagree, 1 = disagree, 2 = slightly disagree, 3 = slightly agree, 4 = agree, 5 = strongly agree, . = missing

Q11. sp11click = my high school mathematics teachers used an electronic response system (such as clickers) to poll students during class
> Values: 1 = yes, 0 = no, . = missing

Q12. sp12graphcalcexam = In high school I was allowed to use graphic calculators on exams
> Values: 2 = always, 1 = sometimes, 0 = never, . = missing

Q13. sp13symbcalc = In high school I was allowed to use calculators that performed symbolic operations on exams (e.g., TI-89, TI-92)
> Values: 2 = yes, 1 = sometimes, 0 = no, . = missing

Q14. Which of the following calculus courses were offered in your high school? *(Mark all that apply)*
sp14calc = Calculus (non-AP)
sp14calcab = AP Calculus AB
sp14calcbc = AP Calculus BC
sp14calcib = International Baccalaureate (IB) calculus
sp14calcol = Online calculus course
sp14coll2yrinhs = Calculus course taught at my high school for which students also received two-year college credit
sp14coll2yr = Calculus course taught at a two-year college for which students also received high school credit
sp14coll4yrinhs = Calculus course taught at my high school for which students also received four-year college or university credit
sp14coll4yr = Calculus course taught at a four-year college for which students also received high school credit
> Values: 0 = not selected, 1 = yes, . = none selected

Q15. (HS math course taking history and characteristics)
Course level of mathematics HS courses
sp15geolevel = Geometry
sp15alg2level = Algebra II
sp15imlevel = Integrated Math
sp15preclevel = Pre-Calculus
sp15triglevel = Trigonometry
sp15statlevel = Statistics (Non-AP)
sp15calclevel = Calculus (Non-AP)
sp15othlevel = Other course taken senior year
> Values: 1 = Regular, 2 = Honors, 3 = IB, 0 = not chosen

Note: If none of these courses was checked at any level (i.e., all above variables = 0), then all these variables were set to missing

Grade Level in High School
sp15geoyear = Geometry
sp15alg2year = Algebra II
sp15imyear = Integrated Math
sp15precyear = Pre-Calculus
sp15trigyear = Trigonometry
sp15statyear = Statistics (Non-AP)
sp15calcyear = Calculus (Non-AP)
sp15othyear = Other course taken senior year
    Values: 8 = eighth grade, 9 = ninth grade, 10 = tenth grade, 11 = eleventh grade, 12 = twelfth grade, . = missing

Final Grade
sp15geograde = Geometry
sp15alg2grade = Algebra II
sp15imgrade = Integrated Math
sp15precgrade = Pre-Calculus
sp15triggrade = Trigonometry
sp15statgrade = Statistics (Non-AP)
sp15calcgrade = Calculus (Non-AP)
sp15othgrade = Other course taken senior year
    Values: "A+" = 4.33, "A" = 4, "A–" = 3.67, … , "F" = 0, "P" = 2.8, missing data = .

Note: The very small category of "P" ("Pass") was assigned the value of 2.8 (between a B and a B-). There are no other values of 2.8. So, if it is desired to eliminate the "P" group, 2.8 can be set to missing. The very small category of "Withdraw" was set to missing.

Q16.   sp16ap = Did you take any AP Calculus or AP Statistics in high school?
        Values: 1 = yes, 0 = no, . = missing

Note: "I don't know" is set to missing. If any information on Q17 was given, "no" and "missing" on Q16 is changed to "yes."

Q17.   (AP course taking history and characteristics)
        AP Exam score (if taken)
        sp17abscore = Calculus AB
        sp17bcscore = Calculus BC
        sp17statscore = AP Statistics
            Values: 1, 2, 3, 4, 5. 0 = exam not taken even though course was taken, . = missing
        Grade Level in High School
        sp17abyear = Calculus AB
        sp17bcyear = Calculus BC
        sp17statyear = AP Statistics
            Values: 9 = ninth grade, 10 = tenth grade, 11 = eleventh grade, 12 = twelfth grade, . = missing

Final Grade
sp17abgrade = Calculus AB
sp17bcgrade = Calculus BC
sp17statgrade = AP Statistics
    Values: "A+" = 4.33, "A" = 4, "A-" = 3.67, … , "F" = 0, missing data = .

Gender of Teacher
sp17abgender = Calculus AB
sp17bcgender = Calculus BC
sp17statgender = AP Statistics
     Values: 0 = female, 1 = male, . = missing data

Q18.   sp18calccol = Did you take a calculus course in COLLEGE prior to this one?
     Values: 1 = yes, 0 = no, . = missing

Q19.   sp19calccolloc = Where was your previous college calculus course taken?
     Values: 1 = At this college or university, 2 = At another 4-year college or university, 3 = At another 2-year college

Q20.   What was the delivery mode of the calculus course you completed in college prior to this one? (**Mark all that apply**)
sp20cconline = Online
sp20cccor = Through correspondence
sp20ccface = Face-to-face with an instructor
     Values: 0 = not selected, 1 = yes, . = none selected

Q21.   Why are you taking this course again? (Mark all that apply)
sp21nocred = It did not count toward the credits I need
sp21grade = I passed, but I need/want a higher grade (e.g., for my major)
sp21nopass = I did not pass the course
sp21drop = I dropped the class
sp21bettergrade = I wanted to get a better grade
sp21understand = I wanted to improve my understanding of calculus
sp21advisor = My college advisor told me to
     Values: 0 = not selected, 1 = yes, . = none selected

Q22.   sp22precalccol = Did you take a pre-calculus course in college prior to this course?
     Values: 1 = yes, 0 = no, . = missing

Q23.   sp23pccloc = Where was your previous college precalculus course taken?
     Values: 1 = At this college or university, 2 = At another 4-year college or university, 3 = At another 2-year college

Q24.   What was the delivery mode of the precalculus course you completed in college prior to this one? (**Mark all that apply**)
sp24pconline = Online
sp24pccor = Through correspondence
sp24pcface = Face-to-face with an instructor
     Values: 0 = not selected, 1 = yes, . = none selected

Q25.   spr25grade = What grade do you expect in this calculus course?
     Values: "A" = 4, "B" = 3, "C" = 2, "D" = 1, "F" = 0, missing data = .

Note: Repeated question. This question was repeated on the end of semester survey (Q1: sqr25grade).

Q26.   spr26calc2 = Do you intend to take Calculus II?
                     Values: 1 = yes, 0 = no, 9 = I don't know yet, . = missing
Note: Repeated question. This question was repeated on the end of semester survey (Q3: sqr26calc2).

Q27.   sp27gradeimp = How important is a good grade in this course in influencing your decision whether or not to
             take Calculus II?
                     Values: 0, 1, 2, 3, 4, 5 (rating scale), 0 = not important at all, 1 = unimportant, 2 = slightly unimportant,
             3 = slightly important, 4 = important, 5 = very important, . = missing

Q28.   spr28c2req = Is Calculus II required for your major?
                     Values: 1 = yes, 0 = no, 9 = I don't know, . = missing

Note: Repeated questions. This question was repeated on the end of semester survey (Q2: sqr28c2req).

Q29.   sp29know = I believe I have the knowledge and abilities to succeed in this course
             sp29understand = I understand the mathematics that I have studied
                     Values: 0, 1, 2, 3, 4, 5 (rating scale), 0 = strongly disagree, 1 = disagree, 2 = slightly disagree,
             3 = slightly agree, 4 = agree, 5 = strongly agree, . = missing

             Note: Repeated questions. The following questions were repeated on the end of semester survey (Q6:
             sqr29confident, sqr29enjoy).
             spr29confident = I am confident in my mathematics abilities
             spr29enjoy = I enjoy doing mathematics
                     Values: 0, 1, 2, 3, 4, 5 (rating scale), 0 = strongly disagree, 1 = disagree, 2 = slightly disagree,
             3 = slightly agree, 4 = agree, 5 = strongly agree, . = missing

Q30.   If I take another calculus course after this one, it will be because (Mark all that apply)
             sp30req = It is required
             sp30want = I want to
                     Values: 0 = not selected, 1 = yes, . = none selected

Note: The following Q31 through Q39 are a block of repeated questions.

Q31.   spr31intend = How certain are you in what you intend to do after college?
                     Values: 0, 1, 2, 3 (rating scale): 0 = "Not at all certain", 3 = "Very certain" , . = missing

Q32.   spr32diffic = When experiencing a difficulty in my math class
                     Values: 0, 1, 2, 3 (rating scale): 0 = "I try hard to figure it out on my own", 3 = "I quickly seek help
             or give up trying" , . = missing

Q33.   spr33unsuccess = For me, making unsuccessful attempts when solving a mathematics problem is
                     Values: 0, 1, 2, 3 (rating scale): 0 = "a natural part of solving the problem", 3 = "an indication of my
             weakness in mathematics" , . = missing

Q34.   spr34success = My success in mathematics PRIMARILY relies on my ability to
                     Values: 0, 1, 2, 3 (rating scale): 0 = "solve specific kinds of problems", 3 = "make connections and
             form logical arguments" , . = missing

Q35.   spr35measure = My score on my mathematics exam is a measure of how well
                     Values: 0, 1, 2, 3 (rating scale): 0 = "I understand the covered material", 3 = "I can do things the way
             the teacher wants" , . = missing

Q36.   spr36choice = If I had a choice
Values: 0, 1, 2, 3 (rating scale): 0 = "I would never take another mathematics course", 3 = "I would continue to take mathematics" , . = missing

Q37.   spr37study = When studying Calculus I in a textbook or in course materials, I tend to
Values: 0, 1, 2, 3 (rating scale): 0 = "memorize it the way it is presented", 3 = "make sense of the material, so that I understand it" , . = missing

Q38.   spr38calc = When solving mathematics problems, graphing calculators or computers help me to
Values: 0, 1, 2, 3 (rating scale): 0 = "understand underlying mathematics ideas", 3 = "find answers to problems" , . = missing

Q39.   spr39instruct = The primary role of a mathematics instructor is to
Values: 0, 1, 2, 3 (rating scale): 0 = "work problems so students know how to do them", 3 = "help students learn to reason through problems on their own" , . = missing

Note: Repeated questions above. These questions (Q31-Q39) were repeated on the end of semester survey (Q7-Q15: sqr31intend-sqr39instruct).

Q40.   sp40relevant = Mathematics instructors should show students how mathematics is relevant
Values: 0, 1, 2, 3, 4, 5 (rating scale): 0 = strongly disagree, 1 = disagree, 2 = mildly disagree, 3 = mildly agree, 4 = agree, 5 = strongly agree, . = missing

Q41.   sp41weak = If I am unable to solve a problem within a few minutes, it is an indication of my weakness in mathematics
sp41exact = Mathematics is about getting exact answers to specific problems
sp41satisfy = The process of solving a problem that involves mathematical reasoning is a satisfying experience
Values: 0, 1, 2, 3, 4, 5 (rating scale): 0 = strongly disagree, 1 = disagree, 2 = slightly disagree, 3 = slightly agree, 4 = agree, 5 = strongly agree, . = missing

Q42.   Please indicate whether each of the following was born in the U.S.
sp42usbornyou = You
sp42usbornfath = Male parent or guardian
sp42usbornmoth = Female parent or guardian
Values: 1 = yes, 0 = no, . = missing

Q43.   sp43fatheduc = What was the highest level of education for your male parent or guardian?
Values: 1 = Did not finish high school, 2 = High school, 3 = Some college, 4 = Four years of college, 5 = Graduate school, . = missing

Q44.   sp44motheduc = What was the highest level of education for your female parent or guardian?
Values: 1 = Did not finish high school, 2 = High school, 3 = Some college, 4 = Four years of college, 5 = Graduate school, . = missing

Q45.   sp45zip = Home zip code when graduating from high school

Note: 00000 = high school outside of U.S.

Q46.   sp46birthdate = Birth date, changed to year only

Q47.   Do the following people see you as a person who is good at mathematics?
sp47mpersonyou = Yourself
sp47mpersonparent = Parents/Relatives
sp47mpersonteach = High school mathematics teacher
sp47mpersonfriend = Friends
        Values: 0, 1, 2, 3, 4, 5 (rating scale): 0 = Not at all, 5 = Very much, . = missing

Q48.   sp48gender = Gender
        Values: 0 = female, 1 = male, . = missing

Q49.   What is your race (Mark all that apply)
sp49white = White
sp49black = Black
sp49asian = Asian
sp49pi = Pacific Islander
sp49amin = American Indian or Alaska Native
        Values: 0 = not selected, 1 = yes, . = no category of Q49 selected
sp49oth = other
        Values: write-in

Q50.   sp50hispanic = Are you of Hispanic origin?
        Values: 1 = yes, 0 = no, . = missing

Q51.   sp51english = Was English the primary spoken language in your household?
        Values: 1 = yes, 0 = no, . = missing

Q52.   sp52yearcoll = What year are you in college?
        Values: 1 = Freshman, 2 = Sophomore, 3 = Junior, 4 = Senior, 5 = Graduate Student, 6 = Other,
. = missing

Q53.   sp53enrtype = What is your current type of college enrollment?
        Values: 1 = Full-time, 0 = Part-time, . = missing

Q54.   sp54homesup = To what degree was your home environment supportive of your studying math?
        Values: 0, 1, 2, 3 (rating scale): 0 = Not at all, 1 = Somewhat, 2 = Strongly, 3 = Very Strongly,
. = missing

Q55.   Who encouraged you to take mathematics classes? (*Mark all that apply*)
sp55encno = No one
sp55encmoth = Mother/female guardian
sp55encfath = Father/male guardian
sp55encsib = Siblings
sp55encrel = Other relative
sp55enccouns = School counselor
sp55encmatht = Math teacher
sp55encotht = Other teacher
sp55enccoach = Coach
        Values: 0 = not selected, 1 = yes, . = none selected

Q56.   sp56hscountry = Where did you attend high school?
        Values: 1 = American school in the United States, 2 = American school abroad, 0 = Other, . = missing
sp56hsforeign = Specify other
        Values: Write-in

Q57. sp57work = Approximately how many hours per week do you expect to work at a job this semester/term?
Values: 1 = 0, 2 = 1-5, 3 = 6-10, 4 = 11-15, 5 = 16-20, 6 = 21-30, 7 = More than 30, . = missing

sp57workl = Approximately how many hours per week do you expect to work at a job this semester/term?
Linearized values (in hours): 0, 3, 8, 13, 18, 25.5, 35, . = missing

Q58. sp58extra = Approximately how many hours per week do you expect to participate in organized extracurricular activities such as sports, college paper, or clubs this semester/term?
Values: 1 = 0, 2 = 1-5, 3 = 6-10, 4 = 11-15, 5 = 16-20, 6 = 21-30, 7 = More than 30, . = missing

sp58extral = Approximately how many hours per week do you expect to participate in organized extracurricular activities such as sports, college paper, or clubs this semester/term?

Linearized values (in hours): 0, 3, 8, 13, 18, 25.5, 35, . = missing

Q59. sp59prep = Approximately how many hours per week do you expect to spend preparing for your classes this semester/term (studying, reading, writing, doing homework or lab work, analyzing data, rehearsing, or other academic activities)?
Values: 1 = 0, 2 = 1-5, 3 = 6-10, 4 = 11-15, 5 = 16-20, 6 = 21-30, 7 = More than 30, . = missing

sp59prepl = Approximately how many hours per week do you expect to spend preparing for your classes this semester/term (studying, reading, writing, doing homework or lab work, analyzing data, rehearsing, or other academic activities)?
Linearized values (in hours): 0, 3, 8, 13, 18, 25.5, 35, . = missing

Q60. sp60career = Which of the following BEST describes your current career goal?
Values: 1 = Medical professional (e.g., doctor, dentist, vet.), 2 = Other health professional (e.g., nurse, medical technician), 3 = Life scientist (e.g., biologist, medical researcher), 4 = Earth/Environmental scientist (e.g., geologist, meteorologist), 5 = Physical Scientist (e.g., chemist, physicist, astronomer), 6 = Engineer, 7 = Computer Scientist, IT, 8 = Mathematician, 9 = Science/Math teacher, 10 = Other teacher, 11 = Social Scientist (e.g., psychologist, sociologist), 12 = Business administration, 13 = Lawyer, 14 = English/Language Arts specialist, 15 = Other non-science related career, 16 = Undecided

Q61. sp61pay = I am anticipating difficulty paying for college
sp61prevcalc = In order to succeed in calculus at a college or university, I must have taken it before
Values: 0, 1, 2, 3, 4, 5 (rating scale): 0 = strongly disagree, 1 = disagree, 2 = slightly disagree, 3 = slightly agree, 4 = agree, 5 = strongly agree, . = missing

Student Post-Survey (End of Term/Semester)

Q1. sqr25grade = What grade do you expect (or did you receive) in this calculus course?
Values: "A" = 4, "B" = 3, "C" = 2, "D" = 1, "F" = 0, missing data = .

Note: Repeated question. This question was repeated from beginning of semester survey (Q25: spr25grade).

Q2. sqr28c2req = Is Calculus II required for your intended major?
Values: 1 = yes, 0 = no, 9 = I'm not sure, . = missing

Note: Repeated question. This question was repeated from beginning of semester survey (Q28: spr28c2req).

Q3. sqr26calc2 = Do you intend to take Calculus II?
Values: 1 = yes, 0 = no, 9 = I'm not sure, . = missing

Note: Repeated question. This question was repeated from beginning of semester survey (Q26: spr26calc2).

Q4.   If you are not intending to take Calculus II, check all reasons that apply.

sq4never = I never intended to take Calculus II

sq4change = I changed my major and now do not need to take Calculus II

sq4exper = My experience in Calculus I made me decide not to take Calculus II

sq4other = I have too many other courses I need to complete

sq4effort = To do well in Calculus II, I would need to spend more time and effort than I can afford

sq4grade = My grade in Calculus I was not good enough for me to continue to Calculus II

sq4understand = I do not believe I understand the ideas of Calculus I well enough to take Calculus II

Values: 0 = not selected, 1 = yes. If the answer to sqr26calc2 is "yes" then all are set to missing. If the answer to sqr26calc2 is "no" or "I'm not sure" and nothing is selected, then all are set to missing

Q5.   sq5initialc2 = When you started this class, did you intend to take Calculus II?

Values: 1 = yes, 0 = no, 9 = I wasn't sure, . = missing

Q6.   sq6interest = This course has increased my interest in taking more mathematics

sq6comput = I am good at computing derivatives and integrals

sq6ideas = I am able to use ideas of calculus (e.g., differentiation, integration) to solve word problems that I have not seen before

sq6prepare = My previous math courses prepared me to succeed in this course

sq6exact = Mathematics is about getting exact answers to specific problems

Values: 0, 1, 2, 3, 4, 5 (rating scale): 0 = strongly disagree, 1 = disagree, 2 = slightly disagree, 3 = slightly agree, 4 = agree, 5 = strongly agree, . = missing

Note: Repeated questions. The following questions were repeated from beginning of semester survey (Q29: spr29confident, spr29enjoy).

sqr29confident = I am confident in my mathematics abilities

sqr29enjoy = I enjoy doing mathematics

Values: 0, 1, 2, 3, 4, 5 (rating scale), 0 = strongly disagree, 1 = disagree, 2 = slightly disagree, 3 = slightly agree, 4 = agree, 5 = strongly agree, . = missing

Note: The following Q7 through Q15 are a block of repeated questions.

Q7.   sqr31intend = How certain are you in what you intend to do after college?

Values: 0, 1, 2, 3 (rating scale): 0 = "Not at all certain", 3 = "Very certain" , . = missing

Q8.   sqr32diffic = When experiencing a difficulty in my math class

Values: 0, 1, 2, 3 (rating scale): 0 = "I try hard to figure it out on my own", 3 = "I quickly seek help or give up trying" , . = missing

Q9.   sqr33unsuccess = For me, making unsuccessful attempts when solving a mathematics problem is

Values: 0, 1, 2, 3 (rating scale): 0 = "a natural part of solving the problem", 3 = "an indication of my weakness in mathematics" , . = missing

Q10.   sqr34success = My success in mathematics PRIMARILY relies on my ability to

Values: 0, 1, 2, 3 (rating scale): 0 = "solve specific kinds of problems", 3 = "make connections and form logical arguments" , . = missing

Q11.   sqr35measure = My score on my mathematics exam is a measure of how well

Values: 0, 1, 2, 3 (rating scale): 0 = "I understand the covered material", 3 = "I can do things the way the teacher wants" , . = missing

Q12.   sqr36choice = If I had a choice

        Values: 0, 1, 2, 3 (rating scale): 0 = "I would never take another mathematics course", 3 = "I would continue to take mathematics" , . = missing

Q13.   sqr37study = When studying Calculus I in a text book or in course materials, I tend to

        Values: 0, 1, 2, 3 (rating scale): 0 = "memorize it the way it is presented", 3 = "make sense of the material, so that I understand it" , . = missing

Q14.   sqr38calc = When solving mathematics problems, graphing calculators or computers help me to

        Values: 0, 1, 2, 3 (rating scale): 0 = "understand underlying mathematics ideas", 3 = "find answers to problems" , . = missing

Q15.   sqr39instruct = The primary role of a mathematics instructor is to

        Values: 0, 1, 2, 3 (rating scale): 0 = "work problems so students know how to do them", 3 = "help students learn to reason through problems on their own" , . = missing

Note: Repeated questions above. These questions (Q7-Q15) were repeated from beginning of semester survey (Q31-Q39: spr31intend-spr39instruct).

Q16.   sq16question = When my calculus instructor asked a question addressed to the whole class, s/he

        Values: 0, 1, 2, 3 (rating scale): 0 = "waited for a student to answer", 3 = "answered to question if no one responded quickly" , . = missing

Q17.   sq17problem = When I asked a question about a problem I was having difficulty solving, my instructor

        Values: 0, 1, 2, 3 (rating scale): 0 = "solved the problem for me", 3 = "helped me figure out how to solve the problem" , . = missing

Q18.   My calculus instructor

sq18ask = asked questions to determine if I understood what was being discussed

sq18listen = listened carefully to my questions and comments

sq18discuss = discussed applications of calculus

sq18time = allowed time for me to understand difficult ideas

sq18solve = helped me become a better problem solver

sq18explain = provided explanations that were understandable

sq18avail = was available to make appointments outside of office hours, if needed

sq18discourage = discouraged me from wanting to continue taking calculus

        Values: 0, 1, 2, 3, 4, 5 (rating scale), 0 = strongly disagree, 1 = disagree, 2 = slightly disagree, 3 = slightly agree, 4 = agree, 5 = strongly agree, . = missing

Q19.   During class time, how frequently did your instructor

sqr19problems = show how to work specific problems

sqr19collab = have students work with one another

sqr19discuss = hold whole-class discussion

sqr19present = have students give presentations

sqr19indiv = have students work individually on problems or tasks

sqr19lecture = lecture

sqr19ask = ask questions

sqr19explain = ask students to explain their thinking

        Values: 0, 1, 2, 3, 4, 5 (rating scale): 0 = Not at all, 5 = Very often, . = missing

Note: Parallel question. This question is parallel to the instructor end of semester survey (Q24: iqr19problems-iqr19explain).

Q20. How frequently did your instructor

sqr20extra = prepare extra material to help students understand calculus concepts or procedures

sqr20homework = require you to explain your thinking on your homework

sqr20exam = require you to explain your thinking on exams

sqr20read = assign sections in your textbook for you to read before coming to class

      Values: 0, 1, 2, 3, 4, 5 (rating scale): 0 = Not at all, 5 = Very often, . = missing

Note: Parallel question. This question is parallel to the instructor end of semester survey (Q25: iqr20extra-iqr20read).

Q21. My calculus instructor

sq21nervous = made students feel nervous during class

sq21encourage = encouraged students to enroll in Calculus II

sq21capable = acted as if I was capable of understanding the key ideas of calculus

sq21comfort = made me feel comfortable in asking questions during class

sq21office = encouraged students to seek help during office hours

sq21mult = presented more than one method for solving problems

sq21english = did not speak English very well

sq21interest = made class interesting

      Values: 0, 1, 2, 3, 4, 5 (rating scale), 0 = strongly disagree, 1 = disagree, 2 = slightly disagree, 3 = slightly agree, 4 = agree, 5 = strongly agree, . = missing

Q22. Indicate how often the following occurred

sq22homework = My instructor assigned homework

sqr22collect = Homework was collected (either hard copy or online)

sqr22quiz = My instructor gave a short quiz

sq22tech = My instructor used technology

      Values: 0, 1, 2, 3, 4 (rating scale), 0 = never, 1 = some class sessions, 2 = about half the class sessions, 3 = most class sessions, 4 = every class session, . = missing

Note: Parallel questions. sqr22collect and sqr22quiz were also on the instructor end of semester survey.

Q23. Which of the following computing technologies did you use during your calculus class? (*Check all that apply.*)

sq23none = None

sq23graph = Graphing calculator

sq23comp = Computers

sq23click = Clickers or some other electronic response system

      Values: 0 = not selected, 1 = yes, . = none selected

Q24. How frequently were the following technologies used during class?

sqr24demgraph = My instructor demonstrated mathematics with a graphing calculator

sqr24graph = I used a graphing calculator

sqr24demcomp = My instructor demonstrated mathematics with a computer algebra system (e.g., Maple, Mathematica, MATLAB)

sqr24comp = I used a computer algebra system (e.g., Maple, Mathematica, MATLAB)

      Values: 0, 1, 2, 3, 4 (rating scale), 0 = never, 1 = some class sessions, 2 = about half the class sessions, 3 = most class sessions, 4 = every class session, . = missing

Note: Parallel question. Q24 was also on the instructor end of semester survey (Q22).

Q25.   How did you use technology during your class? (Check only those that apply)
sq25prob = To find answers to problems
sq25underst = To understand underlying mathematical ideas
sq25check = To check written answers after I worked them out by hand
      Values: 0 = not selected, 1 = yes

Q26.   How did your instructor use technology during your class? (Check only those that apply)
sq26idea = To illustrate ideas
sq26prob = To find answers to problems
sq26check = To check answers after we worked them out by hand
sq26anim = To illustrate motion/dynamic animations
      Values: 0 = not selected, 1 = yes

Q27.   sq27deriv = Does your calculator find the symbolic derivative of a function?
      Values: 1 = yes, 0 = no, 9 = N/A (I don't use a calculator), . = missing

Q28.   sq28graphexam = Were you allowed to use a graphing calculator during your exams?
      Values: 1 = yes, 0 = no, . = missing

Q29.   Assignments completed outside of class time were
sq29online = completed and graded online
sq29returned = graded and returned to me
sq29comment = returned with helpful feedback/comments
sq29group = submitted as a group project
sq29chall = challenging but doable
      Values: 0, 1, 2, 3, 4, 5 (rating scale): 0 = Not at all, 5 = Very often, . = missing

Q30.   The assignments completed *outside of class time* required that I
sqr30word = solve word problems
sqr30diff = solve problems unlike those done in class or in the book
sq30tech = use technology to understand ideas
      Values: 0, 1, 2, 3, 4, 5 (rating scale): 0 = Not at all, 5 = Very often, . = missing

Note: Parallel questions. sqr30word and sqr30diff are somewhat parallel to the instructor end of semester survey Q30.

Q31.   The *exam questions* required that I solve
sqr31word = word problems
sqr31diff = problems unlike those done in class or in the book
      Values: 0, 1, 2, 3, 4, 5 (rating scale): 0 = Not at all, 5 = Very often, . = missing

Note: Parallel questions. Variables are somewhat parallel to the instructor end of semester survey Q31.

Q32.   sq32assess = My calculus exams were a good assessment of what I learned
sq32examfair = My exams were graded fairly
sq32homefair = My homework was graded fairly
      Values: 0, 1, 2, 3, 4, 5 (rating scale), 0 = strongly disagree, 1 = disagree, 2 = slightly disagree,
3 = slightly agree, 4 = agree, 5 = strongly agree, . = missing

Q33. During classsq33contrib = I contributed to class discussions
sq33lost = I was lost and unable to follow the lecture or discussion
sq33asked = I asked questions
sq33copied = I simply copied whatever was written on the board
  Values: 0, 1, 2, 3, 4 (rating scale), 0 = never, 1 = some class sessions, 2 = about half the class sessions, 3 = most class sessions, 4 = every class session, . = missing

Q34. How often did you do the following
sq34text = Read the textbook prior to coming to class
sq34office = Visit your instructor's office hours
sq34online = Use online tutoring.
sq34tutor = Visit a tutor to assist with this course
  Values: 0, 1, 2, 3, 4 (rating scale), 0 = never, 1 = some class sessions, 2 = about half the class sessions, 3 = most class sessions, 4 = every class session, . = missing

Q35. sq35homehelp = The homework for the course helped me learn the material
sq35text = The textbook and/or class materials helped me learn the material
sq35readable = The textbook or reading materials for the course were readable
sq35completed = I completed all my assigned homework
  Values: 0, 1, 2, 3, 4, 5 (rating scale), 0 = strongly disagree, 1 = disagree, 2 = slightly disagree, 3 = slightly agree, 4 = agree, 5 = strongly agree, . = missing

Q36. sq36outside = Did you meet with other students to study or complete homework outside of class?
  Values: 1 = yes, 0 = no, . = missing

Q37. sq37group = Did you belong to a calculus study group organized by your instructor or department?
  Values: 1 = yes, 0 = no, . = missing

Q38. sq38tutor = Does your math department or university provide a walk-in tutor center for mathematics?
  Values: 1 = yes, 0 = no, . = missing

Q39. sq39job = Approximately how many hours per week did you work at a job this semester/term?
  Values: 1 = 0, 2 = 1-5, 3 = 6-10, 4 = 11-15, 5 = 16-20, 6 = 21-30, 7 = More than 30, . = missing

sq39jobl = Approximately how many hours per week did you work at a job this semester/term?
  Linearized values (in hours): 0, 3, 8, 13, 18, 25.5, 35, . = missing

Q40. sq40extra = Approximately how many hours per week did you participate in organized extracurricular activities such as sports, college paper, or clubs?
  Values: 1 = 0, 2 = 1-5, 3 = 6-10, 4 = 11-15, 5 = 16-20, 6 = 21-30, 7 = More than 30, . = missing

sq40extral = Approximately how many hours per week did you participate in organized extracurricular activities such as sports, college paper, or clubs?
  Linearized values (in hours): 0, 3, 8, 13, 18, 25.5, 35, . = missing

Q41. sq41prepareall = Approximately how many hours per week did you spend preparing for all classes (studying, reading, writing, doing homework or lab work, analyzing data, or other academic activities) this semester/term?
  Values: 1 = 0, 2 = 1-5, 3 = 6-10, 4 = 11-15, 5 = 16-20, 6 = 21-30, 7 = More than 30, . = missing

sq41preparealll = Approximately how many hours per week did you spend preparing for all classes (studying, reading, writing, doing homework or lab work, analyzing data, or other academic activities) this semester/term?
> Linearized values (in hours): 0, 3, 8, 13, 18, 25.5, 35, . = missing

Q42. sq42preparecalc = Approximately how many hours per week did you spend preparing for calculus (studying, reading, doing homework or lab work) this semester/term?
> Values: 1 = 0, 2 = 1-5, 3 = 6-10, 4 = 11-15, 5 = 16-20, 6 = 21-30, 7 = More than 30, . = missing

sq42preparecalcl = Approximately how many hours per week did you spend preparing for calculus (studying, reading, doing homework or lab work) this semester/term?
> Linearized values (in hours): 0, 3, 8, 13, 18, 25.5, 35, . = missing

Q43–45 and 47. Removed from maalongdatafile_ANON.csv

Q46. sq46id = Student ID number, . = missing

Q48. sq48grade = Student grade. **Actual grades** provided by departments based on student ID match
> Values: Character variable! Letter grades from "A+" to "F."

sq48gradel = Student grade. **Actual grades** provided by departments based on student ID match
> Linearized values: "A+" = 4.33, "A" = 4, "A-" = 3.67, … , "F" = 0, "AB" = 3.5, etc., missing data = .

Instructor Pre-Survey (Beginning of Term or Semester)

Q1. ip1pos = Your current position is best described as
> Values: 1 = Tenure track faculty (Assistant Professor), 2 = Tenured faculty (Associate or Full Professor), 3 = Other full time faculty, 4 = Part time faculty, 5 = Graduate teaching assistant, 0 = Other, . = missing
> ip1other = Specify Other
> Values: write-in

Q2. ip2office = What best describes your office space?
> Values: 1 = private office, 2 = shared office space with own individual desk, 3 = a desk shared with one other person, 4 = a desk shared with more than one other person, 5 = no office space, . = missing

Q3. ip3calcexp = Indicate the number times you have taught Calculus I in the past five years, including current teaching assignment (*count more than one section in any given term as only one time*)
> Values: 1 = 1, 2 = 2-4, 3 = 5-10, 4 = more than 10, . = missing

ip3calcexpl = Indicate the number times you have taught Calculus I in the past five years, including current teaching assignment (count more than one section in any given term as only one time).
> Linearized values: 1, 3, 7.5, 12, . = missing

Q4. ip4style = How would you describe your teaching of Calculus I?
> Values: 3 = Very innovative, 2 = Somewhat innovative, 1 = Somewhat traditional, 0 = Very traditional, . = missing

Q5. ip5support = From your point of view, how supportive is your department for implementing innovative approaches to teaching Calculus I?
> Values: 0, 1, 2, 3 (rating scale), 0 = not supportive, 1 = somewhat supportive, 2 = moderately supportive, 3 = very supportive, . = missing

Q6.   ip6connect = From your point of view, how successful is your department in creating an environment in which Calculus I students feel they are personally and academically connected to other students studying Calculus I?

   Values: 0, 1, 2, 3, 4 (rating scale), 0 = no effort made, 1 = not successful, 2 = somewhat successful, 3 = moderately successful, 4 = very successful, . = missing

Q7.   ip7textchoice = The Calculus I textbook you use is

   Values: 1 = A common textbook selected by the department, 2 = A textbook I chose from an approved list, 3 = A textbook of my own choosing, 0 = Other, . = missing
   ip7other: Specify Other
   Values: write-in

Q8.   ip8text = What textbook is required for your Calculus I course? Select from the list below or specify a different text if your book is not on the list. Note the distinction between "Early Transcendentals" and standard editions. No distinction is made between single-variable and combined single- and multivariable volumes.

   Values: 1 = Anton/Bivens/Davis—*Calculus*, 2 = Anton/Bivens/Davis—*Calculus: Early Transcendentals*, 3 = Blank/Krantz—*Calculus*, 4 = Edwards/Penney—*Calculus: Early Transcendentals*, 5 = Hass/Weir/Thomas—*University Calculus*, 6 = Hass/Weir/Thomas—*University Calculus: Alternate Edition*, 7 = Hass/Weir/Thomas—*University Calculus: Elements with Early Transcendentals*, 8 = Hughes Hallett et al.—*Calculus*, 9 = Larson/Edwards—*Calculus*, 10 = Larson/Hostetler/Edwards—*Calculus: Early Transcendentals*, 11 = Larson/Hostetler/Edwards—*Essential Calculus*, 12 = Rogawski—*Calculus*, 13 = Rogawski—*Calculus: Early Transcendentals*, 14 = Salas/Hille/Etgen—*Calculus*, 15 = Smith/Minton—*Calculus*, 16 = Smith/Minton—*Calculus: Concepts and Connections*, 17 = Smith/Minton—*Calculus: Early Transcendentals*, 18 = Stewart—*Calculus*, 19 = Stewart—*Calculus: Concepts and Contexts*, 20 = Stewart—*Calculus: Early Transcendentals*, 21 = Stewart—*Essential Calculus*, 22 = Stewart—*Essential Calculus: Early Transcendentals*, 23 = Swokowski—*Calculus*, 24 = Thomas/Weir/Hass/Giordano—*Thomas' Calculus*, 25 = Thomas/Weir/Hass/Giordano—*Thomas' Calculus: Early Transcendentals*, 26 = Varberg/Purcell/Rigdon—*Calculus*, 27 = Varberg/Purcell/Rigdon—*Calculus: Early Transcendentals*, 0 = Other, . = missing
   ip8other: Specify Other
   Values: write-in

Q9.   ip9trad = How long has your current text, including earlier editions, been used on your campus?
   Values: 1 = 4 years or less, 2 = 5-10 years, 3 = more than 10 years, 9 = don't know , . = missing

   ip9tradl = How long has your current text, including earlier editions, been used on your campus?
   Linearized values (in years): 2, 7.5, 12, . = missing ("don't know" was set to missing)

Q10.   ip10instruct = What will be the primary means of instructing students?
   Values: 1 = face-to-face in a classroom, 2 = online via distance learning, 3 = hybrid between face-to-face and online distance learning, . = missing

Q11.   ip11tech = What technology do you permit (but not require) students to use on exams?
   Values: 1 = Technology not permitted, 2 = Graphing calculators that do not perform symbolic algebra, 3 = Graphing calculators that perform symbolic algebra, 4 = Computer algebra system (Maple, Mathematica, MATLAB, etc), 0 = Other, . = missing
   ip11other = Specify Other
   Values: write-in

Q12.   ip12reqtech = What technology do you require students to use on exams?

        Values: 1 = Technology not permitted, 2 = Graphing calculators that do not perform symbolic algebra, 3 = Graphing calculators that perform symbolic algebra, 4 = Computer algebra system (Maple, Mathematica, MATLAB, etc), 0 = Other, . = missing

    ip12other = Specify Other

        Values: write-in

Q13.   ipr13prep = Approximately what percentage of students currently enrolled in your Calculus I course do you expect are academically prepared for the course?

        VALUES: 1 = more than 80%, 2 = between 60 and 80%, 3 = between 40 and 60%, 4 = between 20 and 40%, 5 = less than 20%, . = missing

    ipr13prepl = Approximately what percentage of students currently enrolled in your Calculus I course do you expect are academically prepared for the course?

        Linearized values (in percent): 10, 30, 50, 70, 90, . = missing

Note: Repeated question. This variable is repeated as Q4 on the instructor end of term survey.

Q14.   Estimate the percentage of students currently enrolled in your Calculus I course that will

    ip14wd = withdraw

    ip14df = receive a grade of D or F

    ip14c = receive a grade of C or better

        Values: Percentages

Note: This question is SIMILAR to Q30, 32, 34, 36, 38 on the instructor end of term survey.

Q15.   ip15inst = From your perspective, how strongly does your institution encourage and support the scholarship of teaching and learning (defined as systematic reflection on teaching and learning)?

        Values: 0, 1, 2, 3 (rating scale), 0 = not at all, 1 = somewhat, 2 = moderate, 3 = very strong, . = missing

Q16.   ip16dept = From your perspective, how strongly does your department encourage and support the scholarship of teaching and learning?

        Values: 0, 1, 2, 3 (rating scale), 0 = not at all, 1 = somewhat, 2 = moderate, 3 = very strong, . = missing

Q17.   ip17coll = From your perspective, how valued by your colleagues is the scholarship of teaching?

        Values: 0, 1, 2, 3 (rating scale), 0 = not valued, 1 = somewhat valued, 2 = moderately valued, 3 = very valued, . = missing

Q18.   How strong is your interest in

    ip18calc = Teaching Calculus I

    ip18adv = Teaching more advanced math classes

    ip18aware = Participating in activities that raise your awareness of how students learn key ideas in calculus

    ip18teach = Improving your own teaching

    ip18recruit = Actively recruiting math majors

        Values: 0, 1, 2, 3 (rating scale), 0 = not at all, 1 = mildly strong, 2 = moderately strong, 3 = very strong, . = missing

Note: The following Q19 through Q23 are a block of versions of questions from both the student pre- and post-surveys. (The variable numbers refer to the question numbers in the student pre-survey.)

Q19.   ipr37study = When studying Calculus I in a textbook or in course materials, students tend to
Values: 0, 1, 2, 3, 4, 5 (rating scale): 0 = "Memorize it the way it is presented", 5 = "Make sense of the material, so that I understand it" , . = missing

Q20.   ipr33unsuccess = From your perspective, when students make unsuccessful attempts when solving a Calculus I problem, it is
Values: 0, 1, 2, 3, 4, 5 (rating scale): 0 = "a natural part of solving the problem", 5 = "an indication of their weakness in mathematics" , . = missing

Q21.   ipr34success = From your perspective, student's success in mathematics PRIMARILY relies on their ability to
Values: 0, 1, 2, 3, 4, 5 (rating scale): 0 = "solve specific kinds of problems", 5 = "make connections and form logical arguments" , . = missing

Q22.   ipr38calc = From your perspective, in solving Calculus I problems, graphing calculators or computers help students to
Values: 0, 1, 2, 3, 4, 5 (rating scale): 0 = "understand underlying mathematics ideas", 5 = "find answers to problems" , . = missing

Q23.   ipr39instruct = My primary role of a mathematics instructor is to
Values: 0, 1, 2, 3, 4, 5 (rating scale): 0 = "work problems so students know how to do them", 5 = "help students learn to reason through problems on their own" , . = missing

Note: Q19 through Q23 are versions of questions from both the student pre- and post-surveys, but with a different scale (6-point instead of 4-point).

Q24.   ip24relev = In my teaching of Calculus I, I intend to show students how mathematics is relevant.
Values: 0, 1, 2, 3, 4, 5 (rating scale): 0 = strongly disagree, 1 = disagree, 2 = mildly disagree, 3 = mildly agree, 4 = agree, 5 = strongly agree, . = missing

Q25.   When I prepare to teach a challenging idea in Calculus I,
ip25sub = I break the idea down into subskills
ip25applic = I look for application problems to motivate the idea
ip25coll = I discuss with colleagues the difficulties that students have with the idea
ip25preass = I use pre-assessments in the current class in order to inform how I will teach the idea
ip25tech = I look for ways to use technology to illustrate the idea
ip25text = I follow how the textbook develops the idea
ip25alt = I look to alternate sources for different ways to teach the idea
Values: 0, 1, 2, 3 (rating scale): 0 = never, 1 = occasionally, 2 = frequently, 3 = always, . = missing

Q26.   ip26ta = Does your Calculus I course have recitation sections taught by teaching assistants (TAs)?
Values: 1 = yes, 0 = no, . = missing

Q27.   ip27gender = Gender
Values: 0 = female, 1 = male, . = missing

Q28.   ip28age = Age (in fall 2010)
Values: in years

Q29.   ip29race = Race
Values: 1 = American Indian or Alaskan Native, 2 = Asian, 3 = Black or African American, 4 = Native Hawaiian or Pacific Islander, 5 = White/Caucasian, 0 = Other, . = missing
ip29other = Specify Other
Values: write-in

Q30. ip30eth = Ethnicity
>   Values: 1 = Hispanic or Latino, 0 = Not Hispanic or Latino, . = missing

Q31. ip31degree = Highest degree attained
>   Values: 1 = PhD, 2 = EdD, 3 = Master's, 4 = Bachelor's, . = missing

Q32. ip32degreeyear = Year highest degree obtained
>   Values: years, . = missing

Q33. ip33countryunder = Country in which undergraduate degree was obtained
>   Values: 1 = United States of America, 2 = Andorra, 3 = United Arab Emirates, 4 = Afghanistan, 5 = Antigua & Barbuda, 6 = Anguilla, 7 = Albania, 8 = Armenia, 9 = Netherlands Antilles, 10 = Angola, 11 = Antarctica, 12 = Argentina, 13 = American Samoa, 14 = Austria, 15 = Australia, 16 = Aruba, 17 = Azerbaijan, 18 = Bosnia and Herzegovina, 19 = Barbados, 20 = Bangladesh, 21 = Belgium, 22 = Burkina Faso, 23 = Bulgaria, 24 = Bahrain, 25 = Burundi, 26 = Benin, 27 = Bermuda, 28 = Brunei Darussalam, 29 = Bolivia, 30 = Brazil, 31 = Bahamas, 32 = Bhutan, 33 = Burma (no longer exists), 34 = Bouvet Island, 35 = Botswana, 36 = Belarus, 37 = Belize, 38 = Canada, 39 = Cocos (Keeling) Islands, 40 = Central African Republic, 41 = Congo, 42 = Switzerland, 43 = Côte D'ivoire (Ivory Coast), 44 = Cook Islands, 45 = Chile, 46 = Cameroon, 47 = China, 48 = Colombia, 49 = Costa Rica, 50 = Czechoslovakia (no longer exists), 51 = Cuba, 52 = Cape Verde, 53 = Christmas Island, 54 = Cyprus, 55 = Czech Republic, 56 = German Democratic Republic (no longer exists), 57 = Germany, 58 = Djibouti, 59 = Denmark, 60 = Dominica, 61 = Dominican Republic, 62 = Algeria, 63 = Ecuador, 64 = Estonia, 65 = Egypt, 66 = Western Sahara, 67 = Eritrea, 68 = Spain, 69 = Ethiopia, 70 = Finland, 71 = Fiji, 72 = Falkland Islands (Malvinas), 73 = Micronesia, 74 = Faroe Islands, 75 = France, 76 = France, Metropolitan, 77 = Gabon, 78 = United Kingdom (Great Britain), 79 = Grenada, 80 = Georgia, 81 = French Guiana, 82 = Ghana, 83 = Gibraltar, 84 = Greenland, 85 = Gambia, 86 = Guinea, 87 = Guadeloupe, 88 = Equatorial Guinea, 89 = Greece, 90 = South Georgia and the South Sandwich Islands, 91 = Guatemala, 92 = Guam, 93 = Guinea-Bissau, 94 = Guyana, 95 = Hong Kong, 96 = Heard & McDonald Islands, 97 = Honduras, 98 = Croatia, 99 = Haiti, 100 = Hungary, 101 = Indonesia, 102 = Ireland, 103 = Israel, 104 = India, 105 = British Indian Ocean Territory, 106 = Iraq, 107 = Islamic Republic of Iran, 108 = Iceland, 109 = Italy, 110 = Jamaica, 111 = Jordan, 112 = Japan, 113 = Kenya, 114 = Kyrgyzstan, 115 = Cambodia, 116 = Kiribati, 117 = Comoros, 118 = St. Kitts and Nevis, 119 = Korea, Democratic People's Republic of, 120 = Korea, Republic of, 121 = Kuwait, 122 = Cayman Islands, 123 = Kazakhstan, 124 = Lao People's Democratic Republic, 125 = Lebanon, 126 = Saint Lucia, 127 = Liechtenstein, 128 = Sri Lanka, 129 = Liberia, 130 = Lesotho, 131 = Lithuania, 132 = Luxembourg, 133 = Latvia, 134 = Libyan Arab Jamahiriya, 135 = Morocco, 136 = Monaco, 137 = Moldova, Republic of, 138 = Madagascar, 139 = Marshall Islands, 140 = Mali, 141 = Mongolia, 142 = Myanmar, 143 = Macau, 144 = Northern Mariana Islands, 145 = Martinique, 146 = Mauritania, 147 = Montserrat, 148 = Malta, 149 = Mauritius, 150 = Maldives, 151 = Malawi, 152 = Mexico, 153 = Malaysia, 154 = Mozambique, 155 = Namibia, 156 = New Caledonia, 157 = Niger, 158 = Norfolk Island, 159 = Nigeria, 160 = Nicaragua, 161 = Netherlands, 162 = Norway, 163 = Nepal, 164 = Nauru, 165 = Neutral Zone (no longer exists), 166 = Niue, 167 = New Zealand, 168 = Oman, 169 = Panama, 170 = Peru, 171 = French Polynesia, 172 = Papua New Guinea, 173 = Philippines, 174 = Pakistan, 175 = Poland, 176 = St. Pierre & Miquelon, 177 = Pitcairn, 178 = Puerto Rico, 179 = Portugal, 180 = Palau, 181 = Paraguay, 182 = Qatar, 183 = Réunion, 184 = Romania, 185 = Russian Federation, 186 = Rwanda, 187 = Saudi Arabia, 188 = Solomon Islands, 189 = Seychelles, 190 = Sudan, 191 = Sweden, 192 = Singapore, 193 = St. Helena, 194 = Slovenia, 195 = Svalbard & Jan Mayen Islands, 196 = Slovakia, 197 = Sierra Leone, 198 = San Marino, 199 = Senegal, 200 = Somalia, 201 = Suriname, 202 = Sao Tome & Principe, 203 = Union of Soviet Socialist Republics (no longer exists), 204 = El Salvador, 205 = Syrian Arab Republic, 206 = Swaziland, 207 = Turks & Caicos Islands, 208 = Chad, 209 = French Southern Territories, 210 = Togo, 211 = Thailand, 212 = Tajikistan, 213 = Tokelau, 214 = Turkmenistan, 215 = Tunisia, 216 = Tonga, 217 = East Timor, 218 = Turkey, 219 = Trinidad & Tobago, 220 = Tuvalu, 221 = Taiwan, Province of China, 222 = Tanzania, United Republic of, 223 = Ukraine, 224 = Uganda, 225 = United States Minor Outlying Islands, 226 = Uruguay, 227 = Uzbekistan, 228 = Vatican City State (Holy See), 229 = St. Vincent & the Grenadines, 230 = Venezuela, 231 = British Virgin Islands, 232 = United States Virgin Islands, 233 = Vietnam, 234 = Vanuatu, 235 = Wallis & Futuna Islands, 236 = Samoa, 237 = Democratic Yemen (no longer exists), 238 = Yemen, 239 = Mayotte, 240 = Yugoslavia, 241 = South Africa, 242 = Zambia, 243 = Zaire, 244 = Zimbabwe

Q34. ip34countryhigh = Country in which highest degree was obtained
Values: same as Q33

Q35. ip35field = Highest degree field of study
Values: 1 = Mathematics, 2 = Applied Mathematics, 3 = Statistics, 4 = Mathematics Education, 0 = Other, . = missing
ip35other = Specify Other
Values: write-in

Q36. ip36lastclass = Last day of classes for this fall term
Values: date, . = missing

Instructor Post-Survey (End of Term or Semester)

Q1. iq1number = How many sections of Calculus I did you teach this term? (Note: Multiple sections that met for the same lecture count as one class)
Values: Number

Q2. For each calculus class you taught this term, indicate whether it was an honors section
iq2level1 = Class1
iq2level2 = Class2
iq2level3 = Class3
iq2level4 = Class4
iq2level5 = Class5
Values: 1 = Honors, 0 = Non-Honors, . = missing

Q3. At the end of the term, how many students were enrolled in each calculus class that you taught
iq3enrol1 = Class1
iq3enrol2 = Class2
iq3enrol3 = Class3
iq3enrol4 = Class4
iq3enrol5 = Class5
Values: numbers

Q4. Approximately what percentage of your students were prepared for the course?
iq4prep1 = Class1
iq4prep2 = Class2
iq4prep3 = Class3
iq4prep4 = Class4
iq4prep5 = Class5
Values: 1 = more than 80%, 2 = between 60 and 80%, 3 = between 40 and 60%, 4 = between 20 and 40%, 5 = less than 20%, . = missing

iq4prep1l = Class1 linearized
iq4prep2l = Class2 linearized
iq4prep3l = Class3 linearized
iq4prep4l = Class4 linearized
iq4prep5l = Class5 linearized
Linearized values (in percent): 10, 30, 50, 70, 90, . = missing

Note: The following linearized variable is parallel to Q13 on the instructor beginning of term survey. Calculated as the average of all classes.

iqr13prepl = Approximately what percentage of your students were prepared for the course?
Linearized values: percent, . = missing

Q5.   iq5event = How many times this term did your department or college organize an event (workshop, seminar, meeting, etc.) related to issues of teaching and learning mathematics?
Values: 1 = 0, 2 = once, 3 = twice, 4 = three times, 5 = more than three times 6 = don't know, . = missing

iq5eventl = How many times this term did your department or college organize an event (workshop, seminar, meeting, etc.) related to issues of teaching and learning mathematics?
Linearized values (count): 0, 1, 2, 3, 4, . = missing

Note: "Don't know" was set to missing.

Q6.   iq6attend = How many times this term did you attend an event described in Q5
Values: 1 = 0, 2 = Once, 3 = Twice, 4 = Three times, 5 = More than three times 6 = N/A, . = missing

iq6attendl = How many times this term did you attend an event described in Q5.
Linearized values (count): 0, 1, 2, 3, 4, . = missing

Note: "N/A" was set to missing.

Q7.   iq7office = How many office hours did you hold each week for Calculus I during the current semester?
Values: write-in

Q8.   iq8ta = How many office hours did your TA(s) hold each week for Calculus I during the current semester?
Values: write-in

Q9.   How often did you do the following outside of class
iq9office = Helped students with course content during office hours
iq9nooffice = Helped students with course content outside of office hours
iq9mentor = Mentored students regarding non-course content (e.g., career options, future course)
Values: 0, 1, 2, 3 (rating scale), 0 = never, 1 = infrequently, 2 = frequently, 3 = very frequently, . = missing

Q10.   iq10exam = How many exams, not including the final, did you give?
Values: count, . = missing

Q11.   Indicate how often the following occurred
iqr22quiz = You gave a short quiz
iqr22collect = Students turned in assignments (either hard copy or online)
Values: 0, 1, 2, 3, 4 (rating scale), 0 = never, 1 = some class sessions, 2 = about half the class sessions, 3 = most class sessions, 4 = every class session, . = missing

Note: Parallel question. This question (Q11) is parallel to the student end of semester survey (Q22).

Q12.   iq12format = What was the format of the majority of assignments?
Values: 1 = multiple choice items, 2 = free response questions, 3 = more or less equal amounts of both, 4 = N/A, . = missing

Q13. How were homework assignments submitted? Check all that apply.
iq13paper = on paper, in class
iq13email = electronically via email or fax
iq13online = via an on-line homework system (e.g., WeBWorK, MAPLE T.A.)
iq13na = N/A
   Values: 0 = not selected, 1 = yes, . = none selected

Q14. How were homework assignments graded? Check all that apply.
iq14gradeonline = via an on-line homework system (e.g., WeBWorK, Maple TA)
iq14gradeself = by hand by myself
iq14grader = by hand by a grader
iq14post = via an on-line homework system or distributed to students to check their own work
iq14na = N/A
   Values: 0 = not selected, 1 = yes, . = none selected

Q15. Approximately what percent of each homework assignment (does not need to add up to 100%).
iq15hand = was graded by hand
iq15online = was graded via an on-line homework system
iq15post = was not graded but solutions were posted
iq15nograde = was not graded and solutions were not posted
   Values: percent

Q16. iq16project = How many projects (group or individual) did you assign this term?
   Values: 1 = 0, 2 = 1, 3 = 2, 4 = more than 2 , . = missing

iq16projectl = How many projects (group or individual) did you assign this term?
   Linearized values (count): 0, 1, 2, 3, . = missing

Q17. iq17projectpercent = What percentage of your students' grade was based on projects?
   Values: percentage

Q18. iq18final = In my Calculus I course
   Values: 1 = "a common final was administered to all sections", 2 = "different sections used different final exam questions", 3 = "a combination of both" , . = missing

Q19. iq19finalgrade = How was your final exam for Calculus I graded?
   Values: 1 = "By myself without a rubric", 2 = "By myself using my own rubric", 3 = "By myself using a common rubric", 4 = "By myself with one or more TAs/graders", 5 = "By one or more TAs/graders", 6 = "By a group of instructors using a common rubric", 7 = "Multiple Choice Scantron", 0 = "Other"
iq19other = Specify Other
   Values: write-in

Q20. What other course materials did you make available for students? Check all that apply.
iq20none = none
iq20classnotes = student prepared class notes
iq20lectnotes = instructor prepared lecture notes
iq20supp = supplemental curriculum materials including in-class worksheets and online material
iq20comp = computer animations or interactive software
iq20online = online lectures
   Values: 0 = not selected, 1 = yes, . = none selected (and iq20other empty)
iq20other = other
   Values= write-in

Q21. What technology did you require students to use outside of class? Check all that apply.

iq21prog = Mathematica, Maple, Matlab, etc.

iq21graph = Graphing calculators

iq21online = Online course websites

iq21java = Java applets or other animations

    Values: 0 = not selected, 1 = yes

iq21other = other

    Values= write-in

Q22. How frequently were the following technologies used during class?

iqr24demgraph = Instructor demonstration with a graphing calculator

iqr24graph = Student use of graphing calculators

iqr24demcomp = Instructor demonstration with with computer algebra system (e.g., Maple, Mathematica, MATLAB)

iqr24comp = Student use of a computer algebra system (e.g., Maple, Mathematica, MATLAB)

    Values: 0, 1, 2, 3, 4 (rating scale), 0 = never, 1 = some class sessions, 2 = about half the class sessions, 3 = most class sessions, 4 = every class session, . = missing

Note: Parallel question. Q22 was repeated from the student end of semester survey (Q24).

Q23. When teaching my Calculus I class, I

iq23time = had enough time during class to help students understand difficult ideas

iq23pressure = felt pressured to go through material quickly to cover all the required topics

    Values: 0, 1, 2, 3, 4, 5 (rating scale): 0 = Not at all, 5 = Very often, . = missing

Q24. During class time, how frequently did you

iqr19problems = show how to work specific problems

iqr19collab = have students work with one another

iqr19discuss = hold whole-class discussion

iqr19present = have students give presentations

iqr19indiv = have students work individually on problems or tasks

iqr19lecture = lecture

iqr19ask = ask questions

iqr19explain = ask students to explain their thinking

    Values: 0, 1, 2, 3, 4, 5 (rating scale): 0 = Not at all, 5 = Very often, . = missing

Note: Parallel question. This question is parallel to the student end of semester survey (Q19: sqr19problems-sqr19explain).

Q25. How frequently did you

iqr20extra = prepare extra material to help students understand calculus concepts or procedures

iqr20homework = require students to explain your thinking on assignments

iqr20exam = require students to explain their thinking on exams

iqr20read = assign sections in the textbook for students to read before coming to class

    Values: 0, 1, 2, 3, 4, 5 (rating scale): 0 = Not at all, 5 = Very often, . = missing

Note: Parallel question. This question is parallel to the student end of semester survey (Q20: sqr20extra-sqr20read).

Q26. On a typical assignment, approximately what percentage of the problems focused on (does not need to add up to 100%)

iq26skill = skills and methods for carrying out computations (e.g., methods of determining derivatives and antiderivatives)

iq26graph = graphical interpretation of central ideas

iqr30word = solving routine word problems

iqr30diff = solving complex or unfamiliar word problems

iq26proof = proofs or justifications

   Values: percentages, . = missing

Note: Parallel question. iqr30word and iqr30diff in this question are somewhat parallel to the student end of semester survey (Q30).

Q27. On a typical exam, approximately what percentage of the points focused on (does not need to add up to 100%)

iq27skill = skills and methods for carrying out computations (e.g., methods of determining derivatives and antiderivatives)

iq27graph = graphical interpretation of central ideas

iqr31word = solving standard word problems

iqr31diff = solving complex or unfamiliar word problems

iq27proof = proofs or justifications

   Values: percentages, . = missing

Note: Parallel question. iqr31word and iqr31diff in this question are somewhat parallel to the student end of semester survey (Q31).

Q28. iq28attend = In a typical week, what percentage of students attended each class session?

   Values: percentages, . = missing

Q29. iq29capable = All students in beginning calculus are capable of understanding the ideas of calculus

iq29lect = Calculus students learn best from lectures provided they are clear and well-organized

iq29resp = It is the student's responsibility to address his or her deficiencies with prerequisites

iq29fluent = Understanding ideas in calculus typically comes after achieving procedural fluency

iq29teach = If I had a choice, I would continue to teach calculus

iq29famil = Familiarity with the research literature on how students think about ideas in calculus would be useful for teaching

   Values: 0, 1, 2, 3, 4, 5 (rating scale): 0 = strongly disagree, 1 = disagree, 2 = slightly disagree, 3 = slightly agree, 4 = agree, 5 = strongly agree, . = missing

Q30. Enter the number of students who received the following grades in what you indicated in item 4 above was your first calculus class. (If you only taught one section of Calculus I, enter your data for that section here.)

iq30wd = W/D

iq30f = F

iq30d = D

iq30c = C (includes C– and C+)

iq30b = B (includes B– and B+)

iq30a = A (includes A– and A+)

   Values: counts, . = missing

Note: Similar question to Q14 on the instructor beginning of semester survey

Q31.   iq31other = Select YES to enter grade data for another class
Values: 1 = yes, 0 = no, . = missing

Q32.   Enter the number of students who received the following grades in what you indicated in item 4 above was your second calculus class.
iq32wd = W/D
iq32f = F
iq32d = D
iq32c = C (includes C– and C+)
iq32b = B (includes B– and B+)
iq32a = A (includes A– and A+)
VALUES: counts, . = missing

Note: Similar question to Q14 on the instructor beginning of semester survey

Q33.   iq33other = Select YES to enter grade data for another class
Values: 1 = yes, 0 = no, . = missing

Q34.   Enter the number of students who received the following grades in what you indicated in item 4 above was your third calculus class.
iq34wd = W/D
iq34f = F
iq34d = D
iq34c = C (includes C– and C+)
iq34b = B (includes B– and B+)
iq34a = A (includes A– and A+)
Values: counts, . = missing

Note: Similar question to Q14 on the instructor beginning of semester survey

Q35.   iq35other = Select YES to enter grade data for another class
Values: 1 = yes, 0 = no, . = missing

Q36.   Enter the number of students who received the following grades in what you indicated in item 4 above was your fourth calculus class.
iq36wd = W/D
iq36f = F
iq36d = D
iq36c = C (includes C– and C+)
iq36b = B (includes B– and B+)
iq36a = A (includes A– and A+)
Values: counts, . = missing

Note: Similar question to Q14 on the instructor beginning of semester survey

Q37.   iq37other = Select YES to enter grade data for another class
Values: 1 = yes, 0 = no, . = missing

Q38.   Enter the number of students who received the following grades in what you indicated in item 4 above was your fifth calculus class.

iq38wd = W/D

iq38f = F

iq38d = D

iq38c = C (includes C– and C+)

iq38b = B (includes B– and B+)

iq38a = A (includes A– and A+)

   Values: counts, . = missing

Note: Similar question to Q14 on the instructor beginning of semester survey

Coordinator Survey

Q1.   In your department

c1ack = instructors who excel in the classroom are publicly acknowledged and/or rewarded for their teaching excellence

c1encour = instructors are encouraged to pursue professional development to improve their teaching

c1support = financial support is provided to attend conferences in which the teaching of undergraduate mathematics is a primary focus

c1group = Calculus I instructors meet as a group

   Values: 0, 1, 2, 3 (rating scale): 0 = never, 1 = rarely, 2 = sometimes, 3 = frequently, . = missing

Q2.   In your department

c2unten = What weight is given to excellence in teaching for *untenured* faculty for promotion and compensation?

c2ten = What weight is given to excellence in teaching for *tenured* faculty for promotion and compensation?

   Values: 0, 1, 2, 3 (rating scale): 0 = none, 1 = weak, 2 = moderate, 3 = significant, . = missing

Q3.   Your department

c3access = requests that all invited colloquium speakers include portions of their talks that are accessible to first year students

c3interdis = has interdisciplinary tracks within the undergraduate program (e.g., financial mathematics, mathematical biology)

c3web = has a department website that houses resource materials to support students' entry into the field of mathematics

c3compet = sponsors student participation in math competitions

   Values: 1 = yes, 0 = no, . = missing

Q4.   Your department

c4recruiths = has a program to recruit promising high school students

c4recruitund = has a program to recruit students from undeclared or undecided majors

c4mentor = has a program that matches promising students with faculty mentors

c4match = has a program that matches promising students with upper-classmen or graduate students

c4guest = has a guest lecture series accessible to first year students c4career

c4career = has a career fair specifically targeted at careers in mathematics

c4comm = has a standing department committee for the purpose of promoting mathematics as a major and recruiting/nurturing math students

   Values: 0, 1, 2, 3, 4 (rating scale): 0 = non-existent, 1 = not active, 2 = somewhat active, 3 = active, 4 = very active, . = missing

Q5.   c5act = How many times per year does your department have professional development activities or speakers related to the teaching of undergraduate mathematics?
Values: 1 = 0, 2 = 1-2, 3 = 3-4, 4 = 5 times or more, . = missing

c5actl = How many times per year does your department have professional development activities or speakers related to the teaching of undergraduate mathematics?
Linearized values (times per year): 0, 1.5, 3.5, 5.5, . = missing

Q6.   c6inform = How many times per year does your department arrange opportunities for mathematicians and undergraduates can interact informally?
Values: 1 = 0, 2 = 1-2, 3 = 3-4, 4 = 5 times or more, . = missing

c6informl = How many times per year does your department arrange opportunities for mathematicians and undergraduates can interact informally?
Linearized values (times per year): 0, 1.5, 3.5, 5.5, . = missing

Q7.   Which of the following technologies are provided by your department or institution for use by instructors of your mainstream Calculus I courses? Check all that apply.
c7clickav = clickers available
c7clickrec = clickers recommended
c7clickreq = clickers required
c7clicktr = clickers training available
c7progav = Mathematica, Maple, Matlab, etc. available
c7progrec = Mathematica, Maple, Matlab, etc. recommended
c7progreq = Mathematica, Maple, Matlab, etc. required
c7progtr = Mathematica, Maple, Matlab, etc. training available
c7graphav = graphing calculators available
c7graphrec = graphing calculators recommended
c7graphteq = graphing calculators required
c7graphtr = Graphing calculators training available
c7webav = online course websites available
c7webrec = online course websites recommended
c7webreq = online course websites required
c7webtr = online course websites training available
c7onlav = online homework available
c7onlrec = online homework recommended
c7onlreq = online homework required
c7onltr = online homework training available
c7javaav = Java applets or other computer animations available
c7javarec = Java applets or other computer animations recommended
c7javareq = Java applets or other computer animations required
c7javatr = Java applets or other computer animations training available
Values: 0 = not selected, 1 = yes
c7other = Other technology
Values: write-in

Q8.   c8proj = Are Calculus I courses usually taught in rooms equipped with a computer projections system?
Values: 1 = yes, 0 = no, . = missing

Q9.   If your department has any of the following programs for TAs, please rate the effectiveness of the program
c9mentor = pairs new TAs with faculty mentors
c9class = seminar or class for the purpose of TAs professional development
c9prog = other program (different from the two above) for TA mentoring or professional development
c9interview = interview process to select prospective TAs
c9screen = screen TAs before assigning them a recitation section
c9observe = faculty observation of TAs for the purpose of evaluating their teaching
      Values: 0, 1, 2, 3 (rating scale): 0 = not effective, 1 = minimally effective, 2 = effective, 3 = very effective, . = missing ("not applicable" coded as missing)

Q10.   Check all opportunities available to your Calculus I students
c10hon = Honors sections of Calculus I
c10club = Mathematics club
c10women = Special mathematics programs to encourage women
c10min = Special mathematics programs to encourage minorities
c10contest = Mathematical contests
c10lecture = Special mathematics lectures/colloquia not part of a mathematics club
c10outr = Mathematics outreach to local K-12 schools
c10research = Participation in undergraduate research in mathematics
c10is = Independent study
c10advis = Assigned faculty advisors
      Values: 0 = not selected, 1 = yes, . = missing
c10other = Other
      Values: write-in

Q11.   c11place = Does your department or college administer a mathematics placement test for students entering Calculus I?
      Values: 1 = yes, 0 = no, . = missing

Q12.   Who created your placement test(s)? Check all that apply.
c12own = your department
c12ets = Educational Testing Service (ETS)
c12act = American College Testing Program (ACT)
c12maa = Mathematical Association of America
      Values: 0 = not selected, 1 = yes, . = none selected (and c12other is missing).
c12other = Other
      Values: write-in

Q13.   c13fail = Is it usually the case that students who fail the placement exam for Calculus I are prevented from enrolling in Calculus I?
      Values: 1 = yes, 0 = no, . = missing

Q14.   c14tutor = Does your department or college operate a mathematics tutoring center available to Calculus I students?
      Values: 1 = yes, 0 = no, . = missing

Q15. Check all services available to students through your mathematics tutoring center

c15comp = computer-aided instruction

c15prog = computer software such as Maple, Mathematica, Matlab

c15res = internet resources

c15media = media such as CDs or DVDs

c15group = organized small group tutoring or study sessions

c15us = tutoring by undergraduate students

c15gs = tutoring by graduate students

c15pp = tutoring by paraprofessional staff

c15ptfac = Tutoring by part-time mathematics faculty

c15ftfac = tutoring by full-time mathematics faculty

Values: 0 = not selected, 1 = yes, . = none selected (and c15other is missing).

c15other = Other

Values: write-in

Q16. c16use = Students in Calculus I take advantage of the tutoring center

Values: 0, 1, 2, 3 (rating scale): 0 = strongly disagree, 1 = disagree, 2 = agree, 3 = strongly agree,

. = missing

Reference

College Board Office of Research and Development (1999). *Concordance between SAT I and ACT scores for individual students.* Report RN-07. New York: The College Board.